Volume 2

Mathematics III

Custom Edition for Utah School Districts

Randall I. Charles
Basia Hall
Dan Kennedy
Laurie E. Bass
Allan E. Bellman
Sadie Chavis Bragg
William G. Handlin
Art Johnson
Stuart J. Murphy
Grant Wiggins

PEARSON

Acknowledgments appear on page Z44, which constitutes an extension of this copyright page.

Taken from:

High School Math 2014 Common Core Integrated Math 3 Write-In Student Edition Volume 2
Copyright © 2014 by Pearson Education, Inc.
Published by Pearson Education, Inc.
One Lake Street, Upper Saddle River, New Jersey 07458

Precalculus: Graphical, Numerical, Algebraic, Eighth Edition
By Franklin D. Demana, Bert K. Waits, Gregory D. Foley, Daniel Kennedy
Copyright © 2011 by Pearson Education, Inc.
Published by Addison-Wesley
501 Boylston Street, Suite 900, Boston, MA 02116

High School Math 2014 Common Core Integrated Math 3 Write-In Student Edition Volume 1
Copyright © 2014 by Pearson Education, Inc.
Published by Pearson Education, Inc.
One Lake Street, Upper Saddle River, New Jersey 07458

Pearson Learning Solutions, 501 Boylston Street, Suite 900, Boston, MA 02116
A Pearson Education Company
www.pearsoned.com

Printed in the United States of America

4 5 6 7 8 9 10 V011 18 17 16 15 14

000200010271817094

AH

ISBN 10: 1-269-54676-7
ISBN 13: 978-1-269-54676-8

From the *Authors*

Welcome

Math is a powerful tool with far-reaching applications throughout your life. We have designed a unique and engaging program that will enable you to tap into the power of mathematics and mathematical reasoning. This award-winning program has been developed to align fully to the Common Core State Standards.

Developing mathematical understanding and problem-solving abilities is an ongoing process—a journey both inside and outside the classroom. This course is designed to help make sense of the mathematics you encounter in and out of class each day and to help you develop mathematical proficiency.

You will learn important mathematical principles. You will also learn how the principles are connected to one another and to what you already know. You will learn to solve problems and learn the reasoning that lies behind your solutions. You will also develop the key mathematical practices of the Common Core State Standards.

Each chapter begins with the "big ideas" of the chapter and some essential questions that you will learn to answer. Through this question-and-answer process you will develop your ability to analyze problems independently and solve them in different applications.

Your skills and confidence will increase through practice and review. Work through the problems so you understand the concepts and methods presented and the thinking behind them. Then do the exercises. Ask yourself how new concepts relate to old ones. Make the connections!

Everyone needs help sometimes. You will find that this program has built-in opportunities, both in this text and online, to get help whenever you need it.

The problem-solving and reasoning habits and problem-solving skills you develop in this program will serve you in all your studies and in your daily life. They will prepare you for future success not only as a student, but also as a member of a changing technological society.

Best wishes,

Series *Authors*

Randall I. Charles, Ph.D., is Professor Emeritus in the Department of Mathematics at San Jose State University, San Jose, California. He began his career as a high school mathematics teacher, and he was a mathematics supervisor for five years. Dr. Charles has been a member of several NCTM committees including the writing team for the Curriculum Focal Points. He is the former Vice President of the National Council of Supervisors of Mathematics. Much of his writing and research has been in the area of problem solving. He has authored more than 90 mathematics textbooks for kindergarten through college.

Dan Kennedy, Ph.D., is a classroom teacher and the Lupton Distinguished Professor of Mathematics at the Baylor School in Chattanooga, Tennessee. A frequent speaker at professional meetings on the subject of mathematics education reform, Dr. Kennedy has conducted more than 50 workshops and institutes for high school teachers. He is coauthor of textbooks in calculus and precalculus, and from 1990 to 1994 he chaired the College Board's AP Calculus Development Committee. He is a 1992 Tandy Technology Scholar and a 1995 Presidential Award winner.

Basia Hall currently serves as Manager of Instructional Programs for the Houston Independent School District. With 33 years of teaching experience, Ms. Hall has served as a department chair, instructional supervisor, school improvement facilitator, and professional development trainer. She has developed curricula for Algebra 1, Geometry, and Algebra 2 and co-developed the Texas state mathematics standards. A 1992 Presidential Awardee, Ms. Hall is past president of the Texas Association of Supervisors of Mathematics and is a state representative for the National Council of Supervisors of Mathematics (NCSM).

Consulting *Authors*

Stuart J. Murphy is a visual learning author and consultant. He is a champion of helping students develop visual learning skills so they become more successful students. He is the author of MathStart, a series of children's books that presents mathematical concepts in the context of stories, and *I See I Learn*, a Pre-Kindergarten and Kindergarten learning initiative that focuses on social and emotional skills. A graduate of the Rhode Island School of Design, he has worked extensively in educational publishing and has been on the authorship teams of a number of elementary and high school mathematics programs. He is a frequent presenter at meetings of the National Council of Teachers of Mathematics, the International Reading Association, and other professional organizations.

Grant Wiggins, Ed.D., is the President of Authentic Education in Hopewell, New Jersey. He earned his B.A. from St. John's College in Annapolis and his Ed.D. from Harvard University Dr. Wiggins consults with schools, districts, and state education departments on a variety of reform matters; organizes conferences and workshops; and develops print materials and web resources on curricular change. He is perhaps best known for being the coauthor, with Jay McTighe, of *Understanding by Design*® and *The Understanding by Design*® *Handbook*[1], the award-winning and highly successful materials on curriculum published by ASCD®. His work has been supported by the Pew Charitable Trusts, the Geraldine R. Dodge Foundation, and the National Science Foundation.

[1] ASCD®, publisher of the "Understanding by Design® Handbook" co-authored by Grant Wiggins and registered owner of the trademark "Understanding by Design®", has not authorized or sponsored this work and is in no way affiliated with Pearson or its products.

Program *Authors*

Algebra Topics

Allan E. Bellman, Ph.D., is an Associate Professor of Mathematics Education at the University of Mississippi. He previously taught at the University of California, Davis for 12 years and in public school in Montgomery County, Maryland for 31. He has been an instructor for both the Woodrow Wilson National Fellowship Foundation and the Texas Instruments' T^3 program. Dr. Bellman has expertise in the use of technology in education and assessment-driven instruction and speaks frequently on these topics. He is a recipient of the Tandy Award for Teaching Excellence and has twice been listed in Who's Who Among America's Teachers.

Sadie Chavis Bragg, Ed.D., is Senior Vice President of Academic Affairs and professor of mathematics at the Borough of Manhattan Community College of the City University of New York. She is a past president of the American Mathematical Association of Two-Year Colleges (AMATYC). In recognition for her service to the field of mathematics locally, statewide, nationally, and internationally, she was awarded AMATYC's most prestigious award, The Mathematics Excellence Award for 2010. Dr. Bragg has coauthored more than 60 mathematics textbooks for kindergarten through college.

William G. Handlin, Sr., is a classroom teacher and Department Chair of Mathematics and former Department Chair of Technology Applications at Spring Woods High School in Houston, Texas. Awarded Life Membership in the Texas Congress of Parents and Teachers for his contributions to the well-being of children, Mr. Handlin is also a frequent workshop and seminar leader in professional meetings.

Geometry Topics

Laurie E. Bass is a classroom teacher at the 9–12 division of the Ethical Culture Fieldston School in Riverdale, New York. A classroom teacher for more than 30 years, Ms. Bass has a wide base of teaching experiences, ranging from Grade 6 through Advanced Placement Calculus. She was the recipient of a 2000 Honorable Mention for the Radio Shack National Teacher Awards. She has been a contributing writer for a number of publications, including software-based activities for the Algebra 1 classroom. Among her areas of special interest are cooperative learning for high school students and geometry exploration on the computer. Ms. Bass is a frequent presenter at local, regional, and national conferences.

Art Johnson, Ed.D., is a professor of mathematics education at Boston University. He is a mathematics educator with 32 years of public school teaching experience, a frequent speaker and workshop leader, and the recipient of a number of awards: the Tandy Prize for Teaching Excellence, the Presidential Award for Excellence in Mathematics Teaching, and New Hampshire Teacher of the Year. He was also profiled by the Disney Corporation in the American Teacher of the Year Program. Dr. Johnson has contributed 18 articles to NCTM journals and has authored over 50 books on various aspects of mathematics.

Using **Your Book** with Success

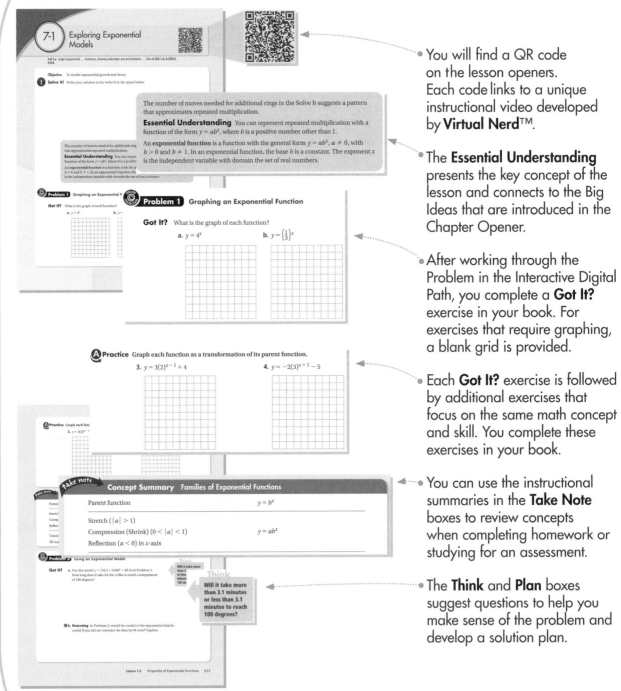

- You will find a QR code on the lesson openers. Each code links to a unique instructional video developed by **Virtual Nerd**™.

- The **Essential Understanding** presents the key concept of the lesson and connects to the Big Ideas that are introduced in the Chapter Opener.

- After working through the Problem in the Interactive Digital Path, you complete a **Got It?** exercise in your book. For exercises that require graphing, a blank grid is provided.

- Each **Got It?** exercise is followed by additional exercises that focus on the same math concept and skill. You complete these exercises in your book.

- You can use the instructional summaries in the **Take Note** boxes to review concepts when completing homework or studying for an assessment.

- The **Think** and **Plan** boxes suggest questions to help you make sense of the problem and develop a solution plan.

At the end of each lesson is a **Lesson Check** that you complete in your book. The Do you know HOW? section focuses on skills and the Do you UNDERSTAND? section targets your understanding of the math concepts related to the skills.

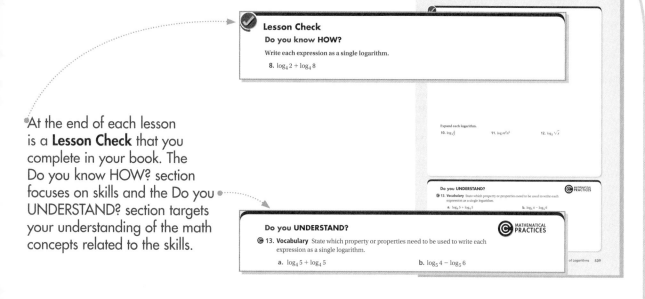

Lesson Check

Do you know HOW?

Write each expression as a single logarithm.

8. $\log_4 2 + \log_4 8$

Expand each logarithm.

10. $\log \frac{x}{3}$ 11. $\log m^2 n^5$ 12. $\log_2 \sqrt{x}$

Do you UNDERSTAND?

13. **Vocabulary** State which property or properties need to be used to write each expression as a single logarithm.

a. $\log_4 5 + \log_4 6$ b. $\log_5 4 - \log_5 6$

Do you UNDERSTAND?

13. **Vocabulary** State which property or properties need to be used to write each expression as a single logarithm.

a. $\log_5 5 + \log_5 5$ b. $\log_5 4 - \log_5 6$

Each lesson ends with **More Practice and Problem Solving** Exercises. You will complete these exercises in your homework notebook or on a separate sheet of paper.

The exercises with the **Common Core logo** help you become more proficient with the Standards for Mathematical Practice. Those with **STEM** logo provide practice with science, technology, or engineering topics.

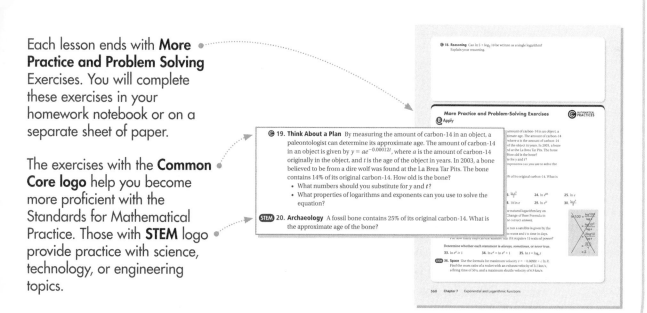

18. **Reasoning** Can $\ln 5 + \log_5 10$ be written as a single logarithm? Explain your reasoning.

More Practice and Problem-Solving Exercises

19. **Think About a Plan** By measuring the amount of carbon-14 in an object, a paleontologist can determine its approximate age. The amount of carbon-14 in an object is given by $y = ae^{-0.00012t}$, where a is the amount of carbon-14 originally in the object, and t is the age of the object in years. In 2003, a bone believed to be from a dire wolf was found at the La Brea Tar Pits. The bone contains 14% of its original carbon-14. How old is the bone?
- What numbers should you substitute for y and t?
- What properties of logarithms and exponents can you use to solve the equation?

20. **Archaeology** A fossil bone contains 25% of its original carbon-14. What is the approximate age of the bone?

What is a **QR code** and how do I use it?

A unique feature of Pearson's *Integrated High School Mathematics* is the QR code on lesson openers. QR codes can be scanned by any electronic device with a camera, such as a smart phone, tablet, and even some laptop computers. The QR codes on the lesson openers link to Virtual Nerd™ tutorial videos that directly relate to the content in the lesson. To learn more about Virtual Nerd tutorial videos and its exclusive dynamic whiteboard, go to virtualnerd.com.

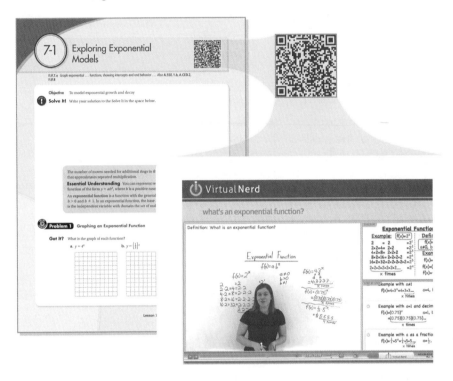

You must have a QR code reader on your mobile device or computer. You can download a QR reader app at the app store for your mobile device.

Step 1: Go to the app store for your camera-enabled smart phone or tablet.

Step 2: Search for "QR" or "QR readers". Download the QR reader app.

Step 3: Open that app and follow the instructions to scan. Whenever you want to scan a QR code, you will need to open the QR reader app first, otherwise you will just end up taking a picture of a QR code.

Step 4: After scanning the QR code, the appropriate Virtual Nerd tutorial video will play.

What **Resources** can I use when studying?

Pearson's *Integrated High School Mathematics* offers a range of resources that you can use out of class.

Student Worktext Your book is more than a textbook. Not only does it have important summaries of key math concepts and skills, it will also have your worked-out solutions to the *Got It?* and *Practice* exercises and your own notes for each lesson or problem. Use your book to:

- Refer back to your worked-out solutions and notes.
- Review the key concepts of each lesson by rereading the *Essential Understanding* and *Take Note* boxes.
- Access video tutorials of the concepts addressed in the lesson by scanning the QR codes.

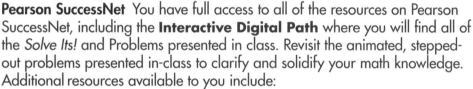

Pearson SuccessNet You have full access to all of the resources on Pearson SuccessNet, including the **Interactive Digital Path** where you will find all of the *Solve Its!* and Problems presented in class. Revisit the animated, stepped-out problems presented in-class to clarify and solidify your math knowledge. Additional resources available to you include:

- Interactive Student Worktext
- Homework Video Tutors in English and Spanish
- Online Glossary with audio in English and Spanish
- MathXL for School Interactive Math Practice
- Math Tools and Online Manipulatives
- Multilingual Handbook
- Assessments with immediate feedback

Mobile eText You may wish to access your student book on the go, either online or offline via download. Pearson's *Integrated High School Mathematics* also offers you a complete mobile etext of the Student Worktext.

- Use the notes, highlight, and bookmark features to personalize your eText.
- Watch animated problem videos with step-by-step instruction for every lesson.

Pearson SuccessNet

Pearson SuccessNet is the gateway to all of the digital components of the program. You can use the online content to review the day's lesson, complete lessons independently, get help with your homework assignments, and prepare for and/or take an assessment. You will be given a username and password to log into www.pearsonsuccessnet.com.

The Homepage

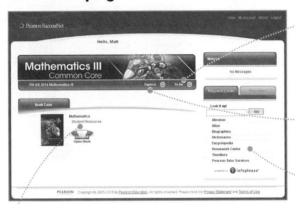

Your eText includes links to animated lesson videos, highlighting and note taking tools, and a visual glossary with audio.

The **To Do** tab contains a list of assignments that you need to complete. You can also access your gradebook and review past assignments.

The **Explore** tab provides you access to the Table of Contents and all of the digital content for the program.

You can also access the following student resources: Practice Worksheets, Homework Video Tutors, and a Multilingual Handbook

Table of Contents

To access the Table of Contents, click on *Explore* from your Homepage.

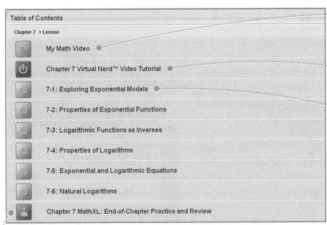

Student-developed videos bring real-life context to mathematics.

Step-by-step video tutorials offer additional support.

Digital lessons include access to animated problems, math tools, homework exercises, and self-assessments.

MathXL for School exercises provide additional practice. Examples and tutorials support every problem, and instant feedback is provided as you complete each exercise.

Interactive Digital Path

To access the **Interactive Digital Path**, click on the appropriate lesson from the Table of Contents.

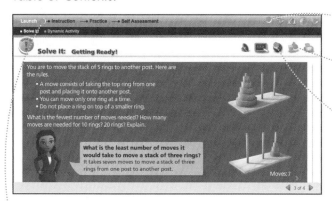

Math Tools help you explore and visualize concepts.

You'll find opportunities to review formulas, properties, and other key concepts.

Interactive Glossary is available in English and Spanish with audio.

Every lesson includes the following:

Launch: Interactive lesson opener connects the math to real-world applications.

Instruction: All lesson problems are stepped out with detailed instruction. You can complete the subsequent *Got It?* exercises in your Student Worktext.

Practice: Exercises from your Student Worktext are available for view.

Self-Assessment: You can take the self-check lesson quiz, and then check your answers on the second screen.

MathXL for School

To access *MathXL for School*, click on the Chapter Review and Practice link from the Table of Contents.

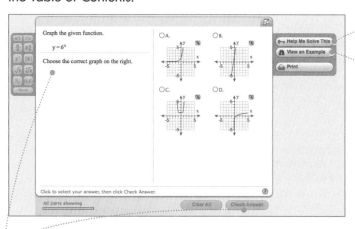

Select **Help Me Solve This** for an interactive step-by-step tutorial.

Select **View an Example** to see a similar worked out problem.

Input your answer and select **Check Answer** to get immediate feedback. After completing the exercise, a new exercise automatically regenerates, so you have unlimited practice opportunities.

Common Core *State Standards*
Mathematics III

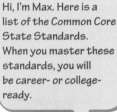

Number and Quantity

Quantities

Reason quantitatively and use units to solve problems

N.Q.2   Define appropriate quantities for the purpose of descriptive modeling.

Algebra

Seeing Structure in Expressions

Interpret the structure of expressions

A.SSE.2   Use the structure of an expression to identify ways to rewrite it. *For example, see $x^4 - y^4$ as $(x^2)^2 - (y^2)^2$, thus recognizing it as a difference of squares that can be factored as $(x^2 - y^2)(x^2 + y^2)$.*

Write expressions in equivalent forms to solve problems

A.SSE.4   Derive the formula for the sum of a finite geometric series (when the common ratio is not 1), and use the formula to solve problems. *For example, calculate mortgage payments.* ★

Arithmetic with Polynomials and Rational Expressions

Understand the relationship between zeros and factors of polynomial

A.APR.2   Know and apply the Remainder Theorem: For a polynomial $p(x)$ and a number a, the remainder on division by $x - a$ is $p(a)$, so $p(a) = 0$ if and only if $(x - a)$ is a factor of $p(x)$.

A.APR.3   Identify zeros of polynomials when suitable factorizations are available, and use the zeros to construct a rough graph of the function defined by the polynomial.

Use polynomial identities to solve problems

A.APR.4   Prove polynomial identities and use them to describe numerical relationships. *For example, the polynomial identity $(x^2 + y^2)^2 = (x^2 - y^2)^2 + (2xy)^2$ can be used to generate Pythagorean triples.*

Rewrite rational expressions

A.APR.6   Rewrite simple rational expressions in different forms; write $a(x)/b(x)$ in the form $q(x) + r(x)/b(x)$, where $a(x)$, $b(x)$, $q(x)$, and $r(x)$ are polynomials with the degree of $r(x)$ less than the degree of $b(x)$, using inspection, long division, or, for the more complicated examples, a computer algebra system.

Creating Equations ★

Create equations that describe numbers or relationships

A.CED.1   Create equations and inequalities in one variable and use them to solve problems. *Include equations arising from linear and quadratic functions, and simple rational and exponential functions.* ★

A.CED.2   Create equations in two or more variables to represent relationships between quantities; graph equations on coordinate axes with labels and scales. ★

Reasoning with Equations and Inequalities

Understand solving equations as a process of reasoning and explain the reasoning

A.REI.1   Explain each step in solving a simple equation as following from the equality of numbers asserted at the previous step, starting from the assumption that the original equation has a solution. Construct a viable argument to justify a solution method.

A.REI.2   Solve simple rational and radical equations in one variable, and give examples showing how extraneous solutions may arise.

Represent and solve equations and inequalities graphically

A.REI.11   Explain why the x-coordinates of the points where the graphs of the equations $y = f(x)$ and $y = g(x)$ intersect are the solutions of the equation $f(x) = g(x)$; find the solutions approximately, e.g., using technology to graph the functions, make tables of values, or find successive approximations. Include cases where $f(x)$ and/or $g(x)$ are linear, polynomial, rational, absolute value, exponential, and logarithmic functions. ★

Functions

Interpreting Functions

Interpret functions that arise in applications in terms of the context

F.IF.4   For a function that models a relationship between two quantities, interpret key features of graphs and tables in terms of the quantities, and sketch graphs showing key features given a verbal description of the relationship. *Key features include: intercepts; intervals where the function is increasing, decreasing, positive, or negative; relative maximums and minimums; symmetries; end behavior; and periodicity.* ★

F.IF.6   Calculate and interpret the average rate of change of a function (presented symbolically or as a table) over a specified interval. Estimate the rate of change from a graph. ★

Analyze functions using different representations

F.IF.7.c   Graph functions expressed symbolically and show key features of the graph, by hand in simple cases and using technology for more complicated cases. Graph polynomial functions, identifying zeros when suitable factorizations are available, and showing end behavior.

F.IF.7.e   Graph functions expressed symbolically and show key features of the graph, by hand in simple cases and using technology for more complicated cases. Graph exponential and logarithmic functions, showing intercepts and end behavior, and trigonometric functions, showing period, midline, and amplitude.

F.IF.9   Compare properties of two functions each represented in a different way (algebraically, graphically, numerically in tables, or by verbal descriptions). *For example, given a graph of one quadratic function and an algebraic expression for another, say which has the larger maximum.*

Building Functions

Build new functions from existing functions

F.BF.3   Identify the effect on the graph of replacing $f(x)$ by $f(x) + k$, $k\, f(x)$, $f(kx)$, and $f(x + k)$ for specific values of k (both positive and negative); find the value of k given the graphs. Experiment with cases and illustrate an explanation of the effects on the graph using technology. *Include recognizing even and odd functions from their graphs and algebraic expressions for them.*

F.BF.4.a   Find inverse functions. Solve an equation of the form $f(x) = c$ for a simple function f that has an inverse and write an expression for the inverse. *For example, $f(x) = 2x^3$ or $f(x) = (x + 1)/(x − 1)$ for $x \neq 1$.*

Linear, Quadratic, and Exponential

Construct and compare linear and exponential models and solve problems

F.LE.4   For exponential models, express as a logarithm the solution to $abct = d$ where a, c, and d are numbers and the base b is 2, 10, or e; evaluate the logarithm using technology.

Trigonometric Functions

Extend the domain of trigonometric functions using the unit circle

F.TF.1   Understand radian measure of an angle as the length of the arc on the unit circle subtended by the angle.

F.TF.2   Explain how the unit circle in the coordinate plane enables the extension of trigonometric functions to all real numbers, interpreted as radian measures of angles traversed counterclockwise around the unit circle.

Model periodic phenomena with trigonometric functions

F.TF.5   Choose trigonometric functions to model periodic phenomena with specified amplitude, frequency, and midline. ★

Prove and apply trigonometric identities

F.TF.8   Prove the Pythagorean identity $\sin^2(\theta) + \cos^2(\theta) = 1$ and use it to find $\sin(\theta)$, $\cos(\theta)$, or $\tan(\theta)$ given $\sin(\theta)$, $\cos(\theta)$, or $\tan(\theta)$ and the quadrant of the angle.

Geometry

Circles

Understand and apply theorems about circles

G.C.3   Construct the inscribed and circumscribed circles of a triangle, and prove properties of angles for a quadrilateral inscribed in a circle.

Geometric Measurement and Dimension

Visualize relationships between two-dimensional and three-dimensional objects

G.GMD.4   Identify the shapes of two-dimensional cross-sections of three-dimensional objects, and identify three-dimensional objects generated by rotations of two-dimensional objects.

Modeling with Geometry

Apply geometric concepts in modeling situations

G.MG.1   Use geometric shapes, their measures, and their properties to describe objects (e.g., modeling a tree trunk or a human torso as a cylinder). ★

G.MG.2   Apply concepts of density based on area and volume in modeling situations (e.g., persons per square mile, BTUs per cubic foot). ★

G.MG.3   Apply geometric methods to solve design problems (e.g., designing an object or structure to satisfy physical constraints or minimize cost; working with typographic grid systems based on ratios). ★

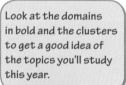

Look at the domains in bold and the clusters to get a good idea of the topics you'll study this year.

Statistics and Probability

Interpreting Categorical and Quantitative Data

Summarize, represent, and interpret data on a single count or measurement variable

S.ID.4   Use the mean and standard deviation of a data set to fit it to a normal distribution and to estimate population percentages. Recognize that there are data sets for which such a procedure is not appropriate. Use calculators, spreadsheets, and tables to estimate areas under the normal curve.

Summarize, represent, and interpret data on two categorical and quantitative variables

S.ID.6a   Represent data on two quantitative variables on a scatter plot, and describe how the variables are related. Fit a function to the data; use functions fitted to data to solve problems in the context of the data. Use given functions or choose a function suggested by the context. *Emphasize linear, quadratic, and exponential models.* ★

S.ID.6.b   Represent data on two quantitative variables on a scatter plot, and describe how the variables are related. Informally assess the fit of a function by plotting and analyzing residuals.

Making Inferences and Justifying Conclusions

Understand and evaluate random processes underlying statistical experiments

S.IC.1   Understand statistics as a process for making inferences about population parameters based on a random sample from that population.

S.IC.2   Decide if a specified model is consistent with results from a given data-generating process, e.g., using simulation. *For example, a model says a spinning coin falls heads up with probability 0.5. Would a result of 5 tails in a row cause you to question the model?*

Make inferences and justify conclusions from sample surveys, experiments, and observational studies

S.IC.3   Recognize the purposes of and differences among sample surveys, experiments, and observational studies; explain how randomization relates to each.

S.IC.4   Use data from a sample survey to estimate a population mean or proportion; develop a margin of error through the use of simulation models for random sampling.

S.IC.5   Use data from a randomized experiment to compare two treatments; use simulations to decide if differences between parameters are significant.

S.IC.6   Evaluate reports based on data.

BIGideas

These Big Ideas are the organizing ideas for the study of important areas of mathematics: algebra, geometry, and statistics.

Stay connected! These Big Ideas will help you understand how the math you study in high school fits together.

Algebra

Properties
- In the transition from arithmetic to algebra, attention shifts from arithmetic operations (addition, subtraction, multiplication, and division) to the use of the properties of these operations.
- All of the facts of arithmetic and algebra follow from certain properties.

Variable
- Quantities are used to form expressions, equations, and inequalities.
- An expression refers to a quantity but does not make a statement about it. An equation (or an inequality) is a statement about the quantities it mentions.
- Using variables in place of numbers in equations (or inequalities) allows the statement of relationships among numbers that are unknown or unspecified.

Equivalence
- A single quantity may be represented by many different expressions.
- The facts about a quantity may be expressed by many different equations (or inequalities).

Solving Equations & Inequalities
- Solving an equation is the process of rewriting the equation to make what it says about its variable(s) as simple as possible.
- Properties of numbers and equality can be used to transform an equation (or inequality) into equivalent, simpler equations (or inequalities) in order to find solutions.
- Useful information about equations and inequalities (including solutions) can be found by analyzing graphs or tables.
- The numbers and types of solutions vary predictably, based on the type of equation.

Proportionality
- Two quantities are proportional if they have the same ratio in each instance where they are measured together.
- Two quantities are inversely proportional if they have the same product in each instance where they are measured together.

Function
- A function is a relationship between variables in which each value of the input variable is associated with a unique value of the output variable.
- Functions can be represented in a variety of ways, such as graphs, tables, equations, or words. Each representation is particularly useful in certain situations.
- Some important families of functions are developed through transformations of the simplest form of the function.
- New functions can be made from other functions by applying arithmetic operations or by applying one function to the output of another.

Modeling
- Many real-world mathematical problems can be represented algebraically. These representations can lead to algebraic solutions.
- A function that models a real-world situation can be used to make estimates or predictions about future occurrences.

Statistics and Probability

Data Collection and Analysis

- Sampling techniques are used to gather data from real-world situations. If the data are representative of the larger population, inferences can be made about that population.
- Biased sampling techniques yield data unlikely to be representative of the larger population.
- Sets of numerical data are described using measures of central tendency and dispersion.

Data Representation

- The most appropriate data representations depend on the type of data—quantitative or qualitative, and univariate or bivariate.
- Line plots, box plots, and histograms are different ways to show distribution of data over a possible range of values.

Probability

- Probability expresses the likelihood that a particular event will occur.
- Data can be used to calculate an experimental probability, and mathematical properties can be used to determine a theoretical probability.
- Either experimental or theoretical probability can be used to make predictions or decisions about future events.
- Various counting methods can be used to develop theoretical probabilities.

Geometry

Visualization

- Visualization can help you see the relationships between two figures and help you connect properties of real objects with two-dimensional drawings of these objects.

Transformations

- Transformations are mathematical functions that model relationships with figures.
- Transformations may be described geometrically or by coordinates.
- Symmetries of figures may be defined and classified by transformations.

Measurement

- Some attributes of geometric figures, such as length, area, volume, and angle measure, are measurable. Units are used to describe these attributes.

Reasoning & Proof

- Definitions establish meanings and remove possible misunderstanding.
- Other truths are more complex and difficult to see. It is often possible to verify complex truths by reasoning from simpler ones using deductive reasoning.

Similarity

- Two geometric figures are similar when corresponding lengths are proportional and corresponding angles are congruent.
- Areas of similar figures are proportional to the squares of their corresponding lengths.
- Volumes of similar figures are proportional to the cubes of their corresponding lengths.

Coordinate Geometry

- A coordinate system on a line is a number line on which points are labeled, corresponding to the real numbers.
- A coordinate system in a plane is formed by two perpendicular number lines, called the x- and y-axes, and the quadrants they form. The coordinate plane can be used to graph many functions.
- It is possible to verify some complex truths using deductive reasoning in combination with the distance, midpoint, and slope formulas.

6

Trigonometric Functions

Functions

Interpreting Functions
Interpret functions that arise in applications in terms of the context
Analyze functions using different representations

Functions

Trigonometric Functions
Extend the domain of trigonometric functions using the unit circle
Model periodic phenomena with trigonometric functions
Prove and apply trigonometric identities

Chapter 6

Sequences and Series

Algebra

Seeing Structure in Expressions
Write expressions in equivalent forms to solve problems

Functions

Building Functions
Build new functions from existing functions

Chapter 7

8

Applying Geometric Concepts

Chapter 8

Geometry
Geometric Measurement and Dimension
Visualize relationships between two-dimensional and
three-dimensional objects

Geometry
Modeling with Geometry
Apply geometric concepts in modeling situations

Honors Appendix

This page intentionally left blank.

Get Ready!

Analyzing Graphs of Rational Functions

Find the vertical asymptotes and holes for the graph of each rational function.

1. $y = \dfrac{2}{x-3}$

2. $y = \dfrac{x+2}{(2x+1)(x-4)}$

Solving Quadratic Equations

Solve each equation.

3. $4x^2 = 25$

4. $x^2 - 23 = 0$

5. $3x^2 = 80$

6. $8x^2 - 44 = 0$

7. $0.5x^2 = 15$

8. $6x^2 - 13 = 11$

Finding the Inverse of a Function

For each function f, find f^{-1} and the domain and range of f and f^{-1}. Determine whether f^{-1} is a function.

9. $f(x) = 5x + 2$

10. $f(x) = \sqrt{3x - 4}$

11. $f(x) = \dfrac{10}{x-1}$

Solving Exponential and Logarithmic Equations

Solve each equation.

12. $4^x = \dfrac{1}{8}$

13. $\log 5x + 1 = -1$

14. $7^{3x} = 500$

15. $\log 3x + \log x = 9$

16. $\log(4x + 3) - \log x = 5$

17. $3^x = 243$

 Looking Ahead Vocabulary

18. If you were to graph the average monthly rainfall for your community for the past 5 years, you would very likely graph a *periodic function*. Why do you think it is called a periodic function?

19. Graph the month-by-month attendance at one of these larger National Parks—The Everglades, Grand Canyon, Yellowstone, or Yosemite—for several years. The pattern that results may resemble a *sine curve*. Describe the features of this curve.

CHAPTER 6

Trigonometric Functions

Big Ideas

1 Modeling
Essential Question: How can you model periodic behavior?

2 Function
Essential Question: If you know the value of sin θ, how can you find cos θ, tan θ, csc θ, sec θ, and cot θ?

3 Equivalence
Essential Question: How do you verify that an equation involving the variable x is an identity?

Domains

- Trigonometric Functions
- Interpreting Functions

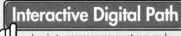

Interactive Digital Path

Log in to **pearsonsuccessnet.com** and click on Interactive Digital Path to access the Solve Its and animated Problems.

Chapter Preview

 ## Vocabulary

English/Spanish Vocabulary Audio Online:

English	Spanish
amplitude, *p. 382*	amplitud
central angle, *p. 395*	ángulo central
cosine, *p. 390, 416*	coseno
cycle, *p. 379*	ciclo
midline, *p. 382*	línea media
period, *p. 379*	período
periodic function, *p. 379*	función periódica
phase shift, *p. 434*	cambio de fase
radian, *p. 395*	radian
sine, *p. 390, 403*	seno
tangent, *p. 425, 427*	tangente
trigonometric identity, *p. 457*	identidad trigonométrica
unit circle, *p. 390*	círculo unitario

6-1 Exploring Periodic Data

F.IF.4 For a function that models a relationship between two quantities, interpret key features of graphs . . . and sketch graphs . . .

Objectives   To identify cycles and periods of periodic functions
To find the amplitude of periodic functions

 Solve It!   Write your solution to the Solve It in the space below.

A **periodic function** is a function that repeats a pattern of *y*-values (outputs) at regular intervals. One complete pattern is a **cycle**. A cycle may begin at any point on the graph of the function. The **period** of a function is the horizontal length—the distance along the *x*-axis—of one cycle. The *x*-value in a periodic function often represents time.

Essential Understanding   Periodic behavior is behavior that repeats over intervals of constant length.

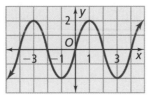

Problem 1   Identifying Cycles and Periods

Got It?   Analyze each periodic function. Identify the cycle in two different ways. What is the period of the function?

a.

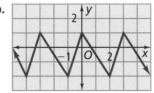

b.

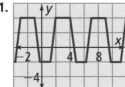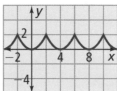

Ⓐ Practice   Identify one cycle in two different ways. Then determine the period of the function.

1.

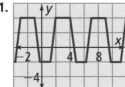

2.

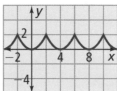

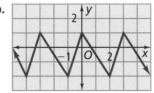

You can analyze the graph of a function to determine if the function is periodic.

Problem 2 **Identifying Periodic Functions**

Got It? Is the function periodic? If it is, what is its period?

Think

Do the *y*-values of the function repeat?

a.
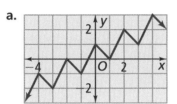

b.
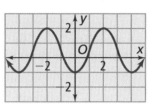

c. Reasoning If the period of a function is 4 seconds, how many cycles does it have in a minute? What is the period of a function that has 180 cycles per minute (for example, a point on a spinning wheel)? Of a function that has 440 cycles per second (for example, a point on the end of a tuning fork)?

Practice Determine whether each function *is* or *is not* periodic. If it is, find the period.

3.
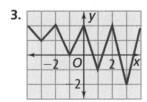

4.
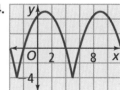

The *amplitude* of a periodic function measures the amount of variation in the function values.

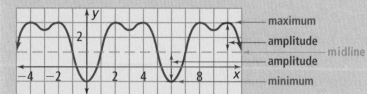

maximum
amplitude
midline
amplitude
minimum

The **midline** is the horizontal line midway between the maximum and minimum values of a periodic function. The **amplitude** is half the difference between the maximum and minimum values of the function.

$$\text{amplitude} = \tfrac{1}{2}(\text{maximum value} - \text{minimum value})$$

Problem 3   Finding Amplitude and Midline of a Periodic Function

Got It?   What is the amplitude of each periodic function? What is the equation of the midline?

a.

b.
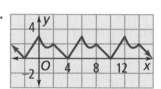

Practice   Find the amplitude of each periodic function, and midline.

5.
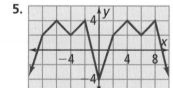

6.
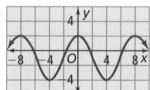

You can model some data with periodic functions. The rotation of a Ferris wheel, the beating of a heart, and the movement of sound waves are all examples of real-world events that generate periodic data.

 **Problem 4** **Using a Periodic Function to Solve a Problem**

Plan

How does identifying the cycle help you?

Got It? What are the period, the amplitude, and the equation of the midline of the green graph in the digital wave display in Problem 4?

ⒶPractice Find the amplitude of the periodic function, and midline.

7.
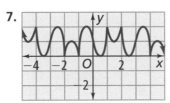

 ## Lesson Check

Do you know HOW?

Determine if the function *is* or *is not* periodic. If it is, find the period.

8.
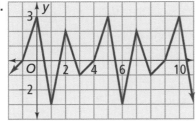

9.
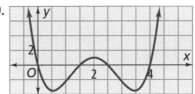

Do you UNDERSTAND?

10. Writing A sound wave can be graphed as a periodic function. Name two more real-world examples of periodic functions.

11. Error Analysis A student looked at the following function and wrote that the amplitude was 2. Describe and correct the student's error.

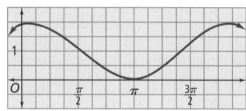

12. Reasoning Suppose f is a periodic function. The period of f is 5 and $f(1) = 2$. What are $f(6)$ and $f(11)$? Explain your reasoning.

13. A wave has a maximum of 6. If its midline is at $y = 1$, what is its minimum?

More Practice and Problem-Solving Exercises

B Apply

Sketch the graph of a sound wave with the given period, amplitude, and midline.

14. period 0.02, amplitude 4, midline 6

15. period 0.005, amplitude 9, midline −5

16. Complete each statement with x or y.

    a. You use ▓-values to compute the amplitude of a function.

    b. You use ▓-values to compute the period of a function.

17. Which of the following could be represented by a periodic function? Explain.

    a. the average monthly temperature in your community, recorded every month for three years

    b. the population in your community, recorded every year for the last 50 years

    c. the number of cars per hour that pass through an intersection near where you live, recorded for two consecutive work days

Ⓒ **18. Writing** What do all periodic functions have in common?

Ⓒ **19. Think About a Plan** A person's pulse rate is the number of times his or her heart beats in one minute. Each cycle in the graph represents one heartbeat. What is the pulse rate?

    • Will you compute the period or the amplitude, or both?

    • Does the graph provide information you do NOT need?

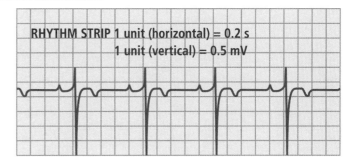

RHYTHM STRIP 1 unit (horizontal) = 0.2 s
1 unit (vertical) = 0.5 mV

20. Health An electrocardiogram (EKG or ECG) measures the electrical activity of a person's heart in millivolts over time. Refer to the graph in the previous exercise.

    a. What is the period of the EKG shown above?

    b. What is the amplitude of the EKG?

21. Open-Ended Sketch a graph of a periodic function that has a period of 3 and an amplitude of 2.

Find the maximum, minimum, and period of each periodic function. Then copy the graph and sketch two more cycles.

22.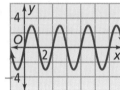

23.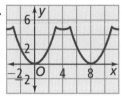

24.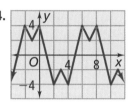

Language Arts Functions that repeat over time are common in everyday life. The English language has many words that stand for common periods of time. State the period of time from which each term derives.

25. annual   **26.** biweekly   **27.** quarterly   **28.** hourly   **29.** circadian

 Challenge

30. Suppose g is a periodic function. The period of g is 24, $g(3) = 67$, and $g(8) = 70$. Find each function value.
   a. $g(27)$ **b.** $g(80)$ **c.** $g(-16)$ **d.** $g(51)$

31. Calendar A day is a basic measure of time. A solar year is about 365.2422 days. We try to keep our calendar in step with the solar year.
   a. If every calendar year had 365 days, by how many days would the calendar year and the solar year differ after 100 years?
   b. If every fourth year had an extra "leap" day added, by how many days would the two systems differ after 100 years?
   c. If every hundred years the "leap" day were omitted, by how many days would the two systems differ after 100 years?
   d. Reasoning Why is it important for the difference between the calendar year and the solar year to be zero?

6-2 Angles and the Unit Circle

Prepares for **F.TF.2** Explain how the unit circle . . . enables the extension of trigonometric functions to all real numbers, interpreted as radian measures of angles traversed counterclockwise around the unit circle. Also prepares for **F.TF.1**

Objectives To work with angles in standard position
To find coordinates of points on the unit circle

 Solve It! Write your solution to the Solve It in the space below.

An angle in the coordinate plane is in **standard position** when the vertex is at the origin and one ray is on the positive x-axis. The ray on the x-axis is the **initial side** of the angle. The other ray is the **terminal side** of the angle.

The measure of an angle in standard position is the amount of rotation from the initial side to the terminal side.

Standard Position

Essential Understanding The measure of an angle in standard position is the input for two important functions. The outputs are the coordinates (called *cosine* and *sine*) of the point on the terminal side of the angle that is 1 unit from the origin.

The measure of an angle is positive when the rotation from the initial side to the terminal side is in the counterclockwise direction. The measure is negative when the rotation is clockwise.

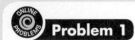

Problem 1 **Measuring Angles in Standard Position**

Got It? What is the measure of the angle shown?

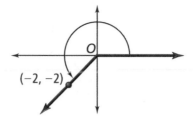

(−2, −2)

**Practice** Find the measure of each angle in standard position.

1.

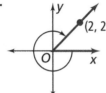

(2, 2)

2. $\left(-\frac{\sqrt{3}}{2}, \frac{1}{2}\right)$

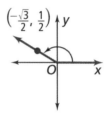

Problem 2 **Sketching Angles in Standard Position**

Got It? What is a sketch of each angle in standard position?

a. $85°$ **b.** $-320°$ **c.** $180°$

Ⓐ Practice Sketch each angle in standard position.

3. $-130°$ **4.** $95°$

Two angles in standard position are **coterminal angles** if they have the same terminal side.

Angles in standard position that have measures $135°$ and $-225°$ are coterminal.

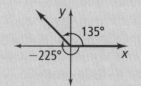

Problem 3   **Identifying Coterminal Angles**

Got It?   Which angles in standard position are coterminal?

A. $-315°$ **B.** $45°$ **C.** $315°$ **D.** $405°$

Ⓐ Practice Find the measure of an angle between $0°$ and $360°$ coterminal with each given angle.

5. $500°$ **6.** $-180°$

In a 360° angle, a point 1 unit from the origin on the terminal ray makes one full rotation about the origin. The resulting circle is a unit circle. The **unit circle** has a radius of 1 unit and its center at the origin of the coordinate plane. Any right triangle formed by the radius of the unit circle has a hypotenuse of 1. Points on the unit circle are related to periodic functions.

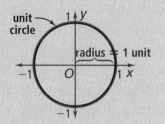

You can use the symbol θ for the measure of an angle in standard position.

take note

Key Concepts   Cosine and Sine of an Angle

Suppose an angle in standard position has measure θ.

The **cosine of θ** (cos θ) is the x-coordinate of the point at which the terminal side of the angle intersects the unit circle. The **sine of θ** (sin θ) is the y-coordinate.

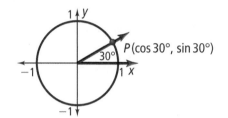

Problem 4   Finding Cosines and Sines of Angles

Got It?   **a.** What are cos θ and sin θ for $\theta = -90°$, $\theta = 360°$, and $\theta = 540°$?

Think

How can you use coterminal angles to find these values?

b. In a triangle, sine and cosine are ratios between side lengths. What ratios produce the values in (a)?

Practice Find the cosine and sine of each angle.

7. $-270°$

8. $720°$

You can find the exact value of sine and cosine for angles that are multiples of 30° or 45°.

 **Problem 5** **Finding Exact Values of Cosine and Sine**

Got It? What are the cosine and sine of the angle?

a. $\theta = -45°$

b. $\theta = 150°$

Plan
How can a sketch of the angle on the unit circle be helpful?

© **c. Reasoning** For an angle θ, can $\cos \theta$ equal $\sin \theta$? Explain.

Practice Find the exact values of the cosine and sine of each angle. Then find the decimal values. Round your answers to the nearest hundredth.

9. $-240°$

10. $315°$

 Lesson Check

Do you know HOW?

Find the measure of each angle in standard position.

11.
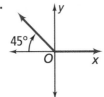

12.
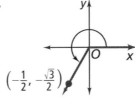

Sketch each angle in standard position. Then find the measure of a coterminal angle.

13. $28°$

14. $325°$

Do you UNDERSTAND?

15. Open-Ended Find a positive and a negative coterminal angle for an angle that measures 1485°.

16. Error Analysis On a test a student wrote that the measure of an angle coterminal to a 50° angle is 310°. Describe and correct the student's error.

More Practice and Problem-Solving Exercises

 **MATHEMATICAL PRACTICES**

B Apply

 Graphing Calculator For each angle θ, find the values of $\cos \theta$ and $\sin \theta$. Round your answers to the nearest hundredth.

17. −95°   **18.** −10°   **19.** 154°   **20.** 90°   **21.** 210°

22. Think About a Plan On an analog clock, the minute hand has moved 128° from the hour. What number will it pass next?
- How can a drawing help you understand the problem?
- How can you find the number of degrees between every two consecutive numbers?

Open-Ended Find a positive and a negative coterminal angle for the given angle.

23. 45°   **24.** 10°   **25.** −675°   **26.** 400°   **27.** 213°

Determine the quadrant or axis where the terminal side of each angle lies.

28. 150°   **29.** 210°   **30.** 540°   **31.** −60°   **32.** 0°

33. Time The time is 2:46 P.M. What is the measure of the angle that the minute hand swept through since 2:00 P.M.?

34. a. Copy and complete the chart at the right.
   b. Suppose you know that cos θ is negative and sin θ is positive. In which quadrant does the terminal side of the angle lie?
   c. Writing Summarize how the quadrant in which the terminal side of an angle lies affects the sign of the sine and cosine of that angle.

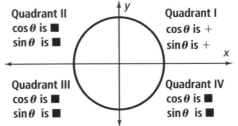

Quadrant II
cos θ is ■
sin θ is ■

Quadrant I
cos θ is +
sin θ is +

Quadrant III
cos θ is ■
sin θ is ■

Quadrant IV
cos θ is ■
sin θ is ■

35. a. Graphing Calculator Use a calculator to find the value of each expression: cos 40°, cos 400°, and cos (−320°).
   b. Reasoning What do you notice about the values you found in part (a)? Explain.

© Challenge

Sketch each angle in standard position. Use the unit circle and a right triangle to find exact values of the cosine and the sine of the angle.

36. −300°   **37.** 120°   **38.** 225°   **39.** −780°   **40.** 1020°

41. Open-Ended Find the measures of four angles in standard position that have a sine of 0.5. (*Hint:* Use the unit circle and right triangles.)

42. Reasoning Suppose θ is an angle in standard position and $\cos \theta = -\frac{1}{2}$ and $\sin \theta = -\frac{\sqrt{3}}{2}$. Can the value of θ be 60°? Can it be −120°? Draw a diagram and justify your reasoning.

6-3 Radian Measure

F.TF.1 Understand radian measure . . . as the length of the arc on the unit circle subtended by the angle. Also prepares for **F.TF.2**

Objectives To use radian measure for angles
To find the length of an arc of a circle

 Solve It! Write your solution to the Solve It in the space below.

A **central angle** of a circle is an angle with a vertex at the center of a circle. An **intercepted arc** is the portion of the circle with endpoints on the sides of the central angle and remaining points within the interior of the angle.

A **radian** is the measure of a central angle that intercepts an arc with length equal to the radius of the circle. Radians, like degrees, measure the amount of rotation from the initial side to the terminal side of an angle. An equivalent definition of the radian measure of a central angle is the length of the arc the angle intercepts on the unit circle.

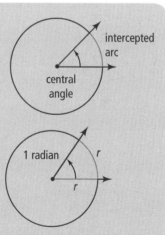

Essential Understanding An angle with a full circle rotation measures 2π radians. An angle with a semicircle rotation measures π radians.

take note

Key Concepts Proportion Relating Radians and Degrees

You can use the proportion $\frac{d°}{180°} = \frac{r \text{ radians}}{\pi \text{ radians}}$ to convert between radians and degrees.

Here's Why It Works Because the circumference of a circle is $2\pi r$, there are 2π radians in any circle. Since 2π radians $= 360°$, it follows that π radians $= 180°$. This equality leads to the following *conversion factors* for converting between radian measure and degree measure.

Key Concepts   Converting Between Radians and Degrees

To convert degrees to radians, multiply by $\frac{\pi \text{ radians}}{180°}$.

To convert radians to degrees, multiply by $\frac{180°}{\pi \text{ radians}}$.

You can use the conversion factors and dimensional analysis to convert between angle measurement systems.

Problem 1   **Using Dimensional Analysis**

Got It?   What is the degree measure of each angle expressed in radians? What is the radian measure of each angle expressed in degrees? (Express radian measures in terms of π.)

Think

How do you know which conversion factor to use?

a. $\frac{\pi}{2}$ radians

b. $225°$

c. 2 radians

d. $150°$

Practice   **1.** Write $-60°$ in radians. Express your answer in terms of π.

2. Write $\frac{11\pi}{10}$ radians in degrees. Round your answer to the nearest degree.

 Problem 2 **Finding Cosine and Sine of a Radian Measure**

Got It?   What are the exact values of $\cos\left(\frac{7\pi}{6}\text{ radians}\right)$ and $\sin\left(\frac{7\pi}{6}\text{ radians}\right)$?

Think
How can a sketch of the angle on the unit circle be helpful?

 Practice   The measure θ of an angle in standard position is given. Find the exact values of $\cos\theta$ and $\sin\theta$ for each angle measure.

3. $-\frac{\pi}{4}$ radians

4. $\frac{2\pi}{3}$ radians

If you know the radius and the measure in radians of a central angle, you can find the length of the intercepted arc.

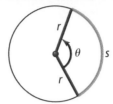

Key Concept Length of an Intercepted Arc

For a circle of radius r and a central angle of measure θ (in radians), the length s of the intercepted arc is $s = r\theta$.

Here's Why It Works The length of the intercepted arc is the same fraction of the circumference of the circle as the central angle is of 2π. So $\frac{\theta}{2\pi} = \frac{s}{C}$. Since $C = 2\pi r$, then $\frac{\theta}{2\pi} = \frac{s}{2\pi r}$. This simplifies to $\theta = \frac{s}{r}$. Multiplying by r results in $s = r\theta$.

Problem 3 Finding the Length of an Arc

Got It?   **a.** What is length b in the circle at the right to the nearest tenth?

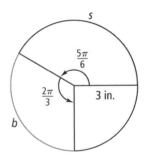

b. Reasoning If the radius of the circle doubled, how would the arc length change?

5. Use the circle to find the length of the indicated arc. Round your answer to the nearest tenth.

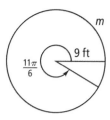

6. Find the length of the arc. Round your answer to the nearest foot.

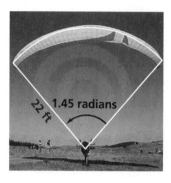

Problem 4 Using Radian Measure to Solve a Problem

Got It? Suppose a satellite orbits 3600 km above Earth's surface and
STEM completed an orbit every 4 h. How far would the satellite have travelled in 1 h?

7. Space A geostationary satellite is positioned 35,800 km above Earth's surface. It takes 24 h to complete one orbit. The radius of Earth is about 6400 km.

    a. What distance does the satellite travel in 1 h? 3 h? 2.5 h? 25 h?

    Ⓒ **b. Reasoning** After how many hours has the satellite traveled 200,000 km?

 Lesson Check

Do you know HOW?

8. Find the radian measure of an angle of 300°.

9. Find the degree measure of an angle of $\frac{3\pi}{4}$ radians.

10. Find the length a.

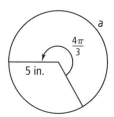

Do you UNDERSTAND?

11. Vocabulary The radius of a circle is 9 cm. A central angle intercepts an arc that is 9 cm. What is the measure of the central angle in radians?

12. Reasoning A certain baker believes that a perfect slice of pie has a central angle of 1 radian. How many "perfect" slices can he get out of one pie?

More Practice and Problem-Solving Exercises

B Apply

13. Think About a Plan Suppose a windshield wiper arm has a length of 22 in. and rotates through an angle of 110°. What distance does the tip of the wiper travel as it moves once across the windshield?

- Which formula can help you answer this question?
- Do you need to convert between degrees and radians?

Determine the quadrant or axis where the terminal side of each angle lies.

14. $\frac{4\pi}{3}$ radians   **15.** $-\frac{5\pi}{4}$ radians   **16.** $-\pi$ radians   **17.** $\frac{6\pi}{5}$ radians

18. **Geography** The 24 lines of longitude that approximate the 24 standard time zones are equally spaced around the equator.
    a. Suppose you use 24 central angles to divide a circle into 24 equal arcs. Express the measure of each angle in degrees and in radians.
    b. The radius of the equator is about 3960 mi. About how wide is each time zone at the equator?
    c. The radius of the Arctic Circle is about 1580 mi. About how wide is each time zone at the Arctic Circle?

Draw an angle in standard position with each given measure. Then find the values of the cosine and sine of the angle.

19. $\frac{7\pi}{4}$ radians   20. $-\frac{2\pi}{3}$ radians   21. $\frac{5\pi}{2}$ radians   22. $\frac{7\pi}{6}$ radians

Ⓒ 23. **Writing** Two angles are measured in radians. Explain how to tell whether the angles are coterminal without rewriting their measures in degrees.

Ⓒ 24. **Open-Ended** Draw an angle in standard position. Draw a circle with its center at the vertex of the angle. Find the measure of the angle in radians and degrees.

25. **Transportation** Suppose the radius of a bicycle wheel is 13 in. (measured to the outside of the tire). Find the number of radians through which a point on the tire turns when the bicycle has moved forward a distance of 12 ft.

Ⓒ 26. **Error Analysis** A student wanted to rewrite $\frac{9\pi}{4}$ radians in degrees. The screen shows her calculation. What error did the student make?

9*π/4*360/2*π

3997.189782

27. **Music** A CD with diameter 12 cm spins in a CD player. Calculate how much farther a point on the outside edge of the CD travels in one revolution than a point 1 cm closer to the center of the CD.

28. **Geography** Assume that Earth is a sphere with radius 3960 miles. A town is at latitude 32° N. Find the distance in miles from the town to the North Pole. (*Hint*: Latitude is measured north and south from the equator.)

Ⓒ **Challenge**

The given angle θ is in standard position. Find the radian measure of the angle that results after the given number of revolutions from the terminal side of θ.

29. $\theta = \frac{\pi}{2}$; 1 clockwise revolution   30. $\theta = -\frac{2\pi}{3}$; 1 counterclockwise revolution

Ⓒ 31. **Reasoning** Use the proportion $\frac{\text{measure of central angle}}{\text{length of intercepted arc}} = \frac{\text{measure of one completed rotation}}{\text{circumference}}$ to derive the formula $s = r\theta$. Use θ for the central angle measure and s for the arc length. Measure the rotation in radians.

6-4 The Sine Function

F.TF.2 Explain how the unit circle . . . enables the extension of trigonometric functions to all real numbers . . .
Also **F.IF.7, F.IF.7.e, F.TF.5**

Objectives To identify properties of the sine function
To graph sine curves

 Solve It! Write your solution to the Solve It in the space below.

The **sine function**, $y = \sin \theta$, matches the measure θ of an angle in standard position with the y-coordinate of a point on the unit circle. This point is where the terminal side of the angle intersects the unit circle.

You can graph the sine function in radians or degrees. In this book, you should use radians unless degrees are specified. For each and every point along the unit circle, the radian measure of the arc has a corresponding sine value. In the graphs below, the points for 1, 2, and 3 radians are marked on the unit circle. The vertical bars represent the sine values of the points on the circle translated onto the sine graph.

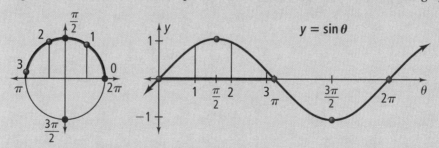

Essential Understanding As the terminal side of an angle rotates about the origin (beginning at 0), its sine value on the unit circle increases from 0 to 1, decreases from 1 to -1, and then increases back to 0.

Problem 1 **Estimating Sine Values Graphically**

Got It? What is a reasonable estimate for each value from the graph? Check your estimate with a calculator.

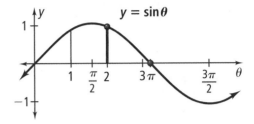

a. sin 3

b. $\sin \frac{3\pi}{2}$

A Practice Use the graph at the right to find the value of $y = \sin \theta$ for each value of θ.

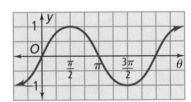

1. 5 radians

2. $\frac{7\pi}{4}$ radians

The graph of a sine function is called a **sine curve**. By varying the period (horizontal length of one cycle), you get different sine curves.

Problem 2 Finding the Period of a Sine Curve

Got It? How many cycles occur in the graph? What is the period of the sine curve?

a.
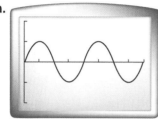

Xmin = 0
Xmax = 4π
Xscl = π/2
Ymin = −2
Ymax = 2
Yscl = 1

b.
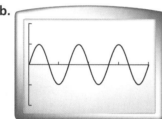

Xmin = 0
Xmax = 4π
Xscl = π/2
Ymin = −2
Ymax = 2
Yscl = 1

A Practice Determine the number of cycles each sine function has in the interval from 0 to 2π. Find the period of each function.

3.
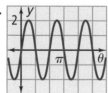

4.
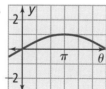

You can also vary the amplitude of a sine curve.

Problem 3 Finding the Amplitude of a Sine Curve

Think

Is the value of *a* always equal to the amplitude of the sine curve?

Got It? The equation of the graph is of the form $y = a \sin x$. What is the amplitude of the sine curve? What is the value of a?

a.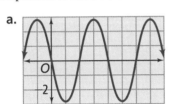

b.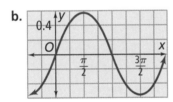

A Practice 5. Determine the number of cycles the sine function has in the interval from 0 to 2π. Find the amplitude and period of the function.

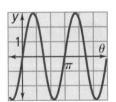

The summary box below lists the properties of sine functions.

 **take note**

Concept Summary Properties of Sine Functions

Suppose $y = a \sin b\theta$, with $a \neq 0$, $b > 0$, and θ in radians.

- $|a|$ is the amplitude of the function.
- b is the number of cycles in the interval from 0 to 2π.
- $\frac{2\pi}{b}$ is the period of the function.

You can use five points equally spaced through one cycle to sketch a sine curve. For $a > 0$, this five-point pattern is *zero–max–zero–min–zero*.

Problem 4 **Sketching a Graph**

 Think
How is the period of the function related to the value of b in the equation?

Got It? What is the graph of one cycle of a sine curve with amplitude 3, period 4π, and $a > 0$? Use the form $y = a \sin b\theta$. What is an equation with $a > 0$ for the sine curve?

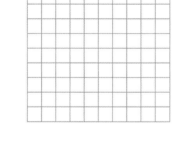

A Practice Sketch one cycle of each sine curve. Assume $a > 0$. Write an equation for each graph.

6. amplitude $\frac{1}{3}$, period π

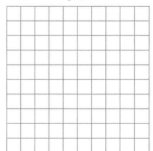

7. amplitude 3, period 2π

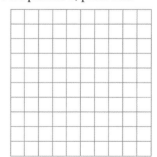

Got It?   What is the graph of one cycle of each sine function?

a. $y = 1.5 \sin 2\theta$

b. $y = 3 \sin \frac{\pi}{2}\theta$

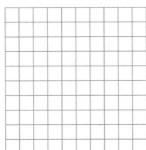 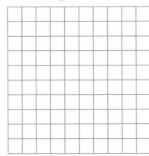

 Practice   Sketch one cycle of the graph of each sine function.

8. $y = -\sin \frac{\pi}{2}\theta$

9. $y = 4 \sin \frac{1}{2}\theta$

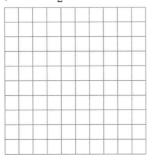 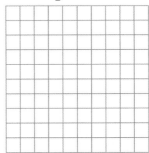

 Problem 6   Using the Sine Function to Model Light Waves

Got It?   The graphs at the right model waves of red, blue, and yellow light. What equation best models red light?

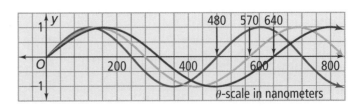

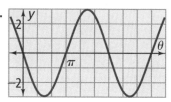 **Practice** Find the period of each sine curve. Then write an equation for each sine function.

10.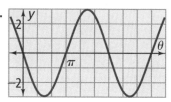

11.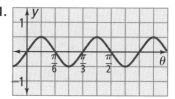

 Lesson Check

Do you know HOW?

12. a. How many cycles does this graph of a sine function have in the interval from 0 to 2π?

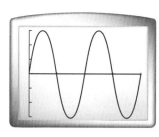

Xmin $= 0$
Xmax $= 2\pi$
Xscl $= \pi/2$
Ymin $= -3$
Ymax $= 3$
Yscl $= 1$

b. What are the amplitude and period?

c. Write an equation for the function.

13. Sketch one cycle of the sine curve that has amplitude 2 and period $\frac{\pi}{3}$.

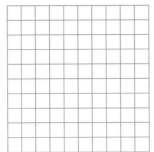

Do you UNDERSTAND?

⊚ 14. Vocabulary What is the difference between one cycle and the period of a sine curve?

⊚ 15. Open-Ended Write a sine function that has a period greater than the period for $y = 5 \sin \frac{\theta}{2}$.

⊚ 16. Error Analysis A student drew this graph for the function $y = -3 \sin \pi\theta$. Describe and correct the student's errors.

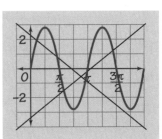

More Practice and Problem-Solving Exercises

MATHEMATICAL
PRACTICES

B Apply

Determine the number of cycles each sine function has in the interval from 0 to 2π. Find the amplitude and period of each function.

17. $y = \sin\theta$

18. $y = \sin 5\theta$

19. $y = \sin \pi\theta$

20. $y = 3\sin\theta$

21. $y = -5\sin\theta$

22. $y = -5\sin 2\pi\theta$

23. Graphing Calculator Graph the functions $y = 3\sin\theta$ and $y = -3\sin\theta$ on the same screen. How are the two graphs related? How does the graph of $y = a\sin b\theta$ change when a is replaced with its opposite?

24. Use the formula Period $= \frac{2\pi}{b}$ to find the period of each sine function.
  a. $y = 1.5\sin 2\theta$
  b. $y = 3\sin\frac{\pi}{2}\theta$

25. Think About a Plan The sound wave for the note A above middle C can be modeled by the function $y = 0.001\sin 880\pi\theta$. Sketch a graph of the sine curve.
  - What is the period of the function?
  - What is the amplitude of the function?
  - How many cycles of the graph are between 0 and 2π?

Find the period and amplitude of each sine function. Then sketch each function from 0 to 2π.

26. $y = -3.5\sin 5\theta$

27. $y = \frac{5}{2}\sin 2\theta$

28. $y = -2\sin 2\pi\theta$

29. $y = 0.4\sin 3\theta$

30. $y = 0.5\sin\frac{\pi}{3}\theta$

31. $y = -1.2\sin\frac{5\pi}{6}\theta$

32. Open-Ended Write the equations of three sine functions with the same amplitude that have periods of 2, 3, and 4. Then sketch all three graphs.

33. Music The sound wave for a certain tuning fork can be modeled by the function $y = 0.001\sin 1320\pi\theta$. Sketch a graph of the sine curve.

34. a. What is the average rate of change of $f(x) = \sin x$ from $x = 0$ to $x = \pi$?
  b. Find two other intervals over which the average rate of change of the sine function is 0.
  c. Reasoning Explain why for any periodic function, you can find an infinite number of intervals over which the average rate of change is 0.

Challenge

STEM **Sound** For sound waves, the period and the frequency of a pitch are reciprocals of each other: period $= \frac{\text{seconds}}{\text{cycle}}$ and frequency $= \frac{\text{cycles}}{\text{second}}$. Write an equation for each pitch. Let $\theta =$ time in seconds. Use $a = 1$.

35. the lowest pitch easily heard by humans: 30 cycles per second

36. the lowest pitch heard by elephants: 15 cycles per second

37. the highest pitch heard by bats: 120,000 cycles per second

Find the period and amplitude of each function. Sketch each function from 0 to 2π.

38. $y = \sin(\theta + 2)$ **39.** $y = \sin(\theta - 3)$ **40.** $y = \sin(2\theta + 4)$

STEM **41. Astronomy** In Houston, Texas, at the spring equinox (March 21), there are 12 hours and 9 minutes of sunlight. The longest and shortest day of the year vary from the equinox by 1 h 55 min. The amount of sunlight during the year can be modeled by a sine function.

a. Define the independent and dependent variables for a function that models the variation in hours of sunlight in Houston.

b. What are the amplitude and period of the function measured in days?

c. Write a function that relates the number of days away from the spring equinox to the variation in hours of sunlight in Houston.

d. **Estimation** Use your function from part (c). In Houston, about how much less sunlight does February 14 have than March 21?

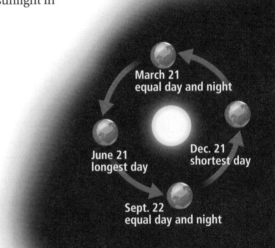

TECHNOLOGY LAB

Use With Lesson 6-4

Graphing Trigonometric Functions

F.IF.7 Graph functions expressed symbolically and show key features of the graph, . . .

Activity 1

MATHEMATICAL PRACTICES

Compare the graphs of $y = \cos x$ from $-360°$ to $360°$ and from -2π to 2π radians.

Step 1 Press **mode** to set the mode to degrees. Adjust the window values. Graph the function.

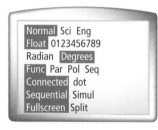

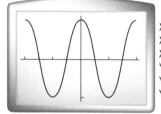

Xmin $= -360$
Xmax $= 360$
Xscl $= 90$
Ymin $= -1.2$
Ymax $= 1.2$
Yscl $= 1$

Step 2 Change the mode to radians. Graph the function.

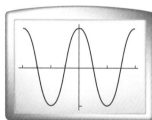

Xmin $= -2\pi$
Xmax $= 2\pi$
Xscl $= \pi/2$
Ymin $= -1.2$
Ymax $= 1.2$
Yscl $= 1$

The graphs appear to be identical. The function has a period of $360°$, or 2π radians.

Activity 2

Graph the function $y = \sin x$. Find $\sin 30°$ and $\sin 150°$.

Step 1 Set the mode to degrees and adjust the window values as shown.

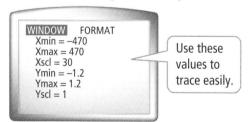

Use these values to trace easily.

Step 2 Graph the function. Use the (trace) key to find the y-values when $x = 30$ and $x = 150$.

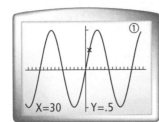
X=30 | Y=.5

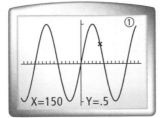
X=150 | Y=.5

Exercises

Use appropriate window values to identify the period of each function in radians and in degrees. Then evaluate each function at 90°.

1. $y = \cos x$

2. $y = \sin x$

3. $y = \sin 3x$

4. $y = -3 \sin x$

5. $y = \cos(x + 30)$

Writing Graph the two functions in the same window. Compare the graphs. How are they similar? How are they different?

6. $y = \sin x$, $y = \cos x$

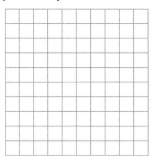

7. $y = \sin x$, $y = \cos\left(x - \frac{\pi}{2}\right)$

8. $y = \sin x$, $y = \cos\left(x + \frac{\pi}{2}\right)$

6-5 The Cosine Function

F.IF.7.e Graph . . . trigonometric functions, showing period, midline, and amplitude. Also **F.IF.7, F.TF.2, F.TF.5**

Objectives To graph and write cosine functions
To solve trigonometric equations

Solve It! Write your solution to the Solve It in the space below.

The **cosine function**, $y = \cos\theta$, matches θ with the x-coordinate of the point on the unit circle where the terminal side of angle θ intersects the unit circle. The symmetry of the set of points $(x, y) = (\cos\theta, \sin\theta)$ on the unit circle guarantees that the graphs of sine and cosine are congruent translations of each other.

Essential Understanding For each and every point along the unit circle the radian measure of the arc has a corresponding cosine value. The colored bars represent the cosine values of the points on the circle translated onto the cosine graph. So as the terminal side of an angle rotates about the origin (beginning at 0°), its cosine value on the unit circle decreases from 1 to −1, and then increases back to 1.

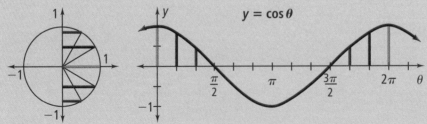

Problem 1 Interpreting a Graph

Got It? Use the graph. What are the domain, period, range, and amplitude of the sine function? Where do the maximum and minimum values occur? Where do the zeros occur?

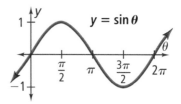

Practice Find the period and amplitude of each cosine function. Determine the values of *x* for $0 \leq x \leq 2\pi$ where the maximum value(s), minimum value(s), and zeros occur.

1.

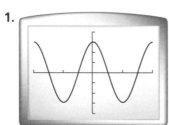

Xmin = -2π
Xmax = 2π
Xscl = π
Ymin = -4
Ymax = 4
Yscl = 1

2.

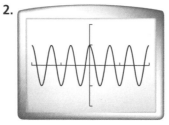

Xmin = -2π
Xmax = 2π
Xscl = π
Ymin = -2
Ymax = 2
Yscl = 1

Concept Summary   Properties of Cosine Functions

Suppose $y = a \cos b\theta$, with $a \neq 0$, $b > 0$, and θ in radians.

- $|a|$ is the amplitude of the function.
- b is the number of cycles in the interval from 0 to 2π.
- $\frac{2\pi}{b}$ is the period of the function.

To graph a cosine function, locate five points equally spaced through one cycle. For $a > 0$, this five-point pattern is *max-zero-min-zero-max*.

ONLINE PROBLEMS **Problem 2**   **Sketching the Graph of a Cosine Function**

Plan

What should you find to graph the function?

Got It?   Sketch one cycle of $y = 2 \cos \frac{\theta}{3}$.

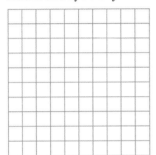

(A) Practice Sketch one cycle of the graph of each cosine function.

3. $y = \cos 2\theta$

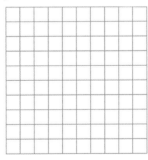

4. $y = -\cos \pi\theta$

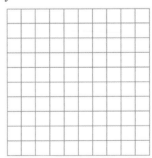

Got It?
STEM

a. Suppose that the water level varies 70 inches between low tide at 8:40 A.M. and high tide at 2:55 P.M. What is a cosine function that models the variation in inches above and below the average water level as a function of the number of hours since 8:40 A.M.?

b. At what point in the cycle does the function cross the midline? What does the midline represent?

Practice

5. Write a cosine function with amplitude π and period 2. Assume that $a > 0$.

6. Write an equation of a cosine function for the graph shown.

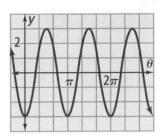

You can solve an equation by graphing to find an exact location along a sine or cosine curve.

Problem 4 **Solving a Cosine Equation**

Got It? What are all solutions to each equation in the interval from 0 to 2π?

a. $3 \cos 2t = -2$ **b.** $-2 \cos \theta = 1.2$

Plan

How can two equations help you find the solutions?

© c. Reasoning In the interval from 0 to 2π, when is $-2 \cos \theta$ less than 1.2? Greater than 1.2?

Practice Solve each equation in the interval from 0 to 2π. Round your answer to the nearest hundredth.

7. $-2 \cos \pi\theta = 0.3$

8. $8 \cos \frac{\pi}{3}t = 5$

 Lesson Check

Do you know HOW?

Sketch the graph of each function in the interval from 0 to 2π.

9. $y = \cos \frac{1}{2}\theta$

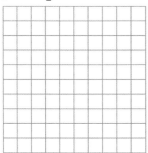

10. $y = 2 \cos \frac{\pi}{3}\theta$

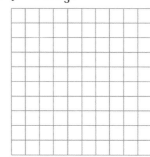

Write a cosine function for each description. Assume that $a > 0$.

11. amplitude 3, period 2π

12. amplitude 1.5, period π

Do you UNDERSTAND?

13. Open-Ended Write a cosine function with amplitude 5 and between 2 and 3 cycles from 0 to 2π.

14. Assume θ is in the interval from 0 to 2π.

    a. For what values of θ is y positive for $y = \cos \theta$?

    b. For what values of θ is y positive for $y = -\sin \theta$?

    c. Reasoning What sine function has the same graph as $y = -3 \cos \frac{2\pi}{3}\theta$?

More Practice and Problem-Solving Exercises

 MATHEMATICAL PRACTICES

B Apply

Identify the period, range, and amplitude of each function.

15. $y = 3 \cos \theta$ **16.** $y = -\cos 2t$ **17.** $y = 2 \cos \frac{1}{2}t$ **18.** $y = \frac{1}{3} \cos \frac{\theta}{2}$

19. $y = 3 \cos\left(-\frac{\theta}{3}\right)$ **20.** $y = -\frac{1}{2} \cos 3\theta$ **21.** $y = 16 \cos \frac{3\pi}{2}t$ **22.** $y = 0.7 \cos \pi t$

© **23. Think About a Plan** In Buenos Aires, Argentina, the average monthly temperature is highest in January and lowest in July, ranging from 83°F to 57°F. Write a cosine function that models the change in temperature according to the month of the year.
  • How can you find the amplitude?
  • What part of the problem describes the length of the cycle?

© **24. Writing** Explain how you can apply what you know about solving cosine equations to solving sine equations. Use $-1 = 6 \sin 2t$ as an example.

Solve each equation in the interval from 0 to 2π. Round your answers to the nearest hundredth.

25. $\sin \theta = 0.6$ **26.** $-3 \sin 2\theta = 1.5$ **27.** $\sin \pi\theta = 1$

Compare the amplitude and period of the cosine functions $f(x)$ and $g(x)$.

28. $f(x) = -\cos 4x$

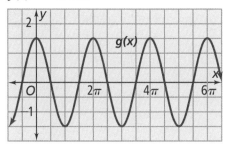

29. $f(x) = 2 \cos 2x$

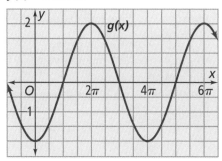

30. a. Solve $-2 \sin \theta = 1.2$ in the interval from 0 to 2π.
  b. Solve $-2 \sin \theta = 1.2$ in the interval $2\pi \le \theta \le 4\pi$. How are these solutions related to the solutions in part (a)?

31. a. Graph the equation $y = -30 \cos\left(\frac{6\pi}{37}t\right)$ from Problem 3.
  b. The independent variable θ represents time (in hours). Find four times at which the water level is the highest.
  c. For how many hours during each cycle is the water level above the line $y = 0$? Below $y = 0$?

STEM **32. Tides** The table at the right shows the times for high tide and low tide of one day. The markings on the side of a local pier showed a high tide of 7 ft and a low tide of 4 ft on the previous day.

Tide Table	
High tide	4:03 A.M.
Low tide	10:14 A.M.
High tide	4:25 P.M.
Low tide	10:36 P.M.

   a. What is the average depth of water at the pier? What is the amplitude of the variation from the average depth?

   b. How long is one cycle of the tide?

   c. Write a cosine function that models the relationship between the depth of water and the time of day. Use $y = 0$ to represent the average depth of water. Use $t = 0$ to represent the time 4:03 A.M.

  ⓔ **d. Reasoning** Suppose your boat needs at least 5 ft of water to approach or leave the pier. Between what times could you come and go?

ⓒ Challenge

33. Graph one cycle of $y = \cos\theta$, one cycle of $y = -\cos\theta$, and one cycle of $y = \cos(-\theta)$ on the same set of axes. Use the unit circle to explain any relationships you see among these graphs.

STEM **34. Biology** A helix is a three-dimensional spiral. The coiled strands of DNA and the edges of twisted crepe paper are examples of helixes. In the diagram, the y-coordinate of each edge illustrates a cosine function. Write an equation for the y-coordinate of one edge.

35. a. Graphing Calculator Graph $y = \cos\theta$ and $y = \cos\left(\theta - \frac{\pi}{2}\right)$ in the interval from 0 to 2π. What translation of the graph of $y = \cos\theta$ produces the graph of $y = \cos\left(\theta - \frac{\pi}{2}\right)$?

   b. Graph $y = \cos\left(\theta - \frac{\pi}{2}\right)$ and $y = \sin\theta$ in the interval from 0 to 2π. What do you notice?

  ⓔ **c. Reasoning** Explain how you could rewrite a sine function as a cosine function.

6-6 The Tangent Function

F.IF.7.e Graph . . . trigonometric functions, showing period, midline, and amplitude. Also **F.IF.7**, **F.TF.2**, **F.TF.5**

Objective   To graph the tangent function

Solve It!   Write your solution to the Solve It in the space below.

The tangent function is closely associated with the sine and cosine functions, but it differs from them in three dramatic ways.

Essential Understanding   The tangent function has infinitely many points of discontinuity, with a vertical asymptote at each point. Its range is all real numbers. Its period is π, half that of both the sine and cosine functions. Its domain is all real numbers except odd multiples of $\frac{\pi}{2}$.

take note

Key Concept   Tangent of an Angle

Suppose the terminal side of an angle θ in standard position intersects the unit circle at the point (x, y). Then the ratio $\frac{y}{x}$ is the **tangent of θ**, denoted $\tan \theta$.

In this diagram, $x = \cos \theta$, $y = \sin \theta$, and $\frac{y}{x} = \tan \theta$.

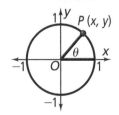

Problem 1 **Finding Tangents Geometrically**

Got It? What is the value of each expression? Do not use a calculator.

Think

Will a graph help?

  a. $\tan \frac{\pi}{2}$

  b. $\tan \frac{2\pi}{3}$

  c. $\tan \left(-\frac{\pi}{4} \right)$

Ⓐ Practice Find each value without using a calculator.

  1. $\tan 2\pi$ **2.** $\tan \left(-\frac{3\pi}{4} \right)$

There is another way to geometrically define tan θ.

The diagram shows the unit circle and the vertical line $x = 1$. The angle θ in standard position determines a point $P(x, y)$.

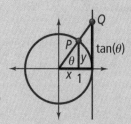

By similar triangles, the length of the vertical red segment divided by the length of the horizontal red segment is equal to $\frac{y}{x}$. The horizontal red segment has length 1 since it is a radius of the unit circle, so the length of the vertical red segment is $\frac{y}{x}$, or tan θ, which is also the *y*-coordinate of Q.

If θ is an angle in standard position and *not* an odd multiple of $\frac{\pi}{2}$, then the line containing the terminal side of θ intersects the line $x = 1$ at a point Q with *y*-coordinate tan θ.

The graph at the right shows one cycle of the **tangent function**, $y = \tan θ$, for $-\frac{\pi}{2} < θ < \frac{\pi}{2}$. The pattern repeats periodically with period π. At $θ = \pm\frac{\pi}{2}$, the line through P fails to intersect the line $x = 1$, so tan θ is undefined.

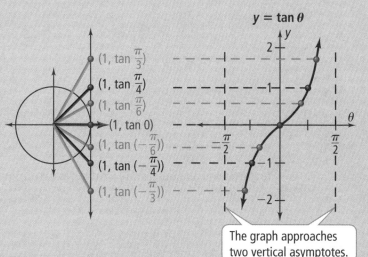

The graph approaches two vertical asymptotes.

take note

Concept Summary   Properties of Tangent Functions

Suppose $y = a \tan bθ$, with $a \neq 0$, $b > 0$, and θ in radians.

- $\frac{\pi}{b}$ is the period of the function.
- One cycle occurs in the interval from $-\frac{\pi}{2b}$ to $\frac{\pi}{2b}$.
- There are vertical asymptotes at each end of the cycle.

You can use asymptotes and three points to sketch one cycle of a tangent curve. As with sine and cosine, the five elements are equally spaced through one cycle. Use the pattern *asymptote-(−a)-zero-(a)-asymptote*. In the graph at the right, $a = b = 1$.

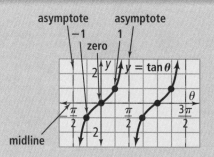

asymptote   asymptote
zero
midline

The next example shows how to use the period, asymptotes, and points to graph a tangent function.

Got It? Sketch two cycles of the graph of each tangent curve.

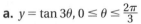

a. $y = \tan 3\theta, 0 \leq \theta \leq \frac{2\pi}{3}$

b. $y = \tan \frac{\pi}{2}\theta, 0 \leq \theta \leq 4$

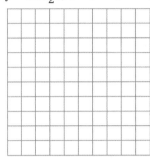

Think

What is the period of each tangent curve?

 Practice **3.** Identify the period and determine where two asymptotes occur for the function $y = \tan 4\theta$.

4. Sketch the graph of $y = \tan(-\theta)$ in the interval from 0 to 2π.

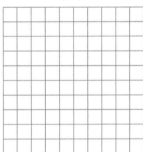

Problem 3 Using the Tangent Function to Solve Problems

Got It? **a.** The function $y = 100 \tan \theta$ models the
STEM height of the triangle, where θ is the angle
indicated (from Problem 3). What is the
height of the triangle when $\theta = 25°$?

b. Reasoning The architect wants the triangle to be at least one story
tall. The average height of a story is 14 ft. What must θ be for the
height of the triangle to be at least 14 ft?

Practice **Graphing Calculator** Graph each function on the interval $0 \le x \le 2\pi$
and $-200 \le y \le 200$. Evaluate each function at $x = \frac{\pi}{4}, \frac{\pi}{2}$, and $\frac{3\pi}{4}$.

5. $y = 50 \tan x$

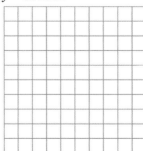

6. $y = -100 \tan x$

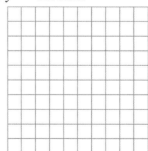

Lesson Check

Do you know HOW?

Find each value without using a calculator.

7. $\tan \frac{\pi}{4}$

8. $\tan \frac{7\pi}{6}$

9. $\tan \left(-\frac{\pi}{4}\right)$

10. $\tan \left(-\frac{3\pi}{3}\right)$

Do you UNDERSTAND?

© 11. Vocabulary Successive asymptotes of a tangent curve are $x = \frac{\pi}{3}$ and $x = -\frac{\pi}{3}$. What is the period?

© **12. Error Analysis** A quiz contained a question asking students to solve the equation $8 = -2 \tan 3\theta$ to the nearest hundredth of a radian. One student did not receive full credit for writing $\theta = -1.33$. Describe and correct the student's error.

© **13. Writing** Explain how you can write a tangent function that has the same period as $y = \sin 4\theta$.

More Practice and Problem-Solving Exercises

B Apply

Identify the period for each tangent function. Then graph each function in the interval from -2π to 2π.

14. $y = \tan \frac{\pi}{6}\theta$

15. $y = \tan 2.5\theta$

16. $y = \tan\left(-\frac{3}{2\pi}\theta\right)$

 Graphing Calculator Solve each equation in the interval from 0 to 2π. Round your answers to the nearest hundredth.

17. $\tan \theta = 2$

18. $\tan \theta = -2$

19. $6 \tan 2\theta = 1$

© **20. a. Open-Ended** Write a tangent function.
    b. Graph the function on the interval -2π to 2π.
    c. Identify the period and the asymptotes of the function.

◎ 21. **Think About a Plan** A quilter is making hexagonal placemats by sewing together six quilted isosceles triangles. Each triangle has a base length of 10 in. The function $y = 5 \tan \theta$ models the height of the triangular quilts, where θ is the measure of one of the base angles. Graph the function. What is the area of the placemat if the triangles are equilateral?

- How can a graph of the function help you find the height of each triangle?
- How can you find the area of each triangle?
- What will be the last step in your solution?

22. **Ceramics** An artist is making triangular ceramic tiles for a triangular patio. The patio will be an equilateral triangle with base 18 ft and height 15.6 ft.
   a. Find the area of the patio in square feet.
   b. The artist uses tiles that are isosceles triangles with base 6 in. The function $y = 3 \tan \theta$ models the height of the triangular tiles, where θ is the measure of one of the base angles. Graph the function. Find the height of the tile when $\theta = 30°$ and when $\theta = 60°$.
   c. Find the area of one tile in square inches when $\theta = 30°$ and when $\theta = 60°$.
   d. Find the number of tiles the patio will require if $\theta = 30°$ and if $\theta = 60°$.

Use the function $y = 200 \tan x$ on the interval $0° \le x \le 141°$. Complete each ordered pair. Round your answers to the nearest whole number.

23. $(45°, \underline{\quad})$ **24.** $(\underline{\quad}°, 0)$ **25.** $(\underline{\quad}°, -200)$ **26.** $(141°, \underline{\quad})$ **27.** $(\underline{\quad}°, 550)$

Write an equation of a tangent function for each graph.

28. 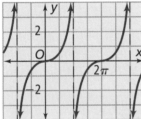 **29.** 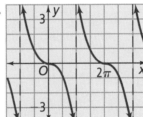 **30.**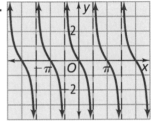

31. **Construction** An architect is designing a hexagonal gazebo. The floor is a hexagon made up of six isosceles triangles. The function $y = 4 \tan \theta$ models the height of one triangle, where θ is the measure of one of the base angles and the base of the triangle is 8 ft long.
   a. Graph the function. Find the height of one triangle when $\theta = 60°$.
   b. Find the area of one triangle in square feet when $\theta = 60°$.
   c. Find the area of the gazebo floor in square feet when the triangles forming the hexagon are equilateral.

32. a. The graph of $y = \frac{1 - \cos x}{\sin x}$ suggests a tangent curve of the form $y = a \tan bx$. Graph the function using the window $[-3\pi, 3\pi]$ by $[-4, 4]$.

   b. What is the period of the curve? What is the value of a?

   c. Find the x-coordinate halfway between a removable discontinuity and the asymptote to its right. Find the corresponding y-coordinate.

   d. Find an equivalent function of the form $y = a \tan bx$.

Ⓒ Challenge

33. Geometry Use the drawing at the right and similar triangles. Justify the statement that $\tan \theta = \frac{\sin \theta}{\cos \theta}$.

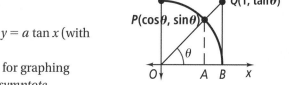

Ⓒ 34. a. Graph $y = \tan x$, $y = a \tan x$ (with $a > 0$), and $y = a \tan x$ (with $a < 0$) on the same coordinate plane.

   b. Reasoning Recall the pattern of five elements for graphing a tangent function: *asymptote-(−1)-zero-(1)-asymptote*. How does the value of a affect this pattern?

Ⓒ 35. Writing How many solutions does the equation $x = \tan x$ have for $0 \leq x \leq 2\pi$? Explain.

6-7 Translating Sine and Cosine Functions

F.TF.5 Choose trigonometric functions to model periodic phenomena . . . Also **F.IF.7, F.IF.7.e, F.BF.3**

Objectives To graph translations of trigonometric functions
To write equations of translations

Solve It! Write your solution to the Solve It in the space below.

Recall that for any function f, you can graph $f(x - h)$ by translating the graph of f by h units horizontally. You can graph $f(x) + k$ by translating the graph of f by k units vertically.

Essential Understanding You can translate periodic functions in the same way that you translate other functions.

Each horizontal translation of certain periodic functions is a **phase shift**.

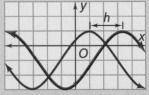

g(x): horizontal translation of f(x)
$$g(x) = f(x - h)$$

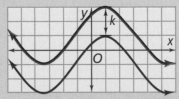

h(x): vertical translation of f(x)
$$h(x) = f(x) + k$$

When $g(x) = f(x - h)$, the value of h is the amount of the shift. If $h > 0$, the shift is to the right. If $h < 0$, the shift is to the left. When $h(x) = f(x) + k$, the value of k is the amount of the midline shift. If $k > 0$, the midline shifts up. If $k < 0$, the midline shifts down.

Problem 1 **Identifying Phase Shifts**

Got It? What is the value of h in each translation? Describe each phase shift (using a phrase such as 3 *units to the left*).

    a. $g(t) = f(t - 5)$

    b. $y = \sin(x + 3)$

> **Think**
> How can you rewrite the equation to help find the value of h?

Ⓐ Practice Determine the value of h in each translation. Describe each phase shift (using a phrase like 3 *units to the left*).

    1. $f(x) = g(x - 3)$

    2. $y = \sin(x + \pi)$

You can analyze a translation to determine how it relates to the parent function.

Problem 2 **Graphing Translations**

Got It? Use the graph of $y = \sin x$ from Problem 2. What is the graph of each translation in the interval $0 \le x \le 2\pi$?

a. $y = \sin x - 2$

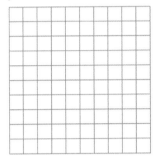

b. $y = \sin(x - 2)$

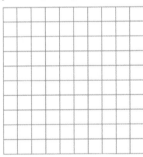

c. Which translation is a phase shift?

d. Which translation gives the graph a new midline?

(A) Practice   **3.** Use the function $f(x)$ at the right. Graph the translation.

$g(x) = f(x + 2)$

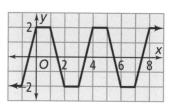

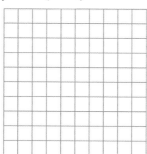

4. Graph the translation of $y = \cos x$ in the interval from 0 to 2π.

$y = \cos(x - \pi)$

You can translate both vertically and horizontally to produce combined translations.

Problem 3   **Graphing a Combined Translation**

Got It?   Use the graph at the right of the parent function $y = \cos x$. What is the graph of each translation in the interval $0 \le x \le 2\pi$?

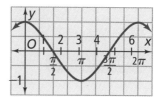

a. $y = \cos(x - 2) + 5$

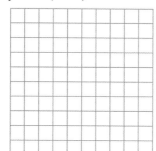

b. $y = \cos(x + 1) + 3$

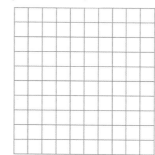

Practice **5.** Describe any phase shift and vertical shift in the graph of
$y = \sin(x - 3) + 2$.

6. Graph the function $y = \cos(x - \pi) - 3$ in the interval from 0 to 2π.

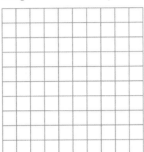

The translations graphed in Problems 2 and 3 belong to the families of the sine and cosine functions.

take note

Concept Summary   Families of Sine and Cosine Functions

Parent Function   **Transformed Function**

$y = \sin x$ $y = a \sin b(x - h) + k$

$y = \cos x$ $y = a \cos b(x - h) + k$

- $|a|$ = amplitude (vertical stretch or shrink)
- $\frac{2\pi}{b}$ = period (when x is in radians and $b > 0$)
- h = phase shift, or horizontal shift
- k = vertical shift ($y = k$ is the midline)

 Problem 4 **Graphing a Translation of $y = \sin 2x$**

Got It? What is the graph of each translation in the interval from 0 to 2π?

a. $y = -3 \sin 2\left(x - \frac{\pi}{3}\right) - \frac{3}{2}$

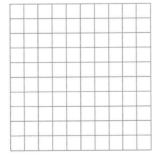

b. $y = 2 \cos \frac{\pi}{2}(x + 1) - 3$

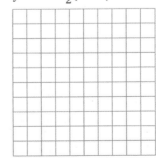

Ⓐ Practice Graph each function in the interval from 0 to 2π.

7. $y = \cos 2\left(x + \frac{\pi}{2}\right) - 2$

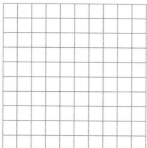

8. $y = 3 \sin \frac{\pi}{2}(x - 2)$

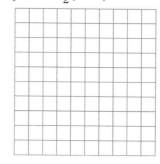

You can write an equation to describe a translation.

 **Problem 5** **Writing Translations**

Got It? What is an equation that models each translation?

a. $y = \cos x$, $\frac{\pi}{2}$ units up

b. $y = 2 \sin x$, $\frac{\pi}{4}$ units to the right

Think

What are a, b, h, and k in $y = a \sin b (x - h) + k$?

Ⓐ Practice Write an equation for each translation.

9. $y = \sin x$, 3 units up

10. $y = \cos x$, 1.5 units to the right

You can write a trigonometric function to model a situation.

Problem 6 **Writing a Trigonometric Function to Model a Situation**

Got It?
STEM

a. Use the model in Problem 6 $(y = 22 \cos \frac{2\pi}{365}(x - 198) + 55$, where x is the days after the start of the calendar year) . What was the average temperature in your town 150 days into the year?

b. What value does the midline of this model represent?

c. Reasoning Can you use this model to predict temperatures for next year? Explain your answer.

Practice **11. Temperature** The table below shows water temperatures at a buoy in the Gulf of Mexico on several days of the year.

STEM

Day of Year	16	47	75	106	136	167	198	228	258	289	319	350
Temperature (°F)	71	69	70	73	77	82	85	86	84	82	78	74

a. Plot the data.

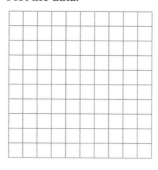

b. Write a cosine model for the data.

Lesson Check

Do you know HOW?

12. Graph $y = \sin\left(x + \frac{\pi}{4}\right)$ in the interval from 0 to 2π.

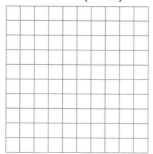

13. Describe any phase shift or vertical shift in the graph of $y = 4 \cos(x - 2) + 9$.

14. What is an equation that shifts $y = \cos x$, 3 units up and $\frac{2\pi}{3}$ units to the right?

Do you UNDERSTAND?

15. Vocabulary Write a sine function that has amplitude 4, period 3π, phase shift π, and vertical shift -5.

16. Error Analysis Two students disagree on the translation for $y = \cos 3\left(x + \frac{\pi}{6}\right)$. Amberly says that it is $\frac{\pi}{2}$ units to the left of $y = \cos 3x$. Scott says that it is $\frac{\pi}{6}$ units to the left of $y = \cos 3x$. Is either student correct? Describe any errors of each student.

More Practice and Problem-Solving Exercises

B Apply

Write an equation for each translation.

17. $y = \cos x$, 3 units to the left and π units up

18. $y = \sin x$, $\frac{\pi}{2}$ units to the right and 3.5 units up

19. Think About a Plan The function $y = 1.5 \sin \frac{\pi}{6}(x - 6) + 2$ represents the average monthly rainfall for a town in central Florida, where x represents the number of the month (January = 1, February = 2, and so on). Rewrite the function using a cosine model.
- How does the graph of $y = \sin x$ translate to the graph of $y = \cos x$?
- What parts of the sine function will stay the same? What must change?

Write a cosine function for each graph. Then write a sine function for each graph.

20.

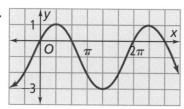

21.

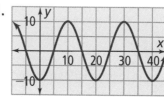

22. The graphs of $y = \sin x$ and $y = \cos x$ are shown at the right.
   a. What phase shift will translate the cosine graph onto the sine graph? Write your answer as an equation in the form $\sin x = \cos (x - h)$.
   b. What phase shift will translate the sine graph onto the cosine graph? Write your answer as an equation in the form $\cos x = \sin (x - h)$.

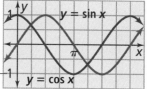

23. a. Open-Ended Draw a periodic function. Find its amplitude and period. Then sketch a translation of your function 3 units down and 4 units to the left.
   b. Reasoning Suppose your original function is $f(x)$. Describe your translation using the form $g(x) = f(x - h) + k$.

24. a. Write $y = 3 \sin (2x - 4) + 1$ in the form $y = a \sin b(x - h) + k$. (*Hint:* Factor where possible.)
   b. Find the amplitude, midline, and period. Describe any translations.

C Challenge

Use a graphing calculator to graph each function in the interval from 0 to 2π. Then sketch each graph.

25. $y = \sin x + x$

26. $y = \sin x + 2x$

27. $y = \cos x - 2x$

28. $y = \cos x + x$

29. $y = \sin(x + \cos x)$

30. $y = \sin(x + 2 \cos x)$

Plotting and Analyzing Residuals

S.ID.6.b Informally assess the fit of a function by . . . analyzing residuals.

MATHEMATICAL PRACTICES

Recall that you can use a *residual plot* to determine whether a particular function is a good fit for a set of data points. A *residual* is the difference between the y-value of a data point and $\hat{y}$, the corresponding y-value of a model for the data set. You can plot each of the points $(x, y - \hat{y})$ on a coordinate plane, and analyze the resulting residual plot to assess whether the function is a good fit for the data. For a good fit, the points in the plot have no apparent pattern.

Activity

Analyze the residual plot to determine whether the model is a good fit for the data.

x	0.4	1.3	2.3	4.1	5.9	7.3	8.7	10.5	11.1	13	13.6	15.4	17.7
y	0.7	2.5	3.6	3.5	0.7	−2	−3.7	−3.4	−2.7	0.83	2	4	2.2

Step 1 Using a graphing calculator, create a scatter plot of the data.

The data appear to be best modeled by a sine function.

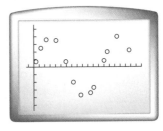

Step 2 Perform a regression.

Press **stat**. Select **CALC** and **SinReg** to find the model. The residuals are stored in the **RESID** list variable.

Step 3 Plot the residuals.

Press **stat plot** 1. Turn on Plot 1 using the list variable used for the x-values of the data set for the Xlist. Place the cursor to select the Ylist. Press **LIST** (2nd **STAT**) and select **RESID**. Press **zoom** 9 to graph.

There is no apparent pattern in the residual plot. When there is no apparent patter in the residual plot, the model is a good fit for the data.

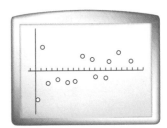

Exercises

In Exercises 1 and 2, use the SinReg function on a graphing calculator to find a sine function that models the data. Then make a residual plot. Does the sine function model the data well? Carefully sketch the residual plot and explain your reasoning.

1.

x	0	0.3	1	2.3	2.9	3.6	4.6	5.6	6.4	7.2
y	0	1.9	3.3	2.2	0.6	−0.9	−1.8	−1.1	0.2	1.2

x	8.3	9.2	10.2	11	12	12.8	13.7	14.8	15.6	16.4
y	1.2	0.2	−0.8	−1.2	−0.7	0.2	0.9	0.9	0.2	−0.6

2.

x	0.2	0.5	1.3	2.6	3.6	4.3	5.5	5.9	7.8	8.6	9.6	10.2
y	0.1	2.9	4.6	3.4	−1.5	−4.2	−4.1	−1.2	5.2	3	0.1	−4.2

3. Find linear, quadratic, cubic, and exponential functions that model the data below using the **LinReg**, **QuadReg**, **CubicReg**, and **ExpReg** functions on a graphing calculator. Determine which functions model the data well by analyzing the residual plots for each function.

x	−1.2	−0.3	0.8	1.5	2.5	3.2	4.1	4.9	5.4	6.3
y	0.43	0.61	0.81	1.74	2.3	2.83	5.66	9.19	12.13	17.15

6-8 Reciprocal Trigonometric Functions

F.IF.7.e Graph . . . trigonometric functions, showing period, midline, and amplitude. Also **F.IF.7, F.TF.2, F.TF.5**

Objectives To evaluate reciprocal trigonometric functions
To graph reciprocal trigonometric functions

 Solve It! Write your solution to the Solve It in the space below.

To solve an equation $ax = b$, you multiply each side by the reciprocal of a. If a is a trigonometric expression, you need to use its reciprocal.

Essential Understanding Cosine, sine, and tangent have reciprocals. Cosine and *secant* are reciprocals, as are sine and *cosecant*. Tangent and *cotangent* are also reciprocals.

take note

Key Concept Cosecant, Secant, and Cotangent Functions

The **cosecant** (csc), **secant** (sec), and **cotangent** (cot) functions are defined using reciprocals. Their domains do not include the real numbers θ that make the denominator zero.

$$\csc \theta = \frac{1}{\sin \theta} \qquad \sec \theta = \frac{1}{\cos \theta} \qquad \cot \theta = \frac{1}{\tan \theta}$$

($\cot \theta = 0$ at odd multiples of $\frac{\pi}{2}$, where $\tan \theta$ is undefined.)

You can use the unit circle to evaluate the reciprocal trigonometric functions directly. Suppose the terminal side of an angle θ in standard position intersects the unit circle at the point (x, y).

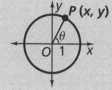

Then $\csc \theta = \frac{1}{y}$, $\sec \theta = \frac{1}{x}$, $\cot \theta = \frac{x}{y}$.

You can use what you know about the unit circle to find exact values for reciprocal trigonometric functions.

Problem 1 Finding Values Geometrically

Got It? What is the exact value of each expression? Do not use a calculator.

a. $\csc \frac{\pi}{3}$

b. $\cot \left(-\frac{5\pi}{4} \right)$

c. $\sec 3\pi$

d. Reasoning Use the unit circle at the right to find $\cot n$, $\csc n$, and $\sec n$. Explain how you found your answers.

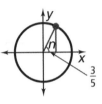

Practice Find each value without using a calculator. If the expression is undefined, write *undefined*.

1. $\csc \frac{7\pi}{6}$

2. $\cot (-\pi)$

Use the reciprocal relationships to evaluate secant, cosecant, or cotangent on a calculator, since most calculators do not have these functions as menu options.

Problem 2 Finding Values with a Calculator

Think

In part (a), can you use the tan⁻¹ key on your calculator to find cot 13?

Got It? What is the decimal value of each expression? Use the radian mode on your calculator. Round your answers to the nearest thousandth.

a. $\cot 13$

b. $\csc 6.5$

c. $\sec 15°$

d. $\sec \frac{3\pi}{2}$

e. Reasoning How can you find the cotangent of an angle without using the tangent key on your calculator?

A Practice Graphing Calculator Use a calculator to find each value. Round your answers to the nearest thousandth.

3. sec 2.5

4. cot $(-32°)$

The graphs of reciprocal trigonometric functions have asymptotes where the functions are undefined.

 Problem 3 **Sketching a Graph**

Think

For what values is cot x undefined?

Got It? What are the graphs of $y = \tan x$ and $y = \cot x$ in the interval from 0 to 2π?

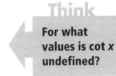

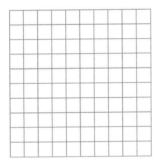

A Practice Graph each function in the interval from 0 to 2π.

5. $y = \sec 2\theta$

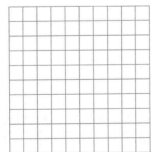

6. $y = \csc 2\theta - 1$

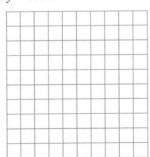

You can use a graphing calculator to graph trigonometric functions quickly.

Problem 4 Using Technology to Graph a Reciprocal Function

Got It? What is the value of csc 45°? Use the graph of the reciprocal trigonometric function.

Ⓐ Practice **Graphing Calculator** Use the graph of the appropriate reciprocal trigonometric function to find each value. Round to four decimal places.

7. csc 130°

8. cot 30°

You can use a reciprocal trigonometric function to solve a real-world problem.

Problem 5 Using Reciprocal Functions to Solve a Problem

Got It? The 601 in the function in Problem 5 is the diner's height above the ground in feet. If the diner is 553 feet above the ground, how far away are objects sighted at angles of 50° and 80°?

Practice

9. **Distance** A woman looks out a window of a building. She is 94 feet above the ground. Her line of sight makes an angle of θ with the building. The distance in feet of an object from the woman is modeled by the function $d = 94 \sec \theta$. How far away are objects sighted at angles of 25° and 55°?

 ## Lesson Check

Do you know HOW?

Find each value without using a calculator.

10. $\csc \frac{\pi}{2}$

11. $\sec \left(-\frac{\pi}{6} \right)$

Use a calculator to find each value. Round your answers to the nearest thousandth.

12. $\csc 1.5$

13. $\sec 42°$

14. An extension ladder leans against a building, forming a 50° angle with the ground. Use the function $y = 21 \csc x + 2$ to find y, the length of the ladder. Round to the nearest tenth of a foot.

Do you UNDERSTAND?

15. Reasoning Explain why the graph of $y = 5 \sec \theta$ has no zeros.

16. Error Analysis On a quiz, a student wrote sec sec 20° + 1 = 0.5155. The teacher marked it wrong. What error did the student make?

17. Compare and Contrast How are the graphs of $y = \sec x$ and $y = \csc x$ alike? How are they different? Could the graph of $y = \csc x$ be a transformation of the graph of $y = \sec x$?

More Practice and Problem-Solving Exercises

MATHEMATICAL PRACTICES

Ⓑ Apply

18. Think About a Plan A communications tower has wires anchoring it to the ground. Each wire is attached to the tower at a height 20 ft above the ground. The length y of the wire is modeled with the function $y = 20 \csc \theta$, where θ is the measure of the angle formed by the wire and the ground. Find the length of wire needed to form an angle of 45°.
- Do you need to graph the function?
- How can you rewrite the function so you can use a calculator?

19. Multiple Representations Write a cosecant model that has the same graph as $y = \sec \theta$.

Match each function with its graph.

20. $y = \dfrac{1}{\sin x}$ **21.** $y = \dfrac{1}{\cos x}$ **22.** $y = -\dfrac{1}{\sin x}$

A. 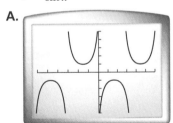   **B.** 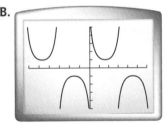   **C.**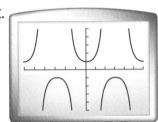

Graph each function in the interval from 0 to 2π.

23. $y = \csc \theta - \dfrac{\pi}{2}$ **24.** $y = \sec \dfrac{1}{4}\theta$ **25.** $y = -\sec \pi\theta$ **26.** $y = \cot \dfrac{\theta}{3}$

27. a. What are the domain, range, and period of $y = \csc x$?
    b. What is the relative minimum in the interval $0 \leq x \leq \pi$?
    c. What is the relative maximum in the interval $\pi \leq x \leq 2\pi$?

© **28. Reasoning** Use the relationship $\csc x = \frac{1}{\sin x}$ to explain why each statement is true.
  a. When the graph of $y = \sin x$ is above the x-axis, so is the graph of $y = \csc x$.
  b. When the graph of $y = \sin x$ is near a y-value of -1, so is the graph of $y = \csc x$.

© **Writing** Explain why each expression is undefined.

29. $\csc 180°$ **30.** $\sec 90°$ **31.** $\cot 0°$

32. Indirect Measurement The fire ladder forms an angle of measure θ with the horizontal. The hinge of the ladder is 35 ft from the building. The function $y = 35 \sec \theta$ models the length y in feet that the fire ladder must be to reach the building.
  a. Graph the function.
  b. In the photo, $\theta = 13°$. What is the ladder's length?
  c. How far is the ladder extended when it forms an angle of 30°?
  d. Suppose the ladder is extended to its full length of 80 ft. What angle does it form with the horizontal? How far up a building can the ladder reach when fully extended? (*Hint*: Use the information in the photo.)

© **33. a.** Graph $y = \tan x$ and $y = \cot x$ on the same axes.
  b. State the domain, range, and asymptotes of each function.
  c. Compare and Contrast Compare the two graphs. How are they alike? How are they different?
  d. Geometry The graph of the tangent function is a reflection image of the graph of the cotangent function. Name at least two reflection lines for such a transformation.

▦ **Graphing Calculator** Graph each function in the interval from 0 to 2π. Describe any phase shift and vertical shift in the graph.

34. $y = \sec 2\theta + 3$ **35.** $y = \sec 2(\theta + \frac{\pi}{2})$ **36.** $y = -2 \sec (x - 4)$

37. $f(x) = 3 \csc (x + 2) - 1$ **38.** $y = \cot 2(x + \pi) + 3$ **39.** $g(x) = 2 \sec\left(3\left(x - \frac{\pi}{6}\right)\right) - 2$

© **40. a.** Graph $y = -\cos x$ and $y = -\sec x$ on the same axes.
  b. State the domain, range, and period of each function.
  c. For which values of x does $-\cos x = -\sec x$? Justify your answer.
  d. Compare and Contrast Compare the two graphs. How are they alike? How are they different?
  e. Reasoning Is the value of $-\sec x$ positive when $-\cos x$ is positive and negative when $-\cos x$ is negative? Justify your answer.

© **41. a. Reasoning** Which expression gives the correct value of $\csc 60°$?
  I. $\sin((60^{-1})°)$ **II.** $(\sin 60°)^{-1}$ **III.** $(\cos 60°)^{-1}$
  b. Which expression in part (a) represents $\sin\left(\frac{1}{60}\right)°$?

© **42. Reasoning** Each branch of $y = \sec x$ and $y = \csc x$ is a curve. Explain why these curves cannot be parabolas. (*Hint:* Do parabolas have asymptotes?)

© **43. Reasoning** Consider the relationship between the graphs of $y = \cos x$ and $y = \cos 3x$. Use the relationship to explain the distance between successive branches of the graphs of $y = \sec x$ and $y = \sec 3x$.

© **44. a.** Graph $y = \cot x$, $y = \cot(2x)$, $y = \cot(-2x)$, and $y = \cot \frac{1}{2}x$ x on the same axes.

     b. Make a Conjecture Describe how the graph of $y = \cot bx$ changes as the value of b changes.

6-9 Trigonometric Identities

F.TF.8 Prove the Pythagorean identity $\sin^2(\theta) + \cos^2(\theta) = 1$ ... find $\sin(\theta)$, $\cos(\theta)$, or $\tan(\theta)$, given $\sin(\theta)$, $\cos(\theta)$, or $\tan(\theta)$, and the quadrant of the angle.

Objective To verify trigonometric identities

Solve It! Write your solution to the Solve It in the space below.

You may recognize $x^2 = 5x - 6$ as an equation that you are to solve to find the few, if any, values of x that make the equation true. On the other hand, you may recognize $\frac{x^5}{x^3} = x^2$ to be an example of an *identity*, an equation in which all values of x make the equation true, except those values for which the expressions in the equation are undefined. (Here, $\frac{x^5}{x^3}$ is not defined for $x = 0$.)

A **trigonometric identity** in one variable is a trigonometric equation that is true for all values of the variable for which all expressions in the equation are defined.

Essential Understanding The interrelationships among the six basic trigonometric functions make it possible to write trigonometric expressions in various equivalent forms, some of which can be significantly easier to work with than others in mathematical applications.

Some trigonometric identities are definitions or follow immediately from definitions.

take note

Key Concept Basic Identities

Reciprocal Identities $\csc\theta = \frac{1}{\sin\theta}$ $\sec\theta = \frac{1}{\cos\theta}$ $\tan\theta = \frac{1}{\cot\theta}$

$\sin\theta = \frac{1}{\csc\theta}$ $\cos\theta = \frac{1}{\sec\theta}$ $\cot\theta = \frac{1}{\tan\theta}$

Tangent Identity $\tan\theta = \frac{\sin\theta}{\cos\theta}$ **Cotangent Identity** $\cot\theta = \frac{\cos\theta}{\sin\theta}$

The *domain of validity* of an identity is the set of values of the variable for which all expressions in the equation are defined.

 **Problem 1** Finding the Domain of Validity

Got It? What is the domain of validity of the trigonometric
identity $\sin\theta = \frac{1}{\csc\theta}$?

Plan

When is $\csc\theta$
undefined?

A) Practice Give the domain of validity for each identity.

1. $\cos\theta\cot\theta = \frac{1}{\sin\theta} - \sin\theta$

2. $\sin\theta\cot\theta = \cos\theta$

You can use known identities to verify other identities. To verify an identity, you can
use previously known identities to transform one side of the equation to look like the
other side.

 Problem 2 Verifying an Identity Using Basic Identities

Got It? Verify the identity $\frac{\csc\theta}{\sec\theta} = \cot\theta$. What is the domain of validity?

Plan

What identities
do you know
that you can use?

Verify each identity. Give the domain of validity for each identity.

3. $\cos\theta \tan\theta = \sin\theta$

4. $\sin\theta \sec\theta = \tan\theta$

You can use the unit circle and the Pythagorean Theorem to verify another identity. The circle with its center at the origin with a radius of 1 is called the unit circle, and has an equation $x^2 + y^2 = 1$.

Every angle θ determines a unique point on the unit circle with x- and y-coordinates $(x, y) = (\cos\theta, \sin\theta)$.

Therefore, for every angle θ,
$(\cos\theta)^2 + (\sin\theta)^2 = 1$ or $\cos^2\theta + \sin^2\theta = 1$.

> This form allows you to write the identity without using parentheses.

This is a Pythagorean identity. You will verify two others in Problem 3.

You can use the basic and Pythagorean identities to verify other identities. To prove identities, transform the expression on one side of the equation to the expression on the other side. It often helps to write everything in terms of sines and cosines.

Problem 3 Verifying a Pythagorean Identity

Got It? **a.** Verify the third Pythagorean identity, $1 + \cot^2\theta = \csc^2\theta$.

b. Reasoning Explain why the domain of validity is not the same for all three Pythagorean identities.

Practice Verify each identity. Give the domain of validity for each identity.

5. $\cos\theta \sec\theta = 1$

6. $\tan\theta \cot\theta = 1$

You have now seen all three Pythagorean identities.

take note

Key Concept   Pythagorean Identities

$$\cos^2\theta + \sin^2\theta = 1 \qquad\qquad 1 + \tan^2\theta = \sec^2\theta \qquad\qquad 1 + \cot^2\theta = \csc^2\theta$$

There are many trigonometric identities. Most do not have specific names.

Problem 4   Verifying an Identity

Got It?   Verify the identity $\sec^2\theta - \sec^2\theta \cos^2\theta = \tan^2\theta$.

Ⓐ Practice   Verify each identity. Give the domain of validity for each identity.

7. $\cot\theta = \csc\theta \cos\theta$

8. $\csc\theta - \sin\theta = \cot\theta \cos\theta$

You can use trigonometric identities to simplify trigonometric expressions.

 Problem 5 **Simplifying an Expression**

Got It? What is a simplified trigonometric expression for $\sec \theta \cot \theta$?

 Practice Simplify each trigonometric expression.

9. $\sec \theta \cos \theta \sin \theta$

10. $\sec^2 \theta - \tan^2 \theta$

✓ **Lesson Check**

Do you know HOW?

Verify each identity.

11. $\tan \theta \csc \theta = \sec \theta$

12. $\csc^2\theta - \cot^2\theta = 1$

13. $\sin\theta\tan\theta = \sec\theta - \cos\theta$

14. Simplify $\tan\theta\cot\theta - \sin^2\theta$.

Do you UNDERSTAND?

15. Vocabulary How does the identity $\cos^2\theta + \sin^2\theta = 1$ relate to the Pythagorean Theorem?

@ **16. Error Analysis** A student simplified the expression $2 - \cos^2\theta$ to $1 - \sin^2\theta$. What error did the student make? What is the correct simplified expression?

More Practice and Problem-Solving Exercises

 Apply

@ **17. Think About a Plan** Simplify the expression $\dfrac{\tan\theta}{\sec\theta - \cos\theta}$.
- Can you write everything in terms of $\sin\theta$, $\cos\theta$, or both?
- Are there any trigonometric identities that can help you simplify the expression?

Simplify each trigonometric expression.

18. $\cos\theta + \sin\theta\tan\theta$

19. $\csc\theta\cos\theta\tan\theta$

20. $\tan\theta(\cot\theta + \tan\theta)$

21. $\sin^2\theta + \cos^2\theta + \tan^2\theta$

22. $\sin\theta(1 + \cot^2\theta)$

23. $\sin^2\theta\csc\theta\sec\theta$

24. $\sec\theta\cos\theta - \cos^2\theta$

25. $\csc\theta - \cos\theta\cot\theta$

26. $\csc^2\theta(1 - \cos^2\theta)$

27. $\dfrac{\csc\theta}{\sin\theta + \cos\theta\cot\theta}$

28. $\dfrac{\cos\theta\csc\theta}{\cot\theta}$

29. $\dfrac{\sin^2\theta\csc\theta\sec\theta}{\tan\theta}$

Express the first trigonometric function in terms of the second.

30. $\sin\theta$, $\cos\theta$

31. $\tan\theta$, $\cos\theta$

32. $\cot\theta$, $\sin\theta$

33. $\csc\theta$, $\cot\theta$

34. $\cot\theta$, $\csc\theta$

35. $\sec\theta$, $\tan\theta$

Verify each identity.

36. $\sin^2\theta\tan^2\theta = \tan^2\theta - \sin^2\theta$

37. $\sec\theta - \sin\theta\tan\theta = \cos\theta$

38. $\sin\theta\cos\theta(\tan\theta + \cot\theta) = 1$

39. $\dfrac{1 - \sin\theta}{\cos\theta} = \dfrac{\cos\theta}{1 + \sin\theta}$

40. $\dfrac{\sec\theta}{\cot\theta + \tan\theta} = \sin\theta$

41. $(\cot\theta + 1)^2 = \csc^2\theta + 2\cot\theta$

42. Express $\cos\theta\csc\theta\cot\theta$ in terms of $\sin\theta$.

43. Express $\dfrac{\cos\theta}{\sec\theta + \tan\theta}$ in terms of $\sin\theta$.

Use the identity $\sin^2\theta + \cos^2\theta = 1$ and the basic identities to answer the following questions. Show all your work.

44. Given that $\sin\theta = 0.5$ and θ is in the first quadrant, what are $\cos\theta$ and $\tan\theta$?

45. Given that $\sin\theta = 0.5$ and θ is in the second quadrant, what are $\cos\theta$ and $\tan\theta$?

46. Given that $\cos\theta = -0.6$ and θ is in the third quadrant, what are $\sin\theta$ and $\tan\theta$?

47. Given that $\sin\theta = 0.48$ and θ is in the second quadrant, what are $\cos\theta$ and $\tan\theta$?

48. Given that $\tan\theta = 1.2$ and θ is in the first quadrant, what are $\sin\theta$ and $\cos\theta$?

49. Given that $\tan\theta = 3.6$ and θ is in the third quadrant, what are $\sin\theta$ and $\cos\theta$?

50. Given that $\sin\theta = 0.2$ and $\tan\theta < 0$, what is $\cos\theta$?

 **Challenge**

51. The unit circle is a useful tool for verifying identities. Use the diagram at the right to verify the identity $\sin(\theta + \pi) = -\sin\theta$.
  a. Explain why the y-coordinate of point P is $\sin(\theta + \pi)$.
  b. Prove that the two triangles shown are congruent.
  c. Use part (b) to show that the two blue segments are congruent.
  d. Use part (c) to show that the y-coordinate of P is $-\sin\theta$.
  e. Use parts (a) and (d) to conclude that $\sin(\theta + \pi) = -\sin\theta$.

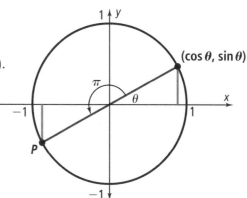

Use the diagram in Exercise 51 to verify each identity.

52. $\cos(\theta + \pi) = -\cos\theta$ **53.** $\tan(\theta + \pi) = \tan\theta$

Simplify each trigonometric expression.

54. $\dfrac{\cot^2\theta - \csc^2\theta}{\tan^2\theta - \sec^2\theta}$ **55.** $(1 - \sin\theta)(1 + \sin\theta)\csc^2\theta + 1$

STEM **56. Physics** When a ray of light passes from one medium into a second, the angle of incidence θ_1 and the angle of refraction θ_2 are related by Snell's law: $n_1 \sin\theta_1 = n_2 \sin\theta_2$, where n_1 is the index of refraction of the first medium and n_2 is the index of refraction of the second medium. How are θ_1 and θ_2 related if $n_2 > n_1$? If $n_2 < n_1$? If $n_2 = n_1$?

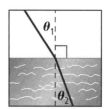

6-10 Area and the Law of Sines

G.SRT.11 Understand and apply the Law of Sines . . . to find unknown measurements in right and non-right triangles . . . Also **G.SRT.9**, **G.SRT.10**

Objectives To find the area of any triangle
To use the Law of Sines

 Solve It! Write your solution to the Solve It in the space below.

Recall from geometry that if you know three parts of a triangle then you can sometimes *solve the triangle*; that is, you can determine its complete shape. This is what the congruence statements SAS, ASA, AAS, SSS were all about.

Essential Understanding If you know two angles and a side of a triangle, you can use trigonometry to solve the triangle. If you know two sides and the included angle, you can find the area of the triangle.

The area of a triangle with base b and height h is $\frac{1}{2}bh$. When you don't know h but you do know an angle measure, there may be another way to find the area.

take note

Formula **Area of a Triangle**

Any $\triangle ABC$ with side lengths a, b, and c has area

$$\tfrac{1}{2}bc \sin A = \tfrac{1}{2}ac \sin B = \tfrac{1}{2}ab \sin C.$$

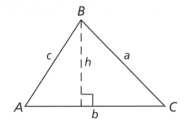

Here's Why It Works The area of the triangle above is $\frac{1}{2}bh$. The altitude h to side AC completes a right triangle. Thus, $\sin A = \frac{h}{c}$, so $h = c \sin A$. Substituting $c \sin A$ for h you get, $\frac{1}{2}bh = \frac{1}{2}bc \sin A$. You can derive $\frac{1}{2}ac \sin B$ and $\frac{1}{2}ab \sin C$ in a similar way.

Problem 1   Finding the Area of a Triangle

Plan

Can you use the
area formula?

Got It?   A triangle has sides of 12 in. and 15 in. The measure of the angle
between them is 24°. What is the area of the triangle?

Ⓐ Practice   Find the area of each triangle. Round your answer to the nearest tenth.

1.

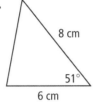

8 cm

51°

6 cm

2.

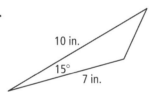

10 in.

15°

7 in.

The relationship $\frac{1}{2}bc \sin A = \frac{1}{2}ac \sin B = 12\,ab \sin C$ yields an important formula
when you divide each expression by $\frac{1}{2}abc$. The formula, known as the Law of Sines,
relates the sines of the angles of a triangle to the lengths of their opposite sides.

take note

Theorem 7   Law of Sines

In any triangle, the ratio of the sine of each angle to its opposite
side is constant. In particular, for $\triangle ABC$, labeled as shown,

$$\frac{\sin A}{a} = \frac{\sin B}{b} = \frac{\sin C}{c}.$$

You can use the Law of Sines to find missing measures of any triangle when you know the measures of

- two angles and any side, or
- two sides and an obtuse angle opposite one of them.
- two sides and an acute angle opposite one of them, where the length of the side opposite the known acute angle is greater than or equal to the length of the remaining known side.

In Problem 2, you know the measures of two angles and a side (AAS). In Problem 3, you know the measures of two sides and an obtuse angle opposite one of them (SSA with A obtuse).

 **Problem 2**   **Finding a Side of a Triangle**

Plan

How can drawing a diagram help?

Got It?   In $\triangle KLM$, $m\angle K = 120°$, $m\angle M = 50°$, and $ML = 35$ yd. What is KL?

A Practice   Use the Law of Sines. Find the measure x to the nearest tenth.

3.

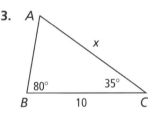

4.

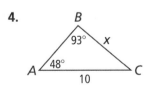

Got It? **a.** In $\triangle PQR$, $m\angle R = 97.5°$, $r = 80$, and $p = 75$. What is $m\angle P$?

b. In Problem 3, can you use the Law of Sines to find the heights of the triangle? Explain your answer.

 Practice Use the Law of Sines. Find the measure x to the nearest tenth.

5.

6.

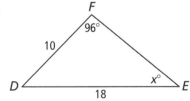

In the SSA case, if the known nonincluded angle is acute, you have an ambiguous situation. Inverse sine is not able to distinguish whether a second angle is, say, 47° or 133°.

In the SAS and SSS congruence situations, the Law of Sines is not useful because you do not have a known angle paired with a known opposite side. You will find out how to solve these triangles in the next lesson.

 **Problem 4**   **Using the Law of Sines to Solve a Problem**

Got It?   A landscaper sights the top of a tree at a 68° angle. She then moves an additional 70 ft directly away from the tree and sights the top at a 43° angle. How tall is the tree to the nearest tenth of a foot?

 Practice   **7. Surveying**   The distance from you to the base of a tower on top of a hill is 2760 ft. The angle of elevation of the base is 26°. The angle of elevation of the top of the tower is 32°. Draw a diagram. Find to the nearest foot the height of the tower above the top of the hill.

 Lesson Check

Do you know HOW?

8. A triangle has sides 2.4 and 9.0 and the measure of the angle between those sides is 98°. What is the area of the triangle?

9. In $\triangle PQR$, $m\angle P = 85°$, $m\angle R = 54°$, and $QR = 30$. What is PR?

10. In $\triangle HJK$, $m\angle J = 14°$, $HK = 6$, and $JK = 11$. What is $m\angle H$?

Do you UNDERSTAND?

11. Vocabulary Suppose you are given information about a triangle according to SSS, SAS, AAS, and ASA. For which of these can you immediately use the Law of Sines to find one of the remaining measures?

12. Error Analysis Suppose you used the Law of Sines and wrote $a = \frac{3 \sin 22°}{\sin 45°}$. Is that the same equation as $a = 3 \sin\left(\frac{22}{45}\right)°$? Explain.

More Practice and Problem-Solving Exercises

B Apply

@ **13. Think About a Plan** One of the congruent sides of an isosceles triangle is 10 cm long. One of the congruent angles has a measure of 54°. Find the perimeter of the triangle. Round your answer to the nearest centimeter.
   - Can drawing a diagram help you solve this problem?
   - What information do you need before finding the perimeter?
   - How can you find that information?

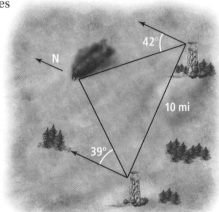

14. Forestry A forest ranger in an observation tower sights a fire 39° east of north. A ranger in a tower 10 miles due east of the first tower sights the fire at 42° west of north. How far is the fire from each tower?

15. Geometry The sides of a triangle are 15 in., 17 in., and 16 in. The smallest angle has a measure of 54°. Find the measure of the largest angle. Round to the nearest degree.

Find the remaining sides and angles of △DEF. Round your answers to the nearest tenth.

16. $m\angle D = 54°$, $m\angle E = 54°$, and $d = 20$ **17.** $m\angle D = 54°$, $e = 8$, and $d = 10$

@ **18. Reasoning** In △ABC, $a = 10$ and $b = 15$.
   a. Does the triangle have a greater area when $m\angle C = 1°$ or when $m\angle C = 50°$?
   b. Does the triangle have a greater area when $m\angle C = 50°$ or when $m\angle C = 179°$?
   c. For what measure of $\angle C$ does △ABC have the greatest area? Explain.

@ **19. Open-Ended** Sketch a triangle. Specify three of its measures, and then use the Law of Sines to find the remaining measures.

Find the area of △ABC. Round your answer to the nearest tenth.

20. $m\angle C = 68°$, $b = 12.9$, $c = 15.2$ **21.** $m\angle A = 52°$, $a = 9.71$, $c = 9.33$

22. $m\angle A = 23°$, $m\angle C = 39°$, $b = 14.6$ **23.** $m\angle B = 87°$, $a = 10.1$, $c = 9.8$

In △ABC, $m\angle A = 40°$ and $m\angle B = 30°$. Find each value to the nearest tenth.

24. Find AC for $BC = 10.5$ m.   **25.** Find BC for $AC = 21.8$ ft.

26. Find AC for $AB = 81.2$ yd.   **27.** Find BC for $AB = 5.9$ cm.

28. Measurement A vacant lot is in the shape of an isosceles triangle. It is between two streets that intersect at an 85.9° angle. Each of the sides of the lot that face these streets is 150 ft long. Find the perimeter of the lot to the nearest foot.

29. a. In the diagram at the right, $m\angle A = 30°$, $AB = 10$, and $BC = BD = 6$. Use the Law of Sines to find $m\angle D$, $m\angle ABD$, and $m\angle ABC$.

b. Reasoning Notice that two sides and a nonincluded angle of $\triangle ABC$ are congruent to the corresponding parts of $\triangle ABD$, but the triangles are not congruent. Must $\triangle EFG$ be congruent to $\triangle ABD$ if $EF = 10$, $FG = 6$, and $\angle E \approx \angle A$? Explain.

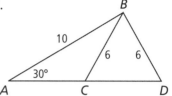

Ⓒ Challenge

30. Sailing Buoys are located in the sea at points A, B, and C. $\angle ACB$ is a right angle. $AC = 3.0$ mi, $BC = 4.0$ mi, and $AB = 5.0$ mi. A ship is located at point D on $\overline{AB}$ so that $m\angle ACD = 30°$. How far is the ship from the buoy at point C? Round your answer to the nearest tenth of a mile.

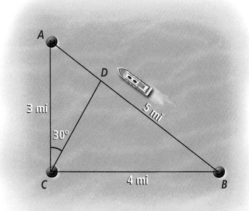

Ⓒ 31. Writing Suppose you know the measures of all three angles of a triangle. Can you use the Law of Sines to find the lengths of the sides? Explain.

The Ambiguous Case

G.SRT.11 Understand and apply the Law of Sines . . . to find unknown measurements in right and non-right triangles . . .

The triangles at the right have one pair of congruent angles and two pairs of congruent sides. But the triangles are not congruent. Notice that the congruent angles are not included by the congruent sides.

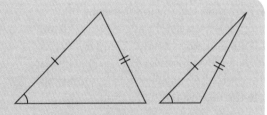

When you know the measures of two sides of a triangle and one of the opposite angles, there may be two triangles with those measurements. You can use the Law of Sines to find the other measures for both triangles.

Example

In each △ABC at the right, $m\angle A = 35°$, $a = 11$, and $b = 15$. Find $m\angle B$.

$\dfrac{\sin A}{a} = \dfrac{\sin B}{b}$ Law of Sines

$\dfrac{\sin 35°}{11} = \dfrac{\sin B}{15}$ Substitute.

$\sin B = \dfrac{15 \sin 35°}{11}$ Solve for $\sin B$.

$m\angle B = \sin^{-1}\left(\dfrac{15 \sin 35°}{11}\right) \approx 51°$ Solve for $m\angle B$. Use a calculator.

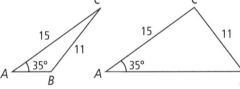

The sine function is also positive in Quadrant II. So another value of $m\angle B$ is about $180° - 51° = 129°$.

Because there are two possible angle measures for $\angle B$, there are two triangles that satisfy the given conditions. In one triangle the angle measures are about $35°$, $51°$, and $94°$. In the other, the angle measures are about $35°$, $129°$, and $16°$.

Exercises

In each $\triangle ABC$, find the measures for $\angle B$ and $\angle C$ that satisfy the given conditions. Draw diagrams to help you decide whether two triangles are possible.

1. $m\angle A = 62°$, $a = 30$, and $b = 32$

2. $m\angle A = 16°$, $a = 12$, and $b = 37.5$

3. $m\angle A = 48°$, $a = 93$, and $b = 125$

4. $m\angle A = 112°$, $a = 16.5$, and $b = 5.4$

5. $m\angle A = 23.6°$, $a = 9.8$, and $b = 17$

6. $m\angle A = 155°$, $a = 12.5$, and $b = 8.4$

7. Multiple Choice You can construct a triangle with compass and straightedge when given three parts of the triangle (except for three angles). Which of the following given sets could result in the ambiguous case?

A Given: three sides

C Given: two angles and a nonincluded side

B Given: two sides and an included angle

D Given: two sides and a nonincluded angle

6-11 The Law of Cosines

G.SRT.10 Prove the Law . . . of Cosines . . . Also **G.SRT.11**

Objective To use the Law of Cosines in finding the measures of sides and angles of a triangle

Solve It! Write your solution to the Solve It in the space below.

The measures of all three sides (SSS) or the measures of two sides and the included angle (SAS) determine a triangle. The Law of Sines does not enable you to solve such a triangle, but the Law of Cosines does.

Essential Understanding If you know the measures of enough parts of a triangle to completely determine the triangle, you can solve the triangle.

The Law of Cosines relates the length of a side of any triangle to the measure of the opposite angle.

take note

Theorem 8   Law of Cosines

In $\triangle ABC$, let a, b, and c represent the lengths of the sides opposite $\angle A$, $\angle B$, and $\angle C$, respectively.

- $a^2 = b^2 + c^2 - 2bc \cos A$

- $b^2 = a^2 + c^2 - 2ac \cos B$

- $c^2 = a^2 + b^2 - 2ab \cos C$

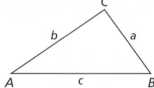

Here's Why It Works

In this $\triangle ABC$ with altitude h, let $AD = x$.

Then $DB = c - x$.

In $\triangle ADC$, $b^2 = x^2 + h^2$

and $\cos A = \frac{x}{b}$ or $x = b \cos A$.

In $\triangle CBD$,

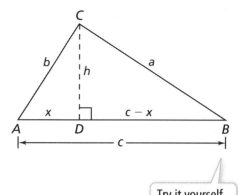

Try it yourself for obtuse $\angle B$.

$a^2 = (c - x)^2 + h^2$	Pythagorean Theorem
$= c^2 - 2cx + x^2 + h^2$	Square the binomial.
$= c^2 - 2cx + b^2$	Substitute b^2 for $x^2 + h^2$.
$= c^2 - 2cb \cos A + b^2$	Substitute $b \cos A$ for x.
$= b^2 + c^2 - 2bc \cos A$	Commutative Properties of Addition and Multiplication

The last equation is the Law of Cosines.

Problem 1   Using the Law of Cosines to Solve a Problem

Got It?   **a.** The lengths of two sides of a triangle are 8 and 10, and the measure of the angle between them is 40°. What is the approximate length of the third side?

b. Reasoning The measure of the included angle for the course in Problem 1 can be between 0° and 180°. Between what lengths can the length of the third side be? Explain your answer.

Practice Use the Law of Cosines. Find length x to the nearest tenth.

1.

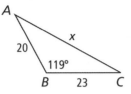

2.

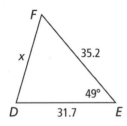

You can also use the Law of Cosines with triangles determined by the measures of all three sides (SSS).

Problem 2 **Finding an Angle Measure**

Got It? The lengths of the sides of a triangle are 10, 14, and 15. What is the measure of the angle opposite the longest side?

Plan
What form of the Law of Cosines should you use?

Practice Use the Law of Cosines. Find x to the nearest tenth.

3.

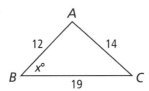

4.

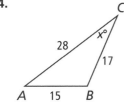

Sometimes you need to use the Law of Cosines followed by the Law of Cosines again or by the Law of Sines.

Problem 3 Finding an Angle Measure

Got It? In $\triangle RST$, $s = 41$, $t = 53$, and $m\angle R = 126°$. What is $m\angle T$?

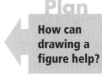

How can drawing a figure help?

Practice Use the Law of Cosines and the Law of Sines. Find x to the nearest tenth.

5.

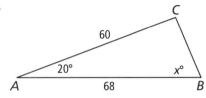

6.

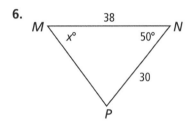

 Lesson Check

Do you know HOW?

7. In $\triangle ABC$, $m\angle B = 26°$, $a = 20$ in., and $c = 10$ in. Find b.

8. In $\triangle ABC$, $a = 8$ m, $b = 5$ m, and $c = 10$ m. Find $m\angle A$.

9. In $\triangle KNP$, $k = 21$ cm, $n = 12$ cm, and $m\angle P = 67°$. Find $m\angle N$.

10. In $\triangle WXY$, $w = 7.7$ ft, $x = 6.4$ ft, and $y = 8.5$ ft. Find $m\angle W$.

Do you UNDERSTAND?

11. Writing Explain how you choose between the Law of Sines and the Law of Cosines when finding the measure of a missing angle or side.

© **12. Error Analysis** A student solved for $m\angle C$, with $a = 11$ m, $b = 17$ m, and $c = 15$ m. What was the student's mistake?

$$\cos C = \frac{15^2 - 11^2 - 17^2}{2(11)(17)}$$

$\cos C \approx -0.495$

$C = \cos^{-1}(-0.495) \approx 119.7°$

More Practice and Problem-Solving Exercises

 MATHEMATICAL PRACTICES

Ⓑ Apply

For each triangle, write the correct form of the Law of Cosines or the Law of Sines to solve for the measure in red. Use only the information given in blue.

13.
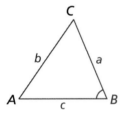

14.
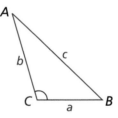

15.
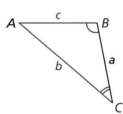

16.
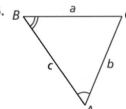

17.
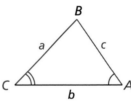

18.
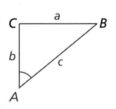

© **19. Think About a Plan** A touring boat was heading toward an island 80 nautical miles due south of where it left port. After traveling 15 nautical miles, it headed 8° east of south to avoid a fleet of commercial fishermen. After traveling 6 nautical miles, it turned to head directly toward the island. How far was the boat from the island at the time it turned?
- Can a diagram help you understand the problem?
- What are you asked to find?
- Which measurements do you need to solve the problem?

20. Sports A softball diamond is a square that is 65 ft on a side. The pitcher's mound is 46 ft from home plate. How far is the pitcher from third base?

Find the remaining sides and angles in each triangle. Round your answers to the nearest tenth.

21.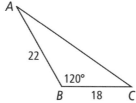

22.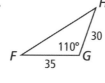

23.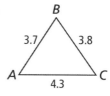

24. **a. Open-Ended** Sketch a triangle. Specify three of its measures so that you can use the Law of Cosines to find the remaining measures.
    b. Solve for the remaining measures of the triangle.

25. **Writing** Given the measures of three angles of a triangle, explain how to find the ratio of the lengths of two sides of the triangle.

26. **Geometry** The lengths of the sides of a triangle are 7.6 cm, 8.2 cm, and 5.2 cm. Find the measure of the largest angle.

27. **Navigation** A pilot is flying from city A to city B, which is 85 mi due north. After flying 20 mi, the pilot must change course and fly 10° east of north to avoid a cloudbank.
    a. If the pilot remains on this course for 20 mi, how far will the plane be from city B?
    b. How many degrees will the pilot have to turn to the left to fly directly to city B? How many degrees from due north is this course?

In $\triangle ABC$, $m\angle A = 53°$ and $c = 7$ cm. Find each value to the nearest tenth.

28. Find $m\angle B$ for $b = 6.2$ cm.

29. Find a for $b = 13.7$ cm.

30. Find a for $b = 11$ cm.

31. Find $m\angle C$ for $b = 15.2$ cm.

32. Find $m\angle B$ for $b = 37$ cm.

33. Find a for $b = 16$ cm.

In $\triangle RST$, $t = 7$ ft and $s = 13$ ft. Find each value to the nearest tenth.

34. Find $m\angle T$ for $r = 11$ ft.

35. Find $m\angle T$ for $r = 6.97$ ft.

36. Find $m\angle S$ for $r = 14$ ft.

37. Find r for $m\angle R = 35°$.

38. Find $m\angle S$ for $m\angle R = 87°$.

39. Find $m\angle R$ for $m\angle S = 70°$.

40. **Geometry** The lengths of the adjacent sides of a parallelogram are 54 cm and 78 cm. The larger angle measures 110°. What is the length of the longer diagonal? Round your answer to the nearest centimeter.

41. **Geometry** The lengths of the adjacent sides of a parallelogram are 21 cm and 14 cm. The smaller angle measures 58°. What is the length of the shorter diagonal? Round your answer to the nearest centimeter.

© **42. Reasoning** Does the Law of Cosines apply to a right triangle? That is, does $c^2 = a^2 + b^2 - 2ab \cos C$ remain true when $\angle C$ is a right angle? Justify your answer.

Challenge

43. a. Find the length of the altitude to $\overline{PQ}$ in the triangle at the right.

b. Find the area of $\triangle PQR$.

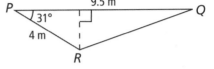

STEM **44. Physics** A pendulum 36 in. long swings 30° from the vertical. How high above the lowest position is the pendulum at the end of its swing? Round your answer to the nearest tenth of an inch.

© **45. Reasoning** If you solve for cos A in the Law of Cosines, you get $\cos A = \frac{b^2 + c^2 - a^2}{2bc}$.

a. Use this formula to explain how cos A can be positive, zero, or negative, depending on how $b^2 + c^2$ compares to a^2.

b. What does this tell you about $\angle A$ in each case?

6-1 Exploring Periodic Data

Quick Review

A **periodic function** repeats a pattern of y-values at regular intervals. One complete pattern is called a **cycle**. A cycle may begin at any point on the graph. The **period** of a function is the length of one cycle. The **midline** is the line located midway between the maximum and the minimum values of the function. The **amplitude** of a periodic function is half the difference between its maximum and minimum values.

Example

What is the period of the periodic function?

One cycle is 5 units long, so the period of the function is 5.

Exercises

1. Determine whether the function below *is* or *is not* periodic. If it is, identify one cycle in two different ways and find the period and amplitude.

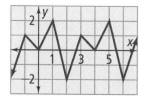

2. Sketch the graph of a wave with a period of 2, an amplitude of 4, and a midline of $y = 1$.

3. Sketch the graph of a wave with a period of 4, an amplitude of 3, and a midline of $y = 0$.

6-2 Angles and the Unit Circle

Quick Review

An angle is in **standard position** if the vertex is at the origin and one ray, the **initial side**, is on the positive x-axis. The other ray is the **terminal side** of the angle. Two angles in standard position are **coterminal** if they have the same terminal side.

The **unit circle** has radius of 1 unit and its center at the origin. The **cosine of θ** ($\cos \theta$) is the x-coordinate of the point where the terminal side of the angle intersects the unit circle. The **sine of θ** ($\sin \theta$) is the y-coordinate.

Example

What are the cosine and sine of $-210°$?

Sketch an angle of $-210°$ in standard position with a unit circle. The terminal side forms a 30°-60°-90° triangle with hypotenuse $= 1$, shorter leg $= \frac{1}{2}$, and longer leg $= \frac{\sqrt{3}}{2}$.

Since the terminal side lies in Quadrant II, $\cos(-210°)$ is negative and $\sin(-210°)$ is positive. $\cos(-210°) = -\frac{\sqrt{3}}{2}$ and $\sin(-210°) = \frac{1}{2}$.

Exercises

4. Find the measurement of the angle in standard position below.

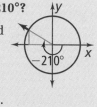

5. Sketch a $-30°$ angle in standard position.

6. Find the measure of an angle between $0°$ and $360°$ coterminal with a $-120°$ angle.

7. Find the exact values of the sine and cosine of $315°$ and $-315°$. Then find the decimal equivalents. Round your answers to the nearest hundredth.

6-3 Radian Measure

Quick Review

A **central angle** of a circle is an angle whose vertex is at the center of a circle and whose sides are radii of the circle. An **intercepted arc** is the portion of the circle whose endpoints are on the sides of the angle and whose remaining points lie in the interior of the angle. A **radian** is the measure of a central angle that intercepts an arc equal in length to a radius of the circle.

Example

What is the radian measure of an angle of $-210°$?

$$-210° = -210° \cdot \frac{\pi}{180°} \text{ radians} = -\frac{7\pi}{6} \text{ radians}$$

Exercises

The measure θ of an angle in standard position is given.

a. Write each degree measure in radians and each radian measure in degrees rounded to the nearest degree.

b. Find the exact values of $\cos \theta$ and $\sin \theta$ for each angle measure.

8. $60°$

9. $-45°$

10. $180°$

11. 2π radians

12. $\frac{5\pi}{6}$ radians

13. $-\frac{3\pi}{4}$ radians

14. Use the circle to find the length of the indicated arc. Round your answer to the nearest tenth.

6-4 The Sine Function

Quick Review

The **sine function** $y = \sin \theta$ matches the measure θ of an angle in standard position with the y-coordinate of a point on the unit circle. This point is where the terminal side of the angle intersects the unit circle. The graph of a sine function is called a **sine curve**.

For the sine function $y = a \sin b\theta$, the amplitude equals $|a|$, there are b cycles from 0 to 2π, and the period is $\frac{2\pi}{b}$.

Example

Determine the number of cycles the sine function $y = -7 \sin 3\theta$ has in the interval from 0 to 2π. Find the amplitude and period of the function.

For $y = -7 \sin 3\theta$, $a = -7$ and $b = 3$. Therefore there are 3 cycles from 0 to 2π. The amplitude is $|a| = |-7| = 7$. The period is $\frac{2\pi}{b} = \frac{2\pi}{3}$.

Exercises

Sketch the graph of each function in the interval from 0 to 2π.

15. $y = 3 \sin \theta$

16. $y = \sin 4\theta$

17. Write an equation of a sine function with $a > 0$, amplitude 4, and period 0.5π.

6-5 The Cosine Function

Quick Review

The **cosine function** $y = \cos\theta$ matches the measure θ of an angle in standard position with the x-coordinate of a point on the unit circle. This point is where the terminal side of the angle intersects the unit circle.

For the cosine function $y = a\cos b\theta$, the amplitude equals $|a|$, there are b cycles from 0 to 2π, and the period is $\frac{2\pi}{b}$.

Example

Find all solutions to $5\cos\theta = -4$ in the interval from 0 to 2π. Round each answer to the nearest hundredth.

On a graphing calculator graph the equations $y = -4$ and $y = 5\cos\theta$.

Use the Intersect feature to find the points at which the two graphs intersect. The graph shows two solutions in the interval. They are $\theta \approx 2.50$ and 3.79.

Exercises

Sketch the graph of each function in the interval from 0 to 2π.

18. $y = 2\cos\left(\frac{\pi}{2}\theta\right)$

19. $y = -\cos 2\theta$

20. Write an equation of a cosine function with $a > 0$, amplitude 3, and period π.

Solve each equation in the interval from 0 to 2π. Round your answer to the nearest hundredth.

21. $3\cos 4\theta = -2$

22. $\cos(\pi\theta) = -0.6$

6-6 The Tangent Function

Quick Review

The **tangent** of an angle θ in standard position is the y-coordinate of the point where the terminal side of the angle intersects the tangent line $x = 1$. A **tangent function** in the form $y = a\tan b\theta$ has a period of $\frac{\pi}{b}$.

Unlike the graphs of the sine and the cosine, the tangent is periodically undefined. At these points, the graph has vertical asymptotes.

Example

What is the period of $y = \tan\frac{\pi}{4}\theta$? Tell where two asymptotes occur.

$$\text{Period } = \frac{\pi}{b} = \frac{\pi}{\frac{\pi}{4}} = 4$$

One cycle occurs in the interval from -2 to 2, so there are asymptotes at $\theta = -2$ and $\theta = 2$.

Exercises

Graph each function in the interval from 0 to 2π. Then evaluate the function at $t = \frac{\pi}{4}$ and $t = \frac{\pi}{2}$. If the tangent is undefined at that point, write *undefined*.

23. $y = \tan\frac{1}{2}t$

24. $y = \tan 3t$

25. $y = 2\tan t$

26. $y = 4\tan 2t$

6-7 Translating Sine and Cosine Functions

Quick Review

Each horizontal translation of certain periodic functions is a **phase shift.** When $g(x) = f(x - h) + k$, the value of h is the amount of the horizontal shift and the value of k is the amount of the vertical shift. $y = k$ is the midline of the graph.

Example

What is an equation for the translation of $y = \sin x$, 2 units to the right and 1 unit up?

2 units to the right means $h = 2$, and 1 unit up means $k = 1$.

An equation is $y = \sin(x - 2) + 1$.

Exercises

Graph each function in the interval from 0 to 2π.

27. $y = \cos\left(x + \frac{\pi}{2}\right)$ **28.** $y = 2\sin x - 4$

29. $y = \sin(x - \pi) + 3$ **30.** $y = \cos(x + \pi) - 1$

Write an equation for each translation.

31. $y = \sin x$, $\frac{\pi}{4}$ units to the right

32. $y = \cos x$, 2 units down

6-8 Reciprocal Trigonometric Functions

Quick Review

The **cosecant** (csc), **secant** (sec), and **cotangent** (cot) functions are defined as reciprocals for all real numbers θ (except those that make a denominator zero).

$$\csc \theta = \frac{1}{\sin \theta} \qquad \sec \theta = \frac{1}{\cos \theta} \qquad \cot \theta = \frac{1}{\tan \theta}$$

Example

Suppose $\sin \theta = -\frac{3}{5}$. Find $\csc \theta$.

$$\csc \theta = \frac{1}{\sin \theta} = \frac{1}{-\frac{3}{5}} = -\frac{5}{3}$$

Exercises

Evaluate each expression. Write your answer in exact form.

33. $\sec(-45°)$ **34.** $\cot 120°$

35. $\csc 150°$ **36.** $\cot(-150°)$

Graph each function in the interval from 0 to 4π.

37. $y = 2\csc \theta$ **38.** $y = \sec \theta - 1$

39. $y = \cot \frac{1}{4}\theta$ **40.** $y = \csc \frac{1}{2}\theta + 2$

6-9 Trigonometric Identities

Quick Review

A **trigonometric identity** is a trigonometric equation that is true for all values except those for which the expressions on either side of the equal sign are undefined.

Reciprocal Identities
$$\csc\theta = \frac{1}{\sin\theta} \qquad \sec\theta = \frac{1}{\cos\theta} \qquad \cot\theta = \frac{1}{\tan\theta}$$

Tangent and Cotangent Identities
$$\tan\theta = \frac{\sin\theta}{\cos\theta} \qquad \cot\theta = \frac{\cos\theta}{\sin\theta}$$

Pythagorean Identities
$$\cos^2\theta + \sin^2\theta = 1 \qquad 1 + \tan^2\theta = \sec^2\theta$$
$$1 + \cot^2\theta = \csc^2\theta$$

Example

Simplify the trigonometric expression $\cot\theta\sec\theta$.

$$\cot\theta\sec\theta = \frac{\cos\theta}{\sin\theta}\cdot\sec\theta \qquad \text{Cotangent identity}$$
$$= \frac{\cos\theta}{\sin\theta}\cdot\frac{1}{\cos\theta} \qquad \text{Reciprocal identity}$$
$$= \frac{1}{\sin\theta} \qquad \text{Simplify.}$$
$$= \csc\theta \qquad \text{Reciprocal identity}$$

Exercises

Verify each identity. Give the domain of validity for each identity.

41. $\sin\theta\tan\theta = \frac{1}{\cos\theta} - \cos\theta$

42. $\cos^2\theta\cot^2\theta = \cot^2\theta - \cos^2\theta$

Simplify each trigonometric expression.

43. $1 - \sin^2\theta$

44. $\frac{\cos\theta}{\sin\theta\cot\theta}$

45. $\csc^2\theta - \cot^2\theta$

46. $\cos^2\theta - 1$

47. $\frac{\sin\theta\cos\theta}{\tan\theta}$

48. $\sec\theta\sin\theta\cot\theta$

6-10 and 6-11 Law of Sines and Law of Cosines

Quick Review

You can use the Law of Sines and the Law of Cosines to find missing measures of a triangle. For $\triangle ABC$:

The **Law of Sines** states that $\frac{\sin A}{a} = \frac{\sin B}{b} = \frac{\sin C}{c}$

The **Law of Cosines**

$$a^2 = b^2 + c^2 - 2bc\cos A \qquad b^2 = a^2 + c^2 - 2ac\cos B$$
$$c^2 = a^2 + b^2 - 2ab\cos C$$

Example

In $\triangle ABC$, $m\angle B = 60°$, $a = 12$, and $c = 8$. What is b to the nearest tenth?

$$b^2 = 12^2 + 8^2 - 2(12)(8)\cos 60° \qquad \text{Law of Cosines}$$
$$b^2 = 112 \qquad \text{Simplify.}$$
$$b \approx 10.6 \qquad \text{Use a calculator.}$$

Exercises

49. Find the area of the triangle. Round your answer to the nearest hundredth.

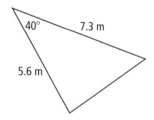

50. In $\triangle LMN$, $m\angle L = 67°$, $m\angle N = 24°$, and $MN = 16$ in. Find LM to the nearest tenth.

51. In $\triangle DEF$, $d = 25$ in., $e = 28$ in., and $f = 20$ in. Find $m\angle F$ to the nearest tenth.

52. In $\triangle GHI$, $h = 8$, $i = 12$, and $m\angle G = 96°$. Find $m\angle I$ to the nearest tenth.

Pull It All Together

Animating a Game

Suzanne is designing a computer game. She uses a coordinate grid and graph, as shown below, to help her design the layout. In the game, a dragonfly will start at the bottom of the circle and then move counterclockwise around it. It will complete one cycle around the circle in 5 seconds.

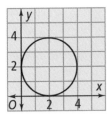

After 8 seconds, a frog jumps out and eats the dragonfly. Suzanne wants to determine the location of the dragonfly when this occurs.

Task Description

Determine the coordinates of the dragonfly when the frog eats it. Round each coordinate to the nearest hundredth.

Get Ready!

Evaluating Functions

For each function, find $f(1), f(2), f(3),$ and $f(4)$.

1. $f(x) = 2x + 7$

2. $f(x) = 5x - 4$

3. $f(x) = 0.2x + 0.7$

4. $f(x) = -5x + 3$

5. $f(x) = 4x - \frac{2}{3}$

6. $f(x) = -3x - 9$

Identifying Mathematical Patterns

Identify a pattern and find the next three numbers in the pattern.

7. $9, 4, -1, -6, \ldots$

8. $1, 2, 4, 8, \ldots$

9. $18, 9, 10, 1, 2, \ldots$

10. $7, 10, 13, 16, \ldots$

Simplifying Complex Fractions

Simplify each complex fraction.

11. $\dfrac{1 - \frac{1}{3}}{\frac{1}{2}}$

12. $\dfrac{\frac{1}{3} + \frac{1}{6}}{\frac{2}{3}}$

13. $\dfrac{1}{1 - \frac{2}{5}}$

14. $\dfrac{1 - \frac{3}{8}}{2 + \frac{1}{4}}$

 Looking Ahead Vocabulary

15. Think of a function and evaluate the function for the input numbers 1, 2, 3, 4, and 5. List the five outputs in order. This list is a *sequence* of numbers. The *sequence* can be infinitely long.

16. Use a linear function to generate a sequence of five numbers. Beginning with the second number, subtract the number that precedes it. Continue doing this until you have found all four differences. Are the results the same? If so, you have discovered that your sequence has a *common difference*.

17. Now use an exponential function to define your sequence of five numbers. Instead of subtracting, divide each number by the number that precedes it. Do this until you find all four quotients. Are these four results the same? If so, you have discovered that your sequence has a *common ratio*.

CHAPTER 7

Sequences and Series

Big Ideas

1 Variable

Essential Question How can you represent the terms of a sequence explicitly? How can you represent them recursively?

2 Equivalence

Essential Question What are equivalent explicit and recursive definitions for an arithmetic sequence?

3 Modeling

Essential Question How can you model a geometric sequence? How can you model its sum?

Ⓒ Domain

• Seeing Structure in Expressions

Interactive Digital Path

Log in to **pearsonsuccessnet.com** and click on Interactive Digital Path to access the Solve Its and animated Problems.

Chapter Preview

 ## Vocabulary

English/Spanish Vocabulary Audio Online:

English	Spanish
arithmetic sequence, *p. 502*	progresión aritmética
arithmetic series, *p. 517*	serie aritmética
common difference, *p. 502*	diferencia común
common ratio, *p. 509*	razón común
converge, *p. 531*	convergir
diverge, *p. 531*	divergir
explicit formula, *p. 493*	fórmula explícita
geometric sequence, *p. 509*	progresión geométrica
geometric series, *p. 529*	serie geométrica
limits, *p. 520*	límites
Pascal's Triangle, *p. 538*	Triángulo de Pascal
recursive formula, *p. 494*	formula recursiva

7-1 Mathematical Patterns

F.BF.1.a Determine an explicit expression, a recursive process, or steps for calculation . . .

Objectives To identify mathematical patterns found in a sequence
To use a formula to find the nth term of a sequence

Solve It! Write your solution to the Solve It in the space below.

Sometimes you can state a rule to describe a pattern. At other times, you have to do a bit of work to find a rule.

Essential Understanding If the numbers in a list follow a pattern, you may be able to relate each number in the list to its numerical position in the list with a rule.

A **sequence** is an ordered list of numbers. Each number in a sequence is a **term of a sequence**. You can represent a term of a sequence by using a variable with a subscript number to indicate its position in the sequence. For example, a_5 is the fifth term in the sequence $a_1, a_2, a_3, a_4, \ldots$.

The subscripts of sequence terms are often positive integers starting with 1. If so, you can generalize a term as a_n, the nth term in the sequence.

1st term	2nd term	3rd term	...	$n-1$ term	nth term	$n+1$ term ...
↓	↓	↓		↓	↓	↓
a_1	a_2	a_3	$\ldots a_{n-1}$	a_n	a_{n+1}	$\ldots$

An **explicit formula** describes the nth term of a sequence using the number n.

For example, in the sequence 2, 4, 6, 8, 10, . . . , the nth term is twice the value of n. You write this as $a_n = 2n$. The table shows how to find a_n by substituting the value of n into the explicit formula.

n	nth term
1	$a_1 = 2(1) = 2$
2	$a_2 = 2(2) = 4$
3	$a_3 = 2(3) = 6$
4	$a_4 = 2(4) = 8$

Problem 1 **Generating a Sequence Using an Explicit Formula**

Plan

Got It? A sequence has an explicit formula $a_n = 12n + 3$. What is term a_{12} in the sequence?

How does the explicit formula help you find the value of a term?

A Practice Find the first six terms of each sequence.

1. $a_n = -5n + 1$

2. $a_n = \frac{1}{2}n^3 - 1$

Sometimes you can see the pattern in a sequence by comparing each term to the one that came before it. For example, in the sequence 133, 130, 127, 124, ..., each term after the first term is equal to three less than the previous term.

A recursive definition for this sequence contains two parts.
(a) an initial condition (the value of the first term): $a_1 = 133$
(b) a **recursive formula** (relates each term after the first term to the one before it):
$a_n = a_{n-1} - 3$, for $n > 1$

 **Problem 2** **Writing a Recursive Definition for a Sequence**

Got It? What is a recursive definition for each sequence? (*Hint:* Look for simple addition or multiplication patterns to relate consecutive terms.)

a. 1, 2, 6, 24, 120, 720, . . .   **b.** 1, 5, 14, 30, 55, . . .

> **Think**
>
> **What pattern do you see in the differences of successive terms?**

 Practice Write a recursive definition for each sequence.

3. 100, 10, 1, 0.1, 0.01, . . .

4. 4, −8, 16, −32, 64, . . .

Recursive definitions can be very helpful when you look at a small section of a sequence. However, if you want to know both a_3 and a_{5000} of a sequence, an explicit formula often works better.

 Problem 3 **Writing an Explicit Formula for a Sequence**

Got It? **a.** What is an explicit formula for the sequence 0, 3, 8, 15, 24, . . . ?
What is the 20th term?

⊚ b. Reasoning Why is using an explicit formula often more efficient than using a recursive definition?

Ⓐ Practice **5.** Write an explicit formula for the sequence $\frac{1}{2}, -\frac{1}{4}, \frac{1}{8}, -\frac{1}{16} \cdots$
Find the tenth term.

6. Find the eighth term of the sequence 2, 1, −2, −7, −14, ...

 **Problem 4** Using Formulas to Find Terms of a Sequence

Got It? In the scenario in Problem 4, if the credit card company were to allow Pierre to continue making no payments, after how many months would his balance exceed $1000?

 7. Exercise You walk 1 mile the first day of your training, 1.2 miles the second day, 1.6 miles the third day, and 2.4 miles the fourth day. If you continue this pattern, how many miles do you walk on the seventh day?

Lesson Check

Do you know HOW?

Find the first five terms of each sequence.

8. $a_n = 5n - 3$

9. $a_n = n^2 - 2n$

10. What is a recursive definition for the sequence 3, 6, 12, 24, . . . ?

11. What is an explicit formula for the sequence 5, 8, 11, 14, . . . ?

Do you UNDERSTAND?

12. Vocabulary Explain the difference between an explicit formula and a recursive definition. Give an example of each.

13. Error Analysis A student writes that $a_n = 3n + 1$ is an explicit formula for the sequence 1, 4, 7, 10, ... Explain the student's error and write a correct explicit formula for the sequence.

More Practice and Problem-Solving Exercises

B Apply

Determine whether each formula is *explicit* or *recursive*. Then find the first five terms of each sequence.

14. $a_n = 2a_{n-1} + 3$, where $a_1 = 3$

15. $a_n = \frac{1}{2}(n)(n-1)$

16. $a_n = (n-5)(n+5)$

17. $a_n = -3a_{n-1}$, where $a_1 = -2$

18. $a_n = -4n^2 - 2$

19. $a_n = 2n^2 + 1$

Use the given rule to write the 4th, 5th, 6th, and 7th terms of each sequence.

20. $a_n = (n+1)^2$

21. $a_n = 2(n-1)^3$

22. $a_n = \frac{n^2}{n+1}$

23. $a_n = \frac{n+1}{n+2}$

24. Think About a Plan You invested money in a company and each month you receive a payment for your investment. Over the first four months, you received $50, $52, $56, and $62. If this pattern continues, how much do you receive in the tenth month?
- What pattern do you see between consecutive terms?
- Can you write a recursive or explicit formula to describe the pattern?
- How can you use your formula to find the amount you receive in the tenth month?

25. Entertainment Suppose you are building towers of cards with levels as displayed below. Copy and complete the table, assuming the pattern continues.

 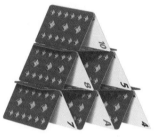

Number of Levels	Cards Needed
1	2
2	7
3	■
4	■
5	■

Find the next two terms in each sequence. Write a formula for the *n*th term. Identify each formula as *explicit* or *recursive*.

26. 5, 8, 11, 14, 17, . . . **27.** 3, 6, 12, 24, 48, . . . **28.** 1, 8, 27, 64, 125, . . .

29. 4, 16, 64, 256, 1024, . . . **30.** 49, 64, 81, 100, 121, . . . **31.** −1, 1, −1, 1, −1, 1, . . .

32. −16, −8, −4, −2, . . . **33.** −75, −68, −61, −54, . . . **34.** 21, 13, 5, −3, . . .

35. a. Open-Ended Write four terms of a sequence of numbers that you can describe both recursively and explicitly.
  b. Write a recursive definition and an explicit formula for your sequence.
  c. Find the 20th term of the sequence by evaluating one of your formulas. Use the other formula to check your work.

36. Geometry Suppose you are stacking boxes in levels that form squares. The numbers of boxes in successive levels form a sequence. The figure at the right shows the top four levels as viewed from above.
  a. How many boxes of equal size would you need for the next lower level?
  b. How many boxes of equal size would you need to add three levels?
  c. Suppose you are stacking a total of 285 boxes. How many levels will you have?

Challenge

37. Geometry The triangular numbers form a sequence. The diagram represents the first three triangular numbers: 1, 3, 6.
   a. Find the fourth and fifth triangular numbers.
   b. Write a recursive formula for the nth triangular number.
   c. Is the explicit formula $a_n = \frac{1}{2}(n^2 + n)$ the correct formula for this sequence? Explain.

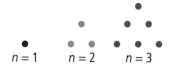

$n = 1 \qquad n = 2 \qquad n = 3$

Use each recursive definition to write an explicit formula for the sequence.

38. $a_1 = 10, a_n = 2a_{n-1}$ **39.** $a_1 = -5, a_n = a_{n-1} - 1$ **40.** $a_1 = 1, a_n = a_{n-1} + 4$

Ⓒ **41. Finance** Use the information in the ad.
   a. Suppose you start a savings account. Write a recursive definition and an explicit formula for the amount of money you would have in the bank at the end of any week.
   b. How much money would you have in the bank after four weeks?
   c. Assume the bank pays interest every four weeks. To calculate your interest, multiply the balance at the end of the four weeks by 0.005. Then add that amount to your account on the last day of the four-week period. Write a recursive formula for the amount of money you have after each interest payment.
   d. Reasoning What is the bank's annual interest rate?

MUN-BANK
is offering a
GREAT deal!
Start a savings
club account by
depositing only
$25 today and
$5 a week
starting next week.

7-2 Arithmetic Sequences

F.BF.1.a Determine an explicit expression, a recursive process, or steps for calculation . . .

Objective To define, identify, and apply arithmetic sequences

Solve It! Write your solution to the Solve It in the space below.

It is sometimes helpful to represent a situation with a sequence of numbers. There are different types of numerical sequences.

Essential Understanding In an *arithmetic sequence*, the difference between any two consecutive terms is always the same number. You can build an arithmetic sequence by adding the same number to each term.

An **arithmetic sequence** is a sequence in which the difference between consecutive terms is constant. This difference is the **common difference**.

take note

Key Concept: Arithmetic Sequence

An arithmetic sequence with a starting value a and common difference d is a sequence of the form

$$a, a + d, a + 2d, a + 3d, \ldots$$

A recursive definition for this sequence has two parts:

$a_1 = a$ initial condition
$a_n = a_{n-1} + d$, for $n > 1$ recursive formula

An explicit definition for this sequence is a single formula:

$a_n = a + (n - 1)d$, for $n \geq 1$

Problem 1 Identifying Arithmetic Sequences

Got It? Is the sequence an arithmetic sequence?

    a. 2, 4, 8, 16, . . .   **b.** 1, 5, 9, 13, 17, . . .

Ⓐ Practice Determine whether each sequence is arithmetic. If so, identify the common difference.

    1. $-21, -18, -15, -12, \ldots$ **2.** 3, 7, 11, 15, . . .

Problem 2 Analyzing Arithmetic Sequences

Got It? **a.** What is the 46th term of the arithmetic sequence that begins 3, 5, 7, . . . ?

Think

What do you need to find additional terms of an arithmetic sequence?

    b. What are the second and third terms of this arithmetic sequence?

                80, _____, _____, 125, . . .

A Practice Find the 32nd term of each sequence.

3. $-9, -8.7, -8.4, \ldots$

4. $101, 105, 109, 113, \ldots$

The **arithmetic mean**, or average, of two numbers x and y is $\frac{x+y}{2}$.

In an arithmetic sequence, the middle term of any three consecutive terms is the arithmetic mean of the other two terms.

Problem 3 Using the Arithmetic Mean

Got It? **a.** The 9th and 11th terms of an arithmetic sequence are 132 and 98. What is the 10th term?

b. Reasoning If you know the 5th and 6th terms of an arithmetic sequence, how can you find term 7 using the arithmetic mean?

Practice Find the missing term of each arithmetic sequence.

5. $-15,$ _____$, 1, \ldots$

6. $25,$ _____$, -10, \ldots$

Problem 4 Using an Explicit Formula for an Arithmetic Sequence

Got It? The numbers of seats in the first 16 rows in a curved section of another arena form an arithmetic sequence. If there are 20 seats in Row 1 and 23 seats in Row 2, how many seats are in Row 16?

Think

How can you find the common difference of the arithmetic sequence?

Practice **7. Savings** A student deposits the same amount of money into her bank account each week. At the end of the second week she has $30 in her account. At the end of the third week she has $45 in her account. How much will she have in her bank account at the end of the ninth week?

Lesson Check

Do you know HOW?

Find the tenth term of each arithmetic sequence.

8. 2, 8, 14, 20, . . .

9. 15, 23, 31, . . .

Find the missing term of each arithmetic sequence.

10. . . . 4, _____, 22, . . .

11. . . . 25, _____, 53, . . .

Do you UNDERSTAND?

12. Vocabulary Explain what it means for a sequence to be an arithmetic sequence.

13. Open-Ended Give an example of a sequence that is not an arithmetic sequence.

More Practice and Problem-Solving Exercises

 MATHEMATICAL PRACTICES

B Apply

Find the 17th term of each sequence.

14. $a_{16} = 18$, $d = 5$

15. $a_{16} = 21$, $d = -3$

16. $a_{18} = -5$, $d = 12$

17. $a_{18} = 32$, $d = -4$

18. $a_{16} = \frac{1}{5}$, $d = \frac{1}{2}$

19. $a_{18} = -9$, $d = -11$

© 20. Think About a Plan The arithmetic mean of the monthly salaries of two employees is $3210. One employee earns $3470 per month. What is the monthly salary of the other employee?
   • What is the given information and what is the unknown?
   • What equation can you use to find the other monthly salary?

© 21. Error Analysis A student claims that the next term of the arithmetic sequence 0, 2, 4, . . . is 8. Explain and correct the student's error.

Find the arithmetic mean a_n of the given terms.

22. $a_{n-1} = 7$, $a_{n+1} = 1$

23. $a_{n-1} = 100$, $a_{n+1} = 140$

24. $a_{n-1} = 4$, $a_{n+1} = -3$

25. $a_{n-1} = 0.3$, $a_{n+1} = 1.9$

26. $a_{n-1} = r$, $a_{n+1} = s$

27. $a_{n-1} = -2x$, $a_{n+1} = 2x$

28. a. Graphing Calculator Use your calculator to generate an arithmetic sequence with a common difference of -7. How could you use a calculator to find the 6th term? The 8th term? The 20th term?
   © b. Reasoning Explain how your answer to part (a) relates to the explicit formula $a_n = a + (n - 1)d$.

Write an explicit and a recursive formula for each sequence.

29. 2, 4, 6, 8, 10, . . .

30. 0, 6, 12, 18, 24, . . .

31. $-5, -4, -3, -2, -1, . . .$

32. $-4, -8, -12, -16, -20, . . .$

33. $-5, -3.5, -2, -0.5, 1, . . .$

34. $-32, -20, -8, 4, 16, . . .$

35. $1, 1\frac{1}{3}, 1\frac{2}{3}, 2, . . .$

36. $0, \frac{1}{8}, \frac{1}{4}, \frac{3}{8}, . . .$

37. $27, 15, 3, -9, -21, . . .$

© 38. Reasoning What information do you need to find a term of a sequence using an explicit formula?

© 39. Writing Describe some advantages and some disadvantages of a recursive formula and an explicit formula. When is it appropriate to use each formula?

40. Transportation Suppose a trolley stops at a certain intersection every 14 min. The first trolley of the day gets to the stop at 6:43 A.M. How long do you have to wait for a trolley if you get to the stop at 8:15 A.M.? At 3:20 P.M.?

Find the missing terms of each arithmetic sequence. (*Hint:* The arithmetic mean of the first and fifth terms is the third term.)

41. $2, a_2, a_3, a_4, -22, \ldots$ **42.** $10, a_2, a_3, a_4, -11.6, \ldots$ **43.** $1, a_2, a_3, a_4, -35, \ldots$

44. $\ldots \frac{13}{5}, a_6, a_7, a_8, \frac{37}{5}, \ldots$ **45.** $17, a_2, a_3, a_4, 17, \ldots$ **46.** $660, a_2, a_3, a_4, 744, \ldots$

47. $\ldots -17, a_4, a_5, a_6, 1, \ldots$ **48.** $\ldots a + 1, a_3, a_4, a_5, a + 17, \ldots$

49. Income The arithmetic mean of the monthly salaries of two people is \$4475. One person earns \$3895 per month. What is the monthly salary of the other person?

ⓒ **50. Reasoning** Suppose you turn the water on in an empty bathtub with vertical sides. After 20 s, the water has reached a level of 1.15 in. You then leave the room. You want to turn the water off when the level in the bathtub is 8.5 in. How many minutes later should you return? (*Hint:* Begin by identifying two terms of an arithmetic sequence.)

ⓒ Challenge

51. In an arithmetic sequence with $a_1 = 4$ and $d = 9$, which term is 184?

52. In an arithmetic sequence with $a_1 = 2$ and $d = -2$, which term is -82?

53. The arithmetic mean of two terms in an arithmetic sequence is 42. One term is 30. Find the other term.

54. The arithmetic mean of two terms in an arithmetic sequence is -6. One term is -20. Find the other term.

Given two terms of each arithmetic sequence, find a_1 and d.

55. $a_3 = 5$ and $a_5 = 11$ **56.** $a_4 = 8$ and $a_7 = 20$ **57.** $a_3 = 32$ and $a_7 = -8$

58. $a_{10} = 17$ and $a_{14} = 34$ **59.** $a_4 = -34.5$ and $a_5 = -12.5$ **60.** $a_4 = -2.4$ and $a_6 = 2$

Find the indicated term of each arithmetic sequence in terms of k.

61. $a_1 = k, d = k + 4; a_9$ **62.** $a_1 = k + 7, d = 2k - 5; a_{11}$

7-3 Geometric Sequences

F.BF.1.a Determine an explicit expression, a recursive process, or steps for calculation . . .

Objective   To define, identify, and apply geometric sequences

Solve It!   Write your solution to the Solve It in the space below.

You build a *geometric sequence* by multiplying each term by a constant.

Essential Understanding   In a *geometric sequence*, the ratio of any term to its preceding term is a constant value.

take note

Key Concept   Geometric Sequence

A **geometric sequence** with a starting value a and a **common ratio** r is a sequence of the form

$$a, ar, ar^2, ar^3, \ldots$$

A recursive definition for the sequence has two parts:
$a_1 = a$ initial condition
$a_n = a_{n-1} \cdot r$, for $n > 1$ recursive formula

An explicit definition for this sequence is a single formula:
$a_n = a_1 \cdot r^{n-1}$, for $n \geq 1$

Got It? Is the sequence geometric? If it is, what are a_1 and r?

a. $2, 4, 8, 16, \ldots$

Think

How do you find the ratios between consecutive terms?

b. $1, 5, 9, 13, 17, \ldots$

c. $2^3, 2^7, 2^{11}, 2^{15}, \ldots$

Practice Determine whether each sequence is geometric. If so, find the common ratio.

1. $1, \frac{1}{2}, \frac{1}{3}, \frac{1}{4}, \ldots$

2. 10, 15, 22.5, 33.75, . . .

 Problem 2 **Analyzing Geometric Sequences**

Got It? What is the 2nd term of the geometric sequence 3, 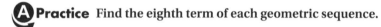, 12, . . . ?

Ⓐ Practice Find the eighth term of each geometric sequence.

3. 10, 5, 2.5, . . .

4. $-30, 7\frac{1}{2}, -1\frac{7}{8}, . . .$

Got It?   **a. Reasoning** In Problem 3, to find the height of the 10th bounce, would you use the recursive or the explicit formula? Explain.

         b. What are the heights of the 6th and 10th bounces?

 Practice   **STEM**   **5. Science** When radioactive substances decay, the amount remaining will form a geometric sequence when measured over constant intervals of time. The table shows the amount of Np-240, a radioactive isotope of Neptunium, initially and after 2 hours. What are the amounts left after 1 hour, 3 hours, and 4 hours?

Hours Elapsed	0	1	2	3	4
Grams of Np-240	1244	■	346	■	■

In a geometric sequence, the square of the middle term of any three consecutive terms is equal to the product of the other two terms. For example, examine the sequence $2, -6, 18, -54, \ldots$.

$$(-6)^2 = 2 \cdot 18 = 36$$

$$2, \underline{-6, 18,} -54, \ldots$$

$$18^2 = (-6)(-54) = 324$$

In an arithmetic sequence, recall that the middle term of any three consecutive terms is the arithmetic mean of the other two terms.

The **geometric mean** of two positive numbers x and y is $\sqrt{xy}$.

Note that the geometric mean is positive by definition. While there are two possible values for the missing term in the geometric sequence $3, \blacksquare, 12, \ldots$, there is only one geometric mean. The geometric mean is one possible value to fill in the geometric sequence. The opposite of the geometric mean is the other.

 **Problem 4** **Using the Geometric Mean**

Think

Is it necessary to find the first term to answer this question?

Got It? The 9th and 11th terms of a geometric sequence are 45 and 80. What are possible values for the 10th term?

A Practice Find the missing term of each geometric sequence. It could be the geometric mean or its opposite.

6. $9180, \underline{\hspace{1cm}}, 255, \ldots$

7. $5, \underline{\hspace{1cm}}, 2.8125, \ldots$

Lesson Check

Do you know HOW?

Determine whether each sequence is geometric. If so, find the common ratio.

8. $5, 10, 15, \ldots$

9. $10, 20, 40, \ldots$

Find the seventh term of each geometric sequence.

10. $1, -3, 9, \ldots$

11. $100, 20, 4, \ldots$

Do you UNDERSTAND?

⊚ 12. Error Analysis To find the third term of the geometric sequence 5, 10, ▦, ▦, 80, your friend says that there are two possible answers—the geometric mean of 5 and 80, and its opposite. Explain your friend's error.

13. Compare and Contrast How is finding a missing term of a geometric sequence using the geometric mean similar to finding a missing term of an arithmetic sequence using the arithmetic mean? How is it different?

More Practice and Problem-Solving Exercises

B Apply

Write an explicit formula for each sequence. Then generate the first five terms.

14. $a_1 = 1, r = 0.5$

15. $a_1 = 100, r = -20$

16. $a_1 = 7, r = 1$

17. $a_1 = 1024, r = 0.5$

18. $a_1 = 4, r = 0.1$

19. $a_1 = 10, r = -1$

Identify each sequence as *arithmetic*, *geometric*, or *neither*. Then find the next two terms.

20. $45, 90, 180, 360, \ldots$

21. $25, 50, 75, 100, \ldots$

22. $3, -3, 3, -3, \ldots$

23. $-5, 10, -20, 40, \ldots$

24. $2, 1, 0.5, 0.25, \ldots$

25. $1, 4, 9, 16, \ldots$

Find the missing terms of each geometric sequence. If necessary, round to the nearest hundredth. (*Hint:* The geometric mean of the first and fifth terms is the third term. Some terms might be negative.)

26. $972, \blacksquare, \blacksquare, \blacksquare, 12, \ldots$

27. $2.5, \blacksquare, \blacksquare, \blacksquare, 202.5, \ldots$

28. $12.5, \blacksquare, \blacksquare, \blacksquare, 5.12, \ldots$

29. $-4, \blacksquare, \blacksquare, \blacksquare, -20\frac{1}{4}$

30. Think About a Plan Suppose a balloon is filled with 5000 cm^3 of helium. It then loses one fourth of its helium each day. How much helium will be left in the balloon at the start of the tenth day?
- How can you write a sequence of numbers to represent this situation?
- Is the sequence arithmetic, geometric, or neither?
- How can you write a formula for this sequence?

31. Athletics During your first week of training for a 100-mile bike event, you bike a total of 10 miles. You increase the distance you bike each week by twenty percent. How many miles do you bike during your twelfth week of training?

32. a. Open-Ended Choose two positive numbers. Find their geometric mean.
   b. Find the common ratio for a geometric sequence that includes the terms from part (a) as its first three terms.
   c. Find the 9th term of the geometric sequence from part (b).
   d. Find the geometric mean of the term from part (c) and the first term of your sequence. What term of the sequence have you just found?

For the geometric sequence 3, 12, 48, 192, ..., find the indicated term.

33. 5th term **34.** 17th term **35.** 20th term **36.** nth term

Find the 10th term of each geometric sequence.

37. $a_9 = 8, r = \frac{1}{2}$ **38.** $a_9 = -5, r = -\frac{1}{2}$

39. $a_{11} = -5, r = -\frac{1}{2}$ **40.** $a_9 = -\frac{1}{3}, r = \frac{1}{2}$

41. Writing Describe the similarities and differences between a common difference and a common ratio.

 **Challenge**

42. Banking Copy and complete the table below. Use the geometric mean. Assume compound interest is earned and no withdrawals are made.

Period 1	Period 2	Period 3
$140.00	■	$145.64
$600.00	■	$627.49
$25.00	■	$32.76
$57.50	■	$60.37
$100.00	■	$111.98
$250.00	■	$276.55

Find a_1 for a geometric sequence with the given terms.

43. $a_5 = 112$ and $a_7 = 448$ **44.** $a_9 = \frac{1}{2}$ and $a_{12} = \frac{1}{16}$

7-4 Arithmetic Series

F.BF.1.a Determine an explicit expression, a recursive process, or steps for calculation . . .

Objective To define arithmetic series and find their sums

 Solve It! Write your solution to the Solve It in the space below.

Just as you found formulas for terms of sequences, you can find formulas for the sums of the terms of sequences.

Essential Understanding When you know two terms and the number of terms in a finite arithmetic sequence, you can find the sum of the terms.

A **series** is the indicated sum of the terms of a sequence. A **finite series**, like a finite sequence, has a first term and a last term, while an **infinite series** continues without end.

Finite sequence	**Finite series**
6, 9, 12, 15, 18	6 + 9 + 12 + 15 + 18 (The sum is 60.)
Infinite sequence	**Infinite series**
3, 7, 11, 15, . . .	3 + 7 + 11 + 15 + $\cdots$

An **arithmetic series** is a series whose terms form an arithmetic sequence (as shown above). When a series has a finite number of terms, you can use a formula involving the first and last term to evaluate the sum.

take note

Property Sum of a Finite Arithmetic Series

The sum S_n of a finite arithmetic series $a_1 + a_2 + a_3 + \cdots + a_n$ is

$$S_n = \frac{n}{2}(a_1 + a_n)$$

where a_1 is the first term, a_n is the nth term, and n is the number of terms.

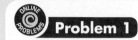

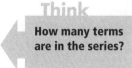

Got It? **a.** What is the sum of the finite arithmetic series
$4 + 9 + 14 + 19 + 24 + \cdots + 99$?

ⓔ b. Reasoning Will the sum of a sequence of even numbers always be an even number? Will the sum of a sequence of odd numbers always be an odd number? Explain.

ⒶPractice Find the sum of each finite arithmetic series.

1. $7 + 14 + 21 + \cdots + 105$

2. $(-3) + (-6) + (-9) + \cdots + (-30)$

Got It? The company in Problem 2 has an alternative bonus plan. It pays a
$5000 bonus if a new salesperson makes 10 sales in the first week and
then improves by *one* sale per week each week thereafter. One salesperson
qualified for this bonus with the minimum number of sales. How many
sales did the salesperson make in week 50? In all 50 weeks?

 **Practice** **3. Grades** A student has taken three math tests so far this semester.
His scores for the first three tests were 75, 79, and 83.

    a. Suppose his test scores continue to improve at the same rate.
What will his grade on the sixth (and final) test be?

    b. What will his total score for all six tests be?

You can use the Greek capital letter sigma, Σ, to indicate a sum. With it, you use *limits* to indicate how many terms you are adding. **Limits** are the least and greatest values of n in the series. You write the limits below and above the Σ to indicate the least and greatest values of n.

For example, you can write the series $3^2 + 4^2 + 5^2 + \cdots + 108^2$ as $\displaystyle\sum_{n=3}^{108} n^2$.

Upper limit: the series ends with $n = 108$.

The explicit formula for each term is n^2.

$$\sum_{n=3}^{108} n^2$$

Lower limit: the series begins with $n = 3$.

For an infinite series, summation notation shows ∞ as the upper limit.

To find the number of terms in a series written in Σ form, subtract the lower limit from the upper limit and add 1.

The number of terms in the series above is $108 - 3 + 1 = 106$.

Problem 3 Writing a Series in Summation Notation

Got It? What is summation notation for the series?

a. $-5 + 2 + 9 + 16 + \cdots + 261 + 268$

Plan

What do you need to write a series in summation notation?

b. $500 + 490 + 480 + \cdots + 20 + 10$

Practice Write each arithmetic series in summation notation.

4. $5 + 8 + 11 + \cdots + 38$

5. $105 + 97 + 89 + \cdots + (-71)$

Key Concept   Summation Notation and Linear Functions

If the explicit formula for the nth term in summation notation is a *linear* function of n, then the series is arithmetic. The slope of the linear function is the common difference between terms of the series.

ONLINE PROBLEMS **Problem 4**   Finding the Sum of a Series

Got It?   What is the sum of each finite series?

a. $\sum\limits_{n=1}^{40}(3n - 8)$

b. $\sum\limits_{n=1}^{4}n^3$

c. $\sum\limits_{n=0}^{100}(-1)^n$

A **Practice** Find the sum of each finite series.

6. $\displaystyle\sum_{n=1}^{10}(3n-4)$

7. $\displaystyle\sum_{n=1}^{3}(-1)^n \cdot 2$

On a graphing calculator, you can find the sum of a finite series by using commands from the **LIST** menu.

Problem 5 **Using a Graphing Calculator to Find the Sum of a Series**

Got It? Use a graphing calculator. What is $\displaystyle\sum_{n=1}^{50}(n^2-n)$?

A **Practice** Use a graphing calculator to find the sum of each series.

8. $\displaystyle\sum_{n=1}^{20}(n^3-10n^2)$

9. $\displaystyle\sum_{n=5}^{25}(n^2-14n+32)$

Lesson Check

Do you know HOW?

Find the sum of each finite arithmetic series.

10. $4 + 7 + 10 + 13 + 16 + 19 + 22$

11. $10 + 20 + 30 + \cdots + 110 + 120$

Write each arithmetic series in summation notation.

12. $3 + 6 + 9 + 12 + 15 + 18 + 21$

13. $1 + 5 + 9 + \cdots + 41 + 45$

Do you UNDERSTAND?

14. Vocabulary What is the difference between an arithmetic sequence and an arithmetic series?

15. Error Analysis A student writes the arithmetic series $3 + 8 + 13 + \cdots + 43$ in summation notation as $\sum_{n=3}^{8} (3 + 5n)$. Describe and correct the error.

16. Reasoning Is it possible to have more than one arithmetic series with four terms whose sum is 44? Explain.

More Practice and Problem-Solving Exercises

B Apply

17. Think About a Plan A meeting room is set up with 16 rows of seats. The number of seats in a row increases by two with each successive row. The first row has 12 seats. What is the total number of seats?
- How can you find the number of seats in each row using an explicit formula?
- What is the number of seats in the 16th row?
- How can you find the sum of the seats in 16 rows?

Determine whether each list is a *sequence* or a *series* and *finite* or *infinite*.

18. 1, 2, 4, 8, 16, 32, . . .

19. 1, 0.5, 0.25, 0.125, 0.0625

20. $5 + 10 + \cdots + 25$

21. $-0.5 - 0.25 - 0.125 - \cdots$

22. $\frac{4}{3}, \frac{7}{3}, \frac{10}{3}, \frac{13}{3}, \frac{16}{3}, \ldots$

23. $2.3 + 4.6 + 9.2 + 18.4$

Each sequence has eight terms. Evaluate each related series.

24. $\frac{1}{2}, \frac{3}{2}, \frac{5}{2}, \ldots, \frac{15}{2}$

25. $1, -1, -3, \ldots, -13$

26. $5, 13, 21, \ldots, 61$

27. $-3.5, -1.25, 1, \ldots, 12.25$

28. $1765, 1414, 1063, \ldots, -692$

29. $-13, -14.5, -16, \ldots, -23.5$

STEM **30.** **Architecture** In a 20-row theater, the number of seats in a row increases by three with each successive row. The first row has 18 seats.
  a. Write an arithmetic series to represent the number of seats in the theater.
  b. Find the total seating capacity of the theater.
  c. Front-row tickets for a concert cost $60. After every 5 rows, the ticket price goes down by $5. What is the total amount of money generated by a full house?

ⓒ **31.** **a.** **Grocery** A supermarket displays cans in a triangle, like the one shown, with two cans in the top row. Write an explicit formula for the sequence of the number of cans.
  b. Use summation notation to write the related series for a triangle with 10 cans in the bottom row.
  c. Suppose the triangle had 17 rows. How many cans would be in the 17th row?
  d. **Reasoning** Could the triangle have 110 cans? 140 cans? Explain.

Evaluate each series to the given term.

32. $2 + 4 + 6 + 8 + \cdots$; 10th term

33. $-5, -25, -45, -\cdots$; 9th term

ⓒ **34.** **a.** **Open-Ended** Write two explicit formulas for arithmetic sequences.
  b. Write the first five terms of each related series.
  c. Use summation notation to rewrite each series.
  d. Evaluate each series.

Ⓒ Challenge

Use the values of a_1 and S_n to find the value of a_n.

35. $a_1 = 4$ and $S_{40} = 6080$; a_{40}

36. $a_1 = -6$ and $S_{50} = -5150$; a_{50}

Find a_1 for each arithmetic series.

37. $S_8 = 440$ and $d = 6$

38. $S_{30} = 240$ and $d = -2$

39. Evaluate S_{10} for the series $x + (x + y) + (x + 2y) + \cdots$

40. Evaluate S_{15} for the series $3x + (3x - 2y) + (3x - 4y) + \cdots$

ACTIVITY LAB

Use With Lesson 7-5

Geometry and Infinite Series

A.SSE.4 Derive the formula for the sum of a finite geometric series (when the common ratio is not 1), and use the formula to solve problems.

> You can use geometric figures to model some infinite series.

Example 1

Geometry Draw a geometric figure to model the series.

$$\frac{1}{2} + \left(\frac{1}{2}\right)^2 + \left(\frac{1}{2}\right)^3 + \ldots + \left(\frac{1}{2}\right)^n + \ldots$$

Draw a square. Shade one half of the square. Then shade one half of the remaining unshaded region. Continue until the square is full.

So the series appears to have a sum of 1.

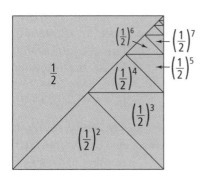

> You can write an infinite series from a geometric model.

Example 2

Geometry Write the series modeled by the trapezoids. Estimate the sum of the series. Explain your reasoning.

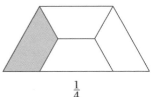 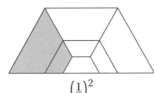 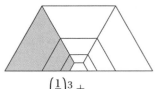

$$\frac{1}{4} \qquad + \qquad \left(\frac{1}{4}\right)^2 \qquad + \qquad \left(\frac{1}{4}\right)^3 + \ldots$$

The shaded region approaches one third of the figure.

So the series $\frac{1}{4} + \left(\frac{1}{4}\right)^2 + \left(\frac{1}{4}\right)^3 + \ldots + \left(\frac{1}{4}\right)^n + \ldots$ appears to have a sum of $\frac{1}{3}$.

Exercises

1. a. Write the series modeled by the figure at the right.

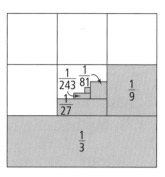

b. Evaluate the series. Explain your reasoning.

2. Draw a figure to model the series. $\frac{1}{5} + \left(\frac{1}{5}\right)^2 + \left(\frac{1}{5}\right)^3 + \ldots + \left(\frac{1}{5}\right)^n + \ldots$

3. Make a Conjecture Consider the series. $\frac{1}{c} + \left(\frac{1}{c}\right)^2 + \left(\frac{1}{c}\right)^3 + \ldots + \left(\frac{1}{c}\right)^n + \ldots, c > 1$

What is the sum of the series? Explain your reasoning.

7-5 Geometric Series

A.SSE.4 Derive the formula for the sum of a finite geometric series . . . and use the formula to solve problems.

Objective To define geometric series and find their sums

 Solve It! Write your solution to the Solve It in the space below.

You can write any whole number that has the same digit in every place as the sum of the terms of a geometric sequence. For example,

$$4444 = 4(10)^0 + 4(10)^1 + 4(10)^2 + 4(10)^3$$

You can write any rational number as an infinite repeating decimal.

For example, $\frac{47}{90} = 0.5222\ldots$

Therefore, you can write any rational number as a number plus the sum of an infinite geometric sequence.

$$0.5222\ldots = 0.5 + 2(0.1)^2 + 2(0.1)^3 + 2(0.1)^4 + \cdots$$

Essential Understanding Just as with finite arithmetic series, you can find the sum of a finite geometric series using a formula. You need to know the first term, the number of terms, and the common ratio.

A **geometric series** is the sum of the terms of a geometric sequence.

take note

Key Concept   Sum of a Finite Geometric Series

The sum S_n of a finite geometric series $a_1 + a_1r + a_1r^2 + \cdots + a_1r^{n-1}, r \neq 1$, is

$$S_n = \frac{a_1(1 - r^n)}{1 - r}$$

where a_1 is the first term, r is the common ratio, and n is the number of terms.

Problem 1   Finding the Sums of Finite Geometric Series

Got It?   What is the sum of the finite geometric series?

a. $-15 + 30 - 60 + 120 - 240 + 480$

Plan

How do you find the common ratio in each of these series?

b. $\displaystyle\sum_{n=1}^{10} 5 \cdot (-2)^{n-1}$

Ⓐ Practice Evaluate the sum of the finite geometric series.

1. $-5 - 10 - 20 - 40 - \cdots - 2560$

2. $\displaystyle\sum_{n=1}^{4} \left(\frac{2}{3}\right)^{n-1}$

The Soldier's Reasonable Request A famous story involves a soldier who rescues his king in battle. The king grants him any prize "within reason" from the riches of the kingdom. The soldier asks for a chessboard with a single kernel of wheat on the first square, two kernels of wheat on the second square, then four, then eight, and so on for all 64 squares of the chessboard. The king decides that the request is reasonable.

See Problem 2 for the outcome.

Problem 2 Using the Geometric Series Formula

Got It? To save money for a vacation, you set aside $100. For each month thereafter, you plan to set aside 10% more than the previous month. How much money will you save in 12 months?

Practice　**3. Financial Planning** In March, a family starts saving for a vacation they are planning for the end of August. The family expects the vacation to cost $1375. They start with $125. Each month they plan to deposit 20% more than the previous month. Will they have enough money for their trip? If not, how much more do they need?

The Rest of the Story A bushel of wheat contains about a million kernels. The total US output of wheat in a recent year was just over 2.1 billion bushels. How many years of production at that level would it take the United States to produce enough wheat to satisfy the soldier's "reasonable" request?

The terms of a geometric series grow rapidly when the common ratio is greater than 1. Likewise, they diminish rapidly when the common ratio is between 0 and 1. In fact, they diminish so rapidly that an *infinite geometric series* has a finite sum.

take note

Key Concept　Infinite Geometric Series

An infinite geometric series with first term a_1 and common ratio $|r| < 1$ has a finite sum

$$S = \frac{a_1}{1 - r}.$$

An infinite geometric series with $|r| \geq 1$ does not have a finite sum.

To say that an infinite series $a_1 + a_2 + a_3 + \cdots$ has a sum means that the *sequence of partial sums* $S_1 = a_1$, $S_2 = a_1 + a_2$, $S_3 = a_1 + a_2 + a_3, \ldots,$ $S_n = a_1 + a_2 + \cdots + a_n, \ldots$ **converges** to a number S as n gets very large.

When an infinite series does not converge to a sum, the series **diverges**. An infinite geometric series with $|r| \geq 1$ diverges.

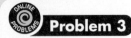

Problem 3 Analyzing Infinite Geometric Series

Got It? Does the infinite series *converge* or *diverge*? If it converges, what is the sum?

Think

When does an infinite geometric series converge?

    a. $\frac{1}{2} + \frac{3}{4} + \frac{9}{8} + \cdots$

    b. $\frac{1}{3} - \frac{1}{9} + \frac{1}{27} - \frac{1}{81} + \cdots$

    c. $\sum_{n=1}^{\infty} \left(\frac{2}{3}\right)^n$

    d. Reasoning Will an infinite geometric series either converge or diverge? Explain.

Practice Determine whether each infinite geometric series *diverges* or *converges*. If the series converges, state the sum.

4. $4 + 2 + 1 + \cdots$

5. $\frac{1}{4} + \frac{1}{2} + 1 + 2 + \cdots$

Evaluate the infinite geometric series.

6. $3 + 2 + \frac{4}{3} + \frac{8}{9} + \cdots$

 ## Lesson Check

Do you know HOW?

Evaluate each finite geometric series.

7. $\frac{1}{5} + \frac{1}{10} + \frac{1}{20} + \frac{1}{40} + \frac{1}{80}$

8. $9 - 6 + 4 - \frac{8}{3} + \frac{16}{9}$

Determine whether each infinite geometric series *diverges* or *converges*.

9. $1 - \frac{1}{6} + \frac{1}{36} - \frac{1}{216} + \cdots$

10. $\frac{1}{64} + \frac{1}{32} + \frac{1}{16} + \cdots$

Do you UNDERSTAND?

@ 11. **Error Analysis** A classmate uses the formula for the sum of an infinite geometric series to evaluate $1 + 1.1 + 1.21 + 1.331 + \cdots$ and gets -10. What error did your classmate make?

@ 12. **Writing** Explain how you can determine whether an infinite geometric series has a sum.

@ 13. **Compare and Contrast** How are the formulas for the sum of a finite arithmetic series and the sum of a finite geometric series similar? How are they different?

B Apply

Determine whether each series is *arithmetic* or *geometric*. Then evaluate the finite series for the specified number of terms.

14. $2 + 4 + 8 + 16 + \cdots; n = 10$

15. $2 + 4 + 6 + 8 + \cdots; n = 20$

16. $-5 + 25 - 125 + 625 - \cdots; n = 9$

17. $6.4 + 8 + 10 + 12.5 + \cdots; n = 7$

18. $1 + 2 + 3 + 4 + \cdots; n = 1000$

19. $81 + 27 + 9 + 3 + \cdots; n = 200$

© 20. Think About a Plan The height a ball bounces is less than the height of the previous bounce due to friction. The heights of the bounces form a geometric sequence. Suppose a ball is dropped from one meter and rebounds to 95% of the height of the previous bounce. What is the total distance traveled by the ball when it comes to rest?
- Does the problem give you enough information to solve the problem?
- How can you write the general term of the sequence?
- What formula should you use to calculate the total distance?

21. Communications Many companies use a telephone chain to notify employees of a closing due to bad weather. Suppose a company's CEO (Chief Executive Officer) calls four people. Then each of these people calls four others, and so on.
- **a.** Make a diagram to show the first three stages in the telephone chain. How many calls are made at each stage?
- **b.** Write the series that represents the total number of calls made through the first six stages.
- **c.** How many employees have been notified after stage six?

22. Graphing Calculator The graph models the sum of the first n terms in the infinite geometric series with $a_1 = 20$ and $r = 0.9$.
- **a.** Write the first four sums of the series.
- **b.** Use the graph to evaluate the series to the 47th term.
- **c.** Write and evaluate the formula for the sum of the series.
- **d.** Graph the formula using the window values shown. Use the graph to verify your answer to part (b).

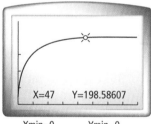

X=47   Y=198.58607

Xmin=0   Ymin=0
Xmax=94   Ymax=250
Xscl=10   Yscl=50

Evaluate each infinite series that has a sum.

23. $\displaystyle\sum_{n=1}^{\infty} \left(\tfrac{1}{5}\right)^{n-1}$

24. $\displaystyle\sum_{n=1}^{\infty} 3\left(\tfrac{1}{4}\right)^{n-1}$

25. $\displaystyle\sum_{n=1}^{\infty} \left(-\tfrac{1}{3}\right)^{n-1}$

26. $\displaystyle\sum_{n=1}^{\infty} 7(2)^{n-1}$

27. $\displaystyle\sum_{n=1}^{\infty} (-0.2)^{n-1}$

© 28. Open-Ended Write an infinite geometric series that converges to 3. Use the formula to evaluate the series.

© 29. Reasoning Find the specified value for each infinite geometric series.
- **a.** $a_1 = 12, S = 96$; find r
- **b.** $S = 12, r = \tfrac{1}{6}$, find a_1

© 30. **Writing** Suppose you are to receive an allowance each week for the next 26 weeks. Would you rather receive (a) $1000 per week or (b) $.02 the first week, $.04 the second week, $.08 the third week, and so on for the 26 weeks? Justify your answer.

© 31. The sum of an infinite geometric series is twice its first term.

   a. **Error Analysis** A student says the common ratio of the series is $\frac{3}{2}$. What is the student's error?

   b. Find the common ratio of the series.

STEM 32. **Physics** Because of friction and air resistance, each swing of a pendulum is a little shorter than the previous one. The lengths of the swings form a geometric sequence. Suppose the first swing of a pendulum has a length of 100 cm and the return swing is 99 cm.

   a. On which swing will the arc first have a length less than 50 cm?

   b. What is the total distance the pendulum has traveled when it comes to rest?

33. Where did the formula for summing finite geometric series come from? Suppose the geometric series has first term a_1 and constant ratio r, so that

$$S_n = a_1 + a_1 r + a_1 r^2 + \cdots + a_1 r^{n-1}.$$

   a. Show that $rS_n = a_1 r + a_1 r^2 + a_1 r^3 + \cdots + a_1 r^n$.

   b. Use part (a) to show that $S_n - rS_n = a_1 - a_1 r^n$.

   c. Use part (b) to show that $S_n = \dfrac{a_1 - a_1 r^n}{1 - r} = \dfrac{a_1(1 - r^n)}{1 - r}$.

© Challenge

34. The function $S(n) = \dfrac{10(1 - 0.8^n)}{0.2}$ represents the sum of the first n terms of an infinite geometric series.

   a. What is the domain of the function?

   b. Find $S(n)$ for $n = 1, 2, 3, \ldots, 10$. Sketch the graph of the function.

   c. Find the sum S of the infinite geometric series.

35. Use the formula for the sum of an infinite geometric series to show that $0.\overline{9} = 1$.
    (*Hint:* $0.\overline{9} = \frac{9}{10} + \frac{9}{100} + \frac{9}{1000} + \cdots$)

7-6 The Binomial Theorem

A.APR.5 Know and apply the Binomial Theorem for the expansion of $(x + y)^n$ . . . with coefficients determined for example by Pascal's Triangle. Also **A.SSE.2**

Objectives To expand a binomial using Pascal's Triangle
To use the Binomial Theorem

Solve It! Write your solution to the Solve It in the space below.

There is a connection between the triangular pattern of numbers in the Solve It and the expansion of $(a + b)^n$.

Essential Understanding You can use a pattern of coefficients and the pattern $a^n, a^{n-1}b, a^{n-2}b^2, \ldots, a^2b^{n-2}, ab^{n-1}, b^n$ to write the expansion of $(a + b)^n$.

You can expand $(a + b)^3$ using the Distributive Property.

$$(a + b)^3 = (a + b)(a + b)(a + b) = a^3 + 3a^2b + 3ab^2 + b^3$$

To **expand** the power of a binomial in general, first multiply as needed. Then write the polynomial in standard form.

Consider the expansions of $(a + b)^n$ for the first few values of n:

Row	Power	Expanded Form	Coefficients Only
0	$(a + b)^0$	1	1
1	$(a + b)^1$	$1a^1 + 1b^1$	1 1
2	$(a + b)^2$	$1a^2 + 2a^1b^1 + 1b^2$	1 2 1
3	$(a + b)^3$	$1a^3 + 3a^2b^1 + 3a^1b^2 + 1b^3$	1 3 3 1
4	$(a + b)^4$	$1a^4 + 4a^3b^1 + 6a^2b^2 + 4a^1b^3 + 1b^4$	1 4 6 4 1

The "coefficients only" column matches the numbers in *Pascal's Triangle.* **Pascal's Triangle**, named for the French mathematician Blaise Pascal (1623–1662), is a triangular array of numbers in which the first and last number of each row is 1. Each of the other numbers in the row is the sum of the two numbers above it.

For example, to generate row 5, use the sums of the adjacent elements in the row above it.

Row	Pascal's Triangle
0	1
1	1 1
2	1 2 1
3	1 3 3 1
4	1 4 6 4 1
5	1 5 10 10 5 1
6	1 6 15 20 15 6 1
7	1 7 21 35 35 21 7 1
8	1 8 28 56 70 56 28 8 1

$$1 \quad\overset{+}{\searrow}\quad 4 \quad\overset{+}{\searrow}\quad 6 \quad\overset{+}{\searrow}\quad 4 \quad\overset{+}{\searrow}\quad 1$$
$$5 \qquad 10 \qquad 10 \qquad 5$$

 Problem 1 Using Pascal's Triangle

Got It? What is the expansion of $(a + b)^8$? Use Pascal's Triangle.

Plan

What row of Pascal's Triangle should you use for this expansion?

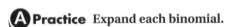 **Practice** Expand each binomial.

1. $(x - 5)^3$

2. $(x + 2)^{10}$

The **Binomial Theorem** gives a general formula for expanding a binomial.

take note

Theorem 9 Binomial Theorem

For every positive integer n,

$$(a + b)^n = P_0 a^n + P_1 a^{n-1}b + P_2 a^{n-2}b^2 + \ldots + P_{n-1}ab^{n-1} + P_n b^n$$

where $P_0, P_1, \ldots, P_n$ are the numbers in the nth row of Pascal's Triangle.

When you use the Binomial Theorem to expand $(x - 2)^4$, $a = x$ and $b = -2$. To expand a binomial such as $(3x - 2)^5$, $a = 3x$; so remember that $a^4 = (3x)^4$ not, $3x^4$.

Problem 2 **Expanding a Binomial**

Think

How can you write the binomial in the form $(a + b)^n$?

Got It? **a.** What is the expansion of $(2x - 3)^4$? Use the Binomial Theorem.

b. Reasoning Consider the following:

$$11^0 = 1 \qquad 11^1 = 11 \qquad 11^2 = 121 \qquad 11^3 = 1331 \qquad 11^4 = 14{,}641$$

Why do these powers of 11 have digits that mirror Pascal's Triangle?

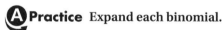 **Practice** Expand each binomial.

3. $(3a - 7)^3$

4. $(4x + 2)^6$

Lesson Check

Do you know HOW?

Use Pascal's Triangle to expand each binomial.

5. $(x + a)^3$

6. $(x - 2)^5$

7. $(2x + 4)^2$

8. $(3a - 2)^3$

Do you UNDERSTAND?

9. Vocabulary Tell whether each expression can be expanded using the Binomial Theorem.

a. $(2a - 6)^4$

b. $(5x^2 + 1)^5$

c. $(x^2 - 3x - 4)^3$

10. Writing Describe the relationship between Pascal's Triangle and the Binomial Theorem.

11. Reasoning Using Pascal's Triangle, determine the number of terms in the expansion of $(x + a)^{12}$. How many terms are there in the expansion of $(x + a)^n$?

More Practice and Problem-Solving Exercises

B Apply

12. Think About a Plan The side length of a cube is $\left(x^2 - \frac{1}{2}\right)$. Determine the volume of the cube.
- Rewrite the binomial as a sum.
- Consider $(a + b)^n$. Identify a and b in the given binomial.
- Which row of Pascal's Triangle can be used to expand the binomial?

13. In the expansion of $(2m + 3n)^9$, one of the terms contains m^3.
- **a.** What is the exponent of n in this term?
- **b.** What is the coefficient of this term?

Find the specified term of each binomial expansion.

14. Fourth term of $(x + 2)^5$

15. Third term of $(x - 3)^6$

16. Third term of $(3x - 1)^5$

17. Fifth term of $(a + 5b^2)^4$

18. Reasoning Explain why the coefficients in the expansion of $(x + 2y)^3$ do not match the numbers in the 3rd row of Pascal's Triangle.

19. Compare and Contrast What are the benefits and challenges of using the Binomial Theorem when expanding $(2x + 3)^2$? Using FOIL? Which method would you choose when expanding $(2x + 3)^6$? Why?

Expand each binomial.

20. $(2x - 2y)^6$ **21.** $(x^2 + 4)^{10}$ **22.** $(x^2 - y^2)^3$ **23.** $(a - b^2)^5$

24. $(3x + 8y)^3$ **25.** $(4x - 7y)^4$ **26.** $(7a + 2y)^{10}$ **27.** $(4x^3 + 2y^2)^6$

28. $(3b - 6)^7$ **29.** $(5a + 2b)^3$ **30.** $(b^2 - 2)^8$ **31.** $(-2y^2 + x)^5$

32. Geometry The side length of a cube is given by the expression $(2x + 8)$. Write a binomial power for the area of a face of the cube and for the volume of the cube. Then use the Binomial Theorem to expand and rewrite the powers in standard form.

ⓒ 33. Writing Explain why the terms of $(x - y)^n$ have alternating positive and negative signs.

ⓒ 34. Error Analysis A student expands $(3x - 8)^4$ as shown below. Describe and correct the student's error.

$$(3x - 8)^4 = (3x)^4 + 4(3x)^3(-8) + 6(3x)^2(-8)^2 + 4(3x)(-8)^3 + (-8)^4$$
$$= 3x^4 - 96x^3 + 1152x^2 - 6144x + 4096$$

ⓒ Challenge

Use the Binomial Theorem to expand each complex expression.

35. $(7 + \sqrt{-16})^5$ **36.** $(\sqrt{-81} - 3)^3$ **37.** $(x^2 - i)^7$

38. The first term in the expansion of a binomial $(ax + by)^n$ is $1024x^{10}$. Find a and n.

39. Determine the coefficient of x^7y in the expansion of $\left(\frac{1}{2}x + \frac{1}{4}y\right)^8$.

40. a. Expand $(1 + i)^4$.
   b. Verify that $1 - i$ is a fourth root of -4 by repeating the process in part (a) for $(1 - i)^4$.

41. Verify that $-1 + i\sqrt{3}$ is a cube root of 8 by expanding $(-1 + i\sqrt{3})^3$.

Mathematical Induction

A.APR.5 Know and apply the Binomial Theorem for the expansion of $(x + y)^n$ . . . with coefficients determined . . . by Pascal's triangle. Also **A.APR.4**

Mathematical induction is a method of proving statements about positive integers. To prove that a statement is true for all positive integers n, follow these steps:

Step 1 Show that the statement is true for $n = 1$. This is called the *base case*.

Step 2 Assume that the statement is true for some positive integer k. This is called the *induction hypothesis*.

Step 3 Show that the statement is true for the next positive integer $k + 1$.

In Steps 2 and 3, you show that if the statement is true for *some* positive integer, it must be true for the next positive integer as well. And since you showed in Step 1 that the statement is true for $n = 1$, this means that the statement must be true for *all* positive integers.

Example 1

Use mathematical induction to prove that $1 + 2 + 3 + \cdots + n = \frac{n(n + 1)}{2}$ for all positive integers n.

Step 1 Show that the statement is true for $n = 1$.

$$1 \stackrel{?}{=} \frac{1(1 + 1)}{2}$$

$$1 \stackrel{?}{=} \frac{1(2)}{2}$$

$$1 = 1$$

Step 2 Assume that the statement is true for some positive integer k.

Assume that $1 + 2 + 3 + \cdots + k = \frac{k(k + 1)}{2}$.

Step 3 Show that the statement is true for the next positive integer $k + 1$.

$$
\begin{aligned}
1 + 2 + 3 + \cdots + k + (k + 1) &= \frac{k(k + 1)}{2} + (k + 1) && \text{Induction hypothesis} \\
&= \frac{k(k + 1) + 2(k + 1)}{2} && \text{Add.} \\
&= \frac{(k + 1)(k + 2)}{2} && \text{Simplify.} \\
&= \frac{(k + 1)[(k + 1) + 1]}{2} && k + 2 = (k + 1) + 1
\end{aligned}
$$

Because the statement is true for $n = 1$ and

$$1 + 2 + 3 + \cdots + k + (k + 1) = \frac{(k + 1)[(k + 1) + 1]}{2},$$

$1 + 2 + 3 + \cdots + n = \frac{n(n + 1)}{2}$ is true for all positive integers n.

Example 2

Use mathematical induction to prove that $\frac{1}{2} + \frac{1}{2^2} + \frac{1}{2^3} + \cdots + \frac{1}{2^n} = 1 - \frac{1}{2^n}$ for all positive integers n.

Step 1 Show that the statement is true for $n = 1$.

$$\frac{1}{2} \overset{?}{=} 1 - \frac{1}{2}$$

$$\frac{1}{2} = \frac{1}{2}$$

Step 2 Assume that the statement is true for some positive integer k.

Assume that $\frac{1}{2} + \frac{1}{2^2} + \frac{1}{2^3} + \cdots + \frac{1}{2^k} = 1 - \frac{1}{2^k}$.

Step 3 Show that the statement is true for the next positive integer $k + 1$.

$$\frac{1}{2} + \frac{1}{2^2} + \frac{1}{2^3} + \cdots + \frac{1}{2^k} + \frac{1}{2^{k+1}} = 1 - \frac{1}{2^k} + \frac{1}{2^{k+1}} \qquad \text{Induction hypothesis}$$

$$= 1 - \frac{1}{2^k}\left(\frac{2}{2}\right) + \frac{1}{2^{k+1}} \qquad \text{Multiply the 2nd term by } \frac{2}{2}.$$

$$= 1 - \frac{2}{2^{k+1}} + \frac{1}{2^{k+1}} \qquad \text{Simplify.}$$

$$= 1 + \frac{-2 + 1}{2^{k+1}}$$

$$= 1 - \frac{1}{2^{k+1}}$$

Because the statement is true for $n = 1$ and $\frac{1}{2} + \frac{1}{2^2} + \frac{1}{2^3} + \cdots + \frac{1}{2^k} + \frac{1}{2^{k+1}} = -\frac{1}{2^{k+1}}$,

$\frac{1}{2} + \frac{1}{2^2} + \frac{1}{2^3} + \cdots + \frac{1}{2^n} = 1 - \frac{1}{2^n}$ is true for all positive integers n.

Exercises

In Exercises 1 and 2, use mathematical induction to prove that each statement is true for all positive integers n.

1. $1 + 3 + 5 + \cdots + (2n - 1) = n^2$

2. $1 \cdot 2 + 2 \cdot 3 + 3 \cdot 4 + \cdots + n(n+1) = \dfrac{n(n+1)(n+2)}{3}$

3. Use mathematical induction in parts (a)–(e) to prove the Binomial Theorem is true for all positive integers n.

    a. Show that the Binomial Theorem is true for $n = 1$.

    b. State the induction hypothesis.

c. Use the induction hypothesis to rewrite the expression $(a + b)^{k+1}$ as the product of $a + b$ and a polynomial.

d. Use the Distributive Property to multiply, then group like terms.

e. Use the properties of Pascal's Triangle to describe the coefficients of the resulting polynomial.

7-1 Mathematical Patterns

Quick Review

A **sequence** is an ordered list of numbers called **terms**.

A **recursive definition** gives the first term and defines the other terms by relating each term after the first term to the one before it.

An **explicit formula** expresses the nth term in a sequence in terms of n, where n is a positive integer.

Example

A sequence has an explicit formula $a_n = n^2$. What are the first three terms of this sequence?

$a_1 = (1)^2 = 1$ Substitute 1 for n and evaluate.

$a_2 = (2)^2 = 4$ Substitute 2 for n and evaluate.

$a_3 = (3)^2 = 9$ Substitute 3 for n and evaluate.

The first three terms are 1, 4, and 9.

Exercises

Find the first five terms of each sequence.

1. $a_n = -2n + 3$

2. $a_n = -n^2 + 2n$

3. $a_n = 2a_{n-1} - 1$, where $a_1 = 2$

4. $a_n = \frac{1}{2}a_{n-1}$, where $a_1 = 20$

Write a recursive definition for each sequence.

5. $5, 22, 39, 56, \ldots$ **6.** $-2, 7, 16, 25, \ldots$

Write an explicit formula for each sequence.

7. $1, 4, 7, 10, \ldots$ **8.** $4, 1.5, -1, -3.5, \ldots$

7-2 Arithmetic Sequences

Quick Review

In an **arithmetic sequence**, the difference between consecutive terms is constant. This difference is the **common difference.**

For an arithmetic sequence, a is the first term, a_n is the nth term, n is the number of the term, and d is the common difference.

An explicit formula is $a_n = a + (n - 1)d$.

A recursive formula is $a_n = a_{n-1} + d$, with $a_1 = a$. The **arithmetic mean** of two numbers x and y is the average of the two numbers $\frac{x + y}{2}$.

Example

What is the missing term of the arithmetic sequence $11, \blacksquare, 27, \ldots$?

$$\text{arithmetic mean} = \frac{11 + 27}{2} = \frac{38}{2} = 19$$

The missing term is 19.

Exercises

Determine whether each sequence is arithmetic. If so, identify the common difference and find the 32nd term of the sequence.

9. $2, 4, 7, 10, \ldots$ **10.** $3, 18, 33, 48, \ldots$

11. $7, 10, 13, 16, \ldots$ **12.** $2, 5, 9, 14, \ldots$

Find the missing term(s) of each arithmetic sequence.

13. $1, \blacksquare, 9, \ldots$ **14.** $104, \blacksquare, 99, \ldots$

15. $-1, \blacksquare, 11 \ldots$ **16.** $-4.6, \blacksquare, -5.2, \ldots$

17. $-13, \blacksquare, \blacksquare, \blacksquare, -3, \ldots$

18. $2, \blacksquare, \blacksquare, \blacksquare, -0.4, \ldots$

Write an explicit formula for each arithmetic sequence.

19. $-2, 7, 16, 25, \ldots$ **20.** $62, 59, 56, 53, \ldots$

7-3 Geometric Sequences

Quick Review

In a **geometric sequence**, the ratio of consecutive terms is constant. This ratio is the **common ratio**.

For a geometric sequence, a is the first term, a_n is the nth term, n is the number of the term, and r is the common ratio.

An explicit formula is $a_n = a \cdot r^{n-1}$.

A recursive formula is $a_n = a_{n-1} \cdot r$, with $a_1 = a$.

The geometric mean of two positive numbers x and y is $\sqrt{xy}$.

Example

What is the sixth term of the geometric sequence that begins 2, 6, 18, . . . ?

$a_1 = 2$ and $r = 6 \div 2 = 3$

$a_6 = 2 \cdot 3^{6-1}$ Substitute 6 for n, 2 for a_1, and 3 for r.

$\quad\quad = 486$

The sixth term is 486.

Exercises

Determine whether each sequence is geometric. If so, identify the common ratio and find the next two terms.

21. $1, \frac{1}{2}, \frac{1}{4}, \frac{1}{8}, \dots$

22. $1, 3, 5, 7, \dots$

23. $3, 3.6, 4.32, 5.184, \dots$

Find the missing term(s) of each geometric sequence.

24. $3, \blacksquare, 12, \dots$

25. $0.004, \blacksquare, 0.4, \dots$

26. $-20, \blacksquare, \blacksquare, \blacksquare, -1.25, \dots$

Write an explicit formula for each geometric sequence.

27. $1, 2, 4, 8, \dots$ **28.** $25, 5, 1, \frac{1}{5}, \dots$

Use an explicit formula to find the 10th term of each geometric sequence.

29. $5, 10, 20, 40, \dots$ **30.** $-3, 6, -12, 24, \dots$

7-4 Arithmetic Series

Quick Review

A **series** is the expression for the sum of the terms of a sequence.

An **arithmetic series** is the sum of the terms of an arithmetic sequence. The sum S_n of the first n terms of an arithmetic series is $S_n = \frac{n}{2}(a_1 + a_n)$. You can use a summation symbol, Σ, and lower and upper **limits** to write a series. The lower limit is the least value of n and the upper limit is the greatest value of n.

Example

What is the sum of the arithmetic series?

$2 + 5 + 8 + 11 + 14 + 17 + 20$

$a_1 = 2$, $a_7 = 20$, and $n = 7$.

$S_7 = \frac{7}{2}(2 + 20)$ Substitute 7 for n, 2 for a_1, and 20 for a_7.

$\quad = 77$ Evaluate.

The sum is 77.

Exercises

Use summation notation to write each arithmetic series for the specified number of terms. Then evaluate the sum.

31. $10 + 7 + 4 + \cdots ; n = 5$

32. $50 + 55 + 60 + \cdots ; n = 7$

33. $6 + 7.4 + 8.8 + \cdots ; n = 11$

34. $21 + 19 + 17 + \cdots ; n = 8$

Find the number of terms in each series, the first term, and the last term. Then evaluate the sum.

35. $\displaystyle\sum_{n=1}^{3} (17n - 25)$ **36.** $\displaystyle\sum_{n=2}^{10} \left(\frac{1}{2}n + 3\right)$

7-5 Geometric Series

Quick Review

A **geometric series** is the sum of the terms of a geometric sequence. The sum S_n of the first n terms of a geometric series is $S_n = \frac{a_1(1 - r^n)}{1 - r}, r \neq 1$.

When an infinite series has a finite sum, the series **converges**. When the series does not converge, the series **diverges**.

In a geometric series, when $|r| < 1$, the series converges to $S = \frac{a_1}{1 - r}$. When $|r| \geq 1$, the series diverges.

Example

What is the sum of the geometric series?

$$5 + 10 + 20 + 40 + 80 + 160$$

$n = 6$, $a_1 = 5$, and $r = 10 \div 5 = 2$.

$S_6 = \frac{5(1 - 2^6)}{1 - 2}$ Substitute 6 for n, 5 for a_1, and 2 for r.

$= 315$ Evaluate.

The sum is 315.

Exercises

Evaluate each finite series for the specified number of terms.

37. $1 + 2 + 4 + \cdots$; $n = 5$

38. $80 - 40 + 20 - \cdots$; $n = 8$

39. $12 + 2 + \frac{1}{3} + \cdots$; $n = 4$

Determine whether each infinite geometric series *converges* or *diverges*. If the series converges, state the sum.

40. $150 + 30 + 6 + \cdots$

41. $2.2 + 2.42 + 2.662 + \cdots$

42. $-10 - 20 - 40 - \cdots$

43. $\frac{2}{3} + \frac{4}{9} + \frac{8}{27} + \cdots$

7-6 The Binomial Theorem

Quick Review

Rows $0-5$ of Pascal's Triangle are shown below.

```
          1
        1   1
      1   2   1
    1   3   3   1
  1   4   6   4   1
1   5   10  10  5   1
```

The **Binomial Theorem** uses Pascal's Triangle to expand binomials. For a positive integer n, $(a + b)^n = P_0 a^n + P_1 a^{n-1}b + P_2 a^{n-2}b^2 + \cdots + P_{n-1}ab^{n-1} + P_n b^n$, where $P_0, P_1, \ldots, P_n$ are the numbers in the nth row of Pascal's Triangle.

Example

Use the binomial theorem to expand $(2x + 3)^3$.

$(2x + 3)^3$

$= 1(2x)^3 + 3(2x)^2(3) + 3(2x)(3)^2 + 1(3)^3$

$= 8x^3 + 36x^2 + 54x + 27$

Exercises

44. How many numbers are in the eighth row of Pascal's Triangle?

45. List the numbers in the eighth row of Pascal's Triangle.

46. How many numbers are in the fifteenth row of Pascal's Triangle?

47. What is the third number in the fifteenth row of Pascal's Triangle?

Use the Binomial Theorem to expand each binomial.

48. $(x + 9)^3$ **49.** $(b + 2)^4$

50. $(3a + 1)^3$ **51.** $(x - 5)^3$

52. $(x - 2y)^3$ **53.** $(3a + 4b)^5$

54. $(x + 1)^6$ **55.** $(2x - 1)^6$

Find the coefficient of the x^2 term in each binomial expansion.

56. $(3x + 4)^3$ **57.** $(ax - c)^4$

 ASSESSMENT

Reconstructing Sales Data

Matthew has a valuable collection of a certain toy car, which is a collector's item. For the last 20 years, the value of the toy car has increased by the same percent each year. The table shows the value of the toy car for several years, as published in a collector's magazine.

Year	Value
2003	$76.00
2004	$79.04
2005	$82.20
2006	$85.49
2007	$88.91
2008	$92.47

Over a span of 7 years, Matthew sold 7 toy cars, with each sale occurring one year after the previous sale and at the published price. His total revenue from the sales was $533.64. However, he cannot remember when he sold the cars, and he is wondering how he can figure this out.

Task Description

Determine the years in which the toy cars were sold.

Get Ready!

Squaring Numbers and Finding Square Roots

Simplify.

1. 3^2

2. 8^2

3. 12^2

4. 15^2

5. $\sqrt{16}$

6. $\sqrt{64}$

7. $\sqrt{100}$

8. $\sqrt{169}$

Solve each quadratic equation.

9. $x^2 = 64$

10. $b^2 - 225 = 0$

11. $a^2 = 144$

Simplifying Radicals

Simplify. Leave your answers in simplified radical form.

12. $\sqrt{8}$

13. $\sqrt{27}$

14. $\sqrt{75}$

15. $4\sqrt{72}$

Area

16. A garden that is 6 ft by 8 ft has a walkway that is 3 ft wide around it. What is the ratio of the area of the garden to the area of the garden and walkway? Write your answer in simplest form.

17. A rectangular rose garden is 8 m by 10 m. One bag of fertilizer can cover 16 m². How many bags of fertilizer will be needed to cover the entire garden?

Classifying Quadrilaterals

Classify each quadrilateral as specifically as possible.

18.

19.

20.

 Looking Ahead Vocabulary

21. Polygons are two-dimensional figures made up of edges and vertices. How can three-dimensional figures be made up of faces, edges, and vertices?

22. The word *locus* comes from the Latin word for "place" or "location." What is the *locus* of a set of points?

Applying Geometric Concepts

Big Ideas

1 Similarity

Essential Questions: How do perimeters and areas of similar polygons compare? How do surface areas and volumes of similar solids compare?

2 Measurement

Essential Question: How do you find the area of a polygon?

3 Visualization

Essential Question: How can you determine the intersection of a solid and a plane?

ⓒ Domains

- Congruence
- Geometric Measurement and Dimension
- Modeling with Geometry

Interactive Digital Path

Log in to **pearsonsuccessnet.com** and click on Interactive Digital Path to access the Solve Its and animated Problems.

Chapter Preview

Vocabulary

English/Spanish Vocabulary Audio Online:

English	Spanish
cross section, *p. 594*	sección de corte
edge, *p. 590*	arista
face, *p. 590*	cara
geometric probability, *p. 581*	probabilidad geométrica
locus, *p. 610*	lugar geométrico
polyhedron, *p. 590*	poliedro
similar solids, *p. 601*	cuerpos geométricos semejantes
vertex, *p. 590*	vértice

8-1 Applying Constructions

G.CO.12 Make formal geometric constructions with . . . compass and straightedge . . . Also **G.CO.13, G.C.3**

Objective To use geometric constructions to solve problems

 Solve It! Write your solution to the Solve It in the space below.

The Solve It involves constructing a square. There are other ways to apply constructions in addition to folding paper.

Essential Understanding You can use a compass, protractor, and straightedge to construct geometric figures.

To **bisect** an angle or segment means to divide the angle or segment into two equal parts.

 **Bisecting an Angle**

Got It? Follow the steps to construct the bisector of $\overline{CD}$.

- Put the compass point on point C. Draw arcs to the left and to the right of $\overline{CD}$.
- Put the compass point on point D. Using the same compass setting, draw an arc to the left and to the right of $\overline{CD}$. Be sure the arcs intersect.
- Draw the line connecting the points of intersections of the arcs.

C
•

•
D

1. Draw a 60°-angle. Then bisect the angle.

2. Draw a 3-inch line segment. Then bisect the segment.

Recall that perpendicular lines form right angles.

Problem 2 Constructing Perpendicular Lines

Think
Which segment
do you need to
bisect?

Got It? First Street is the perpendicular bisector of the section of Front Street between the school and the intersection of Main Street and Front Street. Draw First Street.

• School

Main St.

Front St.

3. The figure below shows the vertical beam of a telephone pole. The points shows the location where the horizontal beam is attached to the vertical beam. Construct the horizontal beam.

4. Explain how to prove that the telephone pole beams drawn in Exercise 3 are perpendicular.

Recall that parallel lines never instersect.

Problem 3 **Constructing Parallel Lines**

Got It? Construct a line parallel to the line below through the given point by constructing two perpendicular lines.

Think

How do you know that the second line you construct is parallel to the given line?

5. A city worker is painting yellow road lines on a highway. The left road line is shown below. Construct the right road line parallel to the given line.

6. Prove that the roads constructed in Exercise 5 are parallel.

To *circumscribe* means to 'draw around'. A **circumscribed circle** is a circle that passes through each vertex of a given polygon.

Got It? A circle can also be *inscribed* in certain polygons. This means that the circle touches each side of a given polygon. Use the steps below to construct an inscribed circle in △*MNP*.

- Bisect ∠*M* and ∠*P*. Label the intersection of the angle bisectors point *Q*.
- Construct a line through *Q* perpendicular to $\overline{MP}$. Label the intersection of the perpendicular line and $\overline{MP}$ as point *R*.
- Draw a circle with center *Q* that passes through *R*.

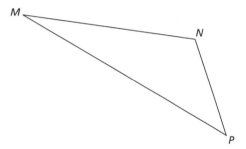

Practice **7.** Construct a circle circumscribed about the isosceles right triangle below.

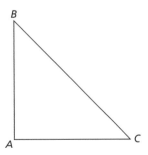

8. Explain how you constructed a circle circumscribed about the right triangle in Exercise 7.

To *inscribe* means to draw inside. An **inscribed polygon** is a polygon in which all vertices of the polygon are on a given circle.

 **Problem 5** Inscribing a Regular Hexagon in a Circle

Got It? You decide to change the company logo from Problem 5 to be an equilateral triangle inscribed in a circle. Explain how you could use the existing logo to create the new logo. Construct the new logo.

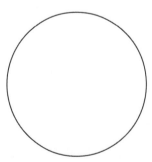

9. Graphic Design Damon is drawing a logo for his new business. He wants the logo to be a square inscribed in a circle. The circular outline of the logo is shown below. Construct the square inscribed in the circle.

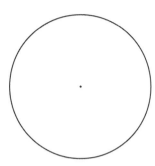

10. Explain how to prove the figure you drew inside the circle is a square.

 Lesson Check

Do you know HOW?

11. Construct a copy of ∠ABC.

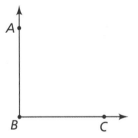

12. Construct the angle bisector of ∠ABC. (Use your copy from Exercise 11.)

Do you UNDERSTAND?

© **13. Vocabulary** What is the difference between a circumscribed circle and an inscribed polygon.

© **14. Reasoning** Suppose you used a narrower compass setting to construct the angle bisector of $\angle ABC$ in Exercise 12. Will you construct a different angle bisector? Explain.

© **15. Compare and Contrast** How are the constructions in Problem 4 and its Got It similar? How are they different?

More Practice and Problem-Solving Exercises

B Apply

In Exercises 16 and 17, construct a figure congruent to the figure given. Check your work with a ruler or a protractor.

16.

17.

18. Describe how to bisect a segment.

☉ 19. Think About a Plan The 2-inch line segment represents the one side of a square table. Copy the segment, then construct a scale model of the top view of the table.
  - How can you copy the segment?
  - How do you construct lines perpendicular to the segment through the endpoints of the segment?
  - How can make sure that each side of the tabletop is the same length?

20. Draw a line segment. Construct an equilateral triangle with the segment as one side. Describe the steps in your construction.

21. Construct a 30°-60°-90° triangle. (*Hint*: Use the construction from Exercise 20.)

22. Sports An indoor soccer field has a length that is twice its width.
  a. Construct a drawing of the soccer field.
  b. Describe the steps in your construction.

23. a. Construct a circle inscribed in a square.
  b. Describe the steps in your construction from part (a).

24. Draw $\overline{ST}$.
  a. Construct a trisection of $\overline{ST}$ by following the steps below.
    - Draw $\overrightarrow{SR}$ to form $\angle RST$.
    - Choose a point X on $\overrightarrow{SR}$.
    - Copy $\overline{SX}$ with endpoint at X along $\overrightarrow{SR}$ in the opposite direction of point S. Label the new endpoint of the copied segment point Y.
    - Copy $\overline{SX}$ with endpoint Y along $\overrightarrow{SR}$ in the opposite direction of point S. Label the new endpoint of the copied segment point Z.
    - Draw $\overline{ZT}$. Construct lines through points X and Y that are parallel to $\overline{ZT}$.
  b. Show that the parallel lines in the last step of the construction trisect $\overline{ST}$.

25. Copy the number line below, and the point *X* on the number line.

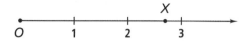

a. Construct $\sqrt{X}$ by following the steps below.

- Draw a circle of radius 1 with center *O*.
- Extend the number line to the left so that it intersects the circle at point *P*.
- Find the midpoint of $\overline{XP}$. Label the midpoint *Q*.
- Draw a circle with center *Q* and radius *QP*.
- Construct a line through *O* perpendicular to the number line. Let the intersection of this line and the circle from the previous step be *R*. The length of $\overline{RO}$ is $\sqrt{X}$.

b. Prove that $RO = \sqrt{X}$. (*Hint*: Draw $\overline{RP}$ and $\overline{RX}$. Use the fact that $\triangle PRO \sim \triangle RXO$ to write a proportion of side lengths of the two triangles.)

26. Golden Rectangle Rectangles in which the ratio of the length to the width is $1 + \sqrt{5} : 2$ are *golden rectangles*. A golden rectangle can be divided into a square and a rectangle that is similar to the original rectangle.

a. Construct a golden rectangle by following the steps below.

- Draw square *FGHJ*.
- Construct the midpoint of $\overline{FJ}$. Label the midpoint *I*.
- Extend $\overline{FJ}$ in the direction of *J*.
- Place the compass at *I*. Make the width of the compass *IH*. Draw an arc that intersects the extended segment. Label the intersection *K*.
- Construct a line at *K* perpendicular to $\overline{FK}$.
- Extend $\overline{GH}$ to intersect the perpendicular line constructed in the previous step at point *L*. *GLKF* is a golden rectangle, where rectangle *JHLK* is similar to rectangle *GLKF*.

b. Show that $IK = \frac{\sqrt{5}}{2}FJ$. (*Hint*: Consider $\triangle IHJ$.)

c. Show that $JK = \frac{\sqrt{5} - 1}{2}FJ$.

d. Show that *FGLK* is similar to *HJKL* by showing that $\frac{FK}{GF} = \frac{HJ}{JK}$.

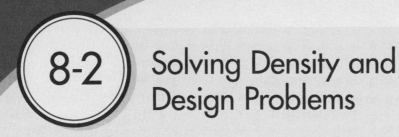

8-2 Solving Density and Design Problems

G.MG.2 Apply concepts of density based on area and volume in modeling situations . . . Also **G.MG.3**

Objective   To find the density of objects

 Solve It!   Write your solution to the Solve It in the space below.

The Solve It involves finding the area per person of your classroom. *Density* is a measure based on area or volume that you can use to describe real-world situations.

Essential Understanding You can use geometric methods to solve real-world problems.

To find the **density** of an object, divide its mass by its volume. To find **population density**, divide the number of individuals in the population by the total area or volume that they occupy.

 **Problem 1** **Finding Population Density**

Got It?   A fish tank is shown below. There are 36 fish in the tank. What is the population density of the fish tank?

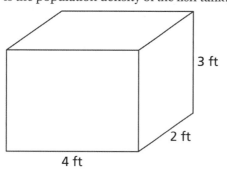

3 ft

2 ft

4 ft

Plan

What do you need to know to find the population density?

Practice   **1.** An outline of a city map is shown. The population of the city is 23,023 people. What is the population density of the city?

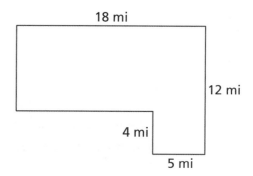

18 mi

12 mi

4 mi

5 mi

2. The aquarium can accommodate medium-size fish.

   a. What is the population density of the aquarium if it holds two fish?

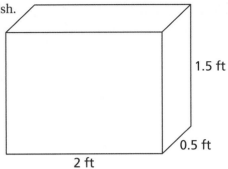

1.5 ft

0.5 ft

2 ft

   b. An aquarium in the shape of a cube has 2 ft edges. Based on the population density you found in part (a), how many medium size fish can this aquarium hold?

You can also use geometric methods to solve design problems.

Problem 2 **Solving a Design Problem**

Got It? The company in Problem 2 decides to change the base of the block of cheese to be an isosceles right triangle while maintaining its volume. What dimensions should the company choose for the blocks of cheese in order to minimize the surface area? Round your answer to the nearest tenth.

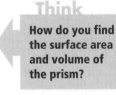

Think

How do you find the surface area and volume of the prism?

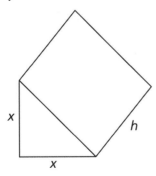

x

h

x

Practice

3. A company wants to manufacture packaging boxes in the shape of rectangular prisms. Each box will have a volume of 12,000 cubic inches. The company wants to choose the dimensions of a box with side lengths h in., $8x$ in., and $12x$ in., so that the box's surface area is minimized. What dimensions should the company choose for the boxes? Round your answer to the nearest tenth.

4. A designer wants to manufacture storage crates in the shape of rectangular prisms with an open top. Each crate will have a volume of 1944 cubic inches. The designer wants to choose the dimensions of a crate with length $1.5x$ in., width x in., and height h in., so that the crate's surface area is minimized. What dimensions should the company choose for the boxes? Round your answer to the nearest tenth.

Lesson Check

Do you know HOW?

5. What two measures are needed to find the density of an object?

6. How can you minimize the surface area of an object with a fixed volume?

7. How do you find population density?

Do you UNDERSTAND?

 **8. Vocabulary** What does *population* refer to in the term *population density*?

9. **Open-Ended** Describe a situation in which you might want to minimize the surface area of an object with a fixed volume.

 10. **Error Analysis** The volume of a block of iron is 12 cm³ and its mass is 94.44 grams. A classmate said the density of iron was 0.13 g/cm³. Explain his error.

More Practice and Problem-Solving Exercises

B Apply

11. New York City has an area of 303 square miles. In 2011, New York City had a population of 8,244,910. What was the population density of New York City in 2011?

12. The state of Connecticut has an area of 4,845 square miles. In 2011, Connecticut had a population of 3,580,709. What was the population density of Connecticut in 2011?

13. **Think About a Plan** You want to manufacture soup cans in the shape of a cylinder. Each can will have a volume of 1099 cubic centimeters. You want to choose the dimensions so that the surface area is minimized. What dimensions should you choose for the cans?
    - What formula should you use for the volume of a cylinder?
    - What formula should you use for the surface area of a cylinder?
    - How can you use a calculator to find the dimensions for each can?

14. A designer wants to manufacture storage bins in the shape of rectangular prisms. Each bin will have a volume of 9 cubic feet. The designer wants to choose the dimensions of a bin so that the bases of the prism are squares and the bin's surface area is minimized. What dimensions should the designer choose for the bins?

15. Error Analysis The population of a city is 293,908 and the area is 142 square miles. A classmate said the population density can be found by dividing 142 square miles by 293,908 people. What is her mistake?

STEM 16. Metals The table shows the mass and volume of different metals. Find the density of each.

Density

Substance	Mass (grams)	Volume (cm^3)
Aluminum	135	50
Cesium	308.8	160
Gold	482.5	25
Lead	339	30

a. Aluminum
b. Cesium
c. Gold
d. Lead

17. The table shows the population and area of several countries.

Country	Population	Area (km^2)
Singapore	5,183,700	710
Bhutan	738,267	38,394
Bangladesh	152,518,015	147,570
South Korea	48,456,369	99,538

a. What is the population density of Singapore?
b. What is the population density of Bhutan?
c. What is the population density of Bangladesh?
d. What is the population density of South Korea?

18. A florist recommends that you should grow 4 Flower *A* plants per square foot, and 9 Flower *B* plants per square foot. If you want to grow 50 plants each of Flower *A* and Flower *B*, how many more square feet of garden space do you need for the Flower *A* plants than the Flower *B* plants?

19. Japan has 127,960,000 people living on 377,944 square kilometers of land. Belgium has 11,007,020 people living on 30,528 square kilometers of land. How many fewer people live on a square kilometer of land in Japan than in Belgium?

20. **Buoyancy** Buoyancy is the upward force that a fluid applies to an object less dense than itself. This means an object will float if the density of the object is less than the density of the fluid is displaces. Water has a density of 1 g/cm³.

   a. A beach ball has a volume of 1800 cm³ and a mass of 630 grams. What is the density of the beach ball?

   b. Will the beach ball float? Explain.

STEM 21. **Energy** Natural gas is measured by volume, in cubic feet. A cubic foot of gas is the amount of gas needed to fill a volume of one cubic foot under certain conditions of pressure and temperature. The energy content of natural gas is measured in British Thermal Units, or BTUs. One BTU is the amount of heat needed to raise one pound of water 1°F. One cubic foot of propane has 2516 BTUs, and one cubic foot of natural gas has 1030 BTUs.

   a. How much natural gas will a 100,000 BTU/hr furnace will use in one hour? Explain.

   b. How much propane gas will a 100,000 BTU/hr furnace will use in one hour? Explain.

   c. How many times more energy does propane contain than natural gas, using a 100,000 BTU/hr furnace? Explain.

8-3 Perimeters and Areas of Similar Figures

G.MG.1 Use geometric shapes, their measures, and their properties to describe objects . . . Also **G.MG.2, G.MG.3**

Objective To find the perimeters and areas of similar polygons

Solve It! Write your solution to the Solve It in the space below.

In the Solve It, you compared the areas of similar figures.

Essential Understanding You can use ratios to compare the perimeters and areas of similar figures.

take note

Theorem 10 Perimeters and Areas of Similar Figures

If the scale factor of two similar figures is $\frac{a}{b}$, then

(1) the ratio of their perimeters is $\frac{a}{b}$, and

(2) the ratio of their areas is $\frac{a^2}{b^2}$.

Got It?   Two similar polygons have corresponding sides in the ratio 5 : 7.

     a. What is the ratio (larger to smaller) of their perimeters?

     b. What is the ratio (larger to smaller) of their areas?

Ⓐ Practice   The figures in each pair are similar. Compare the first figure to the second. Give the ratio of the perimeters and the ratio of the areas.

1.

14 cm

21 cm

2.

15 in.   25 in.

When you know the area of one of two similar polygons, you can use a proportion to find the area of the other polygon.

Problem 2 **Finding Areas Using Similar Figures**

Think

What is the ratio of the areas?

Got It?   The scale factor of two similar parallelograms is $\frac{3}{4}$. The area of the larger parallelogram is 96 in.^{2}. What is the area of the smaller parallelogram?

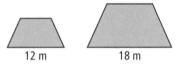**Practice** The figures in each pair are similar. The area of one figure is given. Find the area of the other figure to the nearest whole number.

3.

12 m   18 m

Area of larger trapezoid = 121 m^2

4.

3 m

11 m

Area of smaller hexagon = 23 m^2

Problem 3 Applying Area Ratios

Got It?   **a.** The scale factor of the dimensions of two similar pieces of window glass is 3 : 5. The smaller piece costs $2.50. How much should the larger piece cost?

b. Reasoning In Problem 3, why is it important that *each* dimension is 2.5 times the corresponding dimension of the original plot? Explain.

Practice 5. **Remodeling** The scale factor of the dimensions of two similar wood floors is 4:3. It costs $216 to refinish the smaller wood floor. At that rate, how much would it cost to refinish the larger wood floor?

6. **Decorating** An embroidered placemat costs $3.95. An embroidered tablecloth is similar to the placemat, but four times as long and four times as wide. How much would you expect to pay for the tablecloth?

When you know the ratio of the areas of two similar figures, you can work backward to find the ratio of their perimeters.

 **Problem 4** Finding Perimeter Ratios

Got It? The areas of two similar rectangles are 1875 ft^2 and 135 ft^2. What is the ratio of their perimeters?

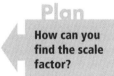

Plan

How can you find the scale factor?

A Practice Find the scale factor and the ratio of perimeters for each pair of similar figures.

7. two trapezoids with areas 49 cm² and 9 cm²

8. two equilateral triangles with areas $16\sqrt{3}$ ft² and $\sqrt{3}$ ft²

 Lesson Check

Do you know HOW?

The figures in each pair are similar. What is the ratio of the perimeters and the ratio of the areas?

9.

4 cm   6 cm

10.

12 in.   9 in.

11. In Exercise 10, if the area of the smaller triangle is about 39 ft^2, what is the area of the larger triangle to the nearest tenth?

12. The areas of two similar rhombuses are 48 m^2 and 128 m^2. What is the ratio of their perimeters?

Do you UNDERSTAND?

13. Reasoning How does the ratio of the areas of two similar figures compare to the ratio of their perimeters? Explain.

14. Reasoning The area of one rectangle is twice the area of another. What is the ratio of their perimeters? How do you know?

15. Error Analysis Your friend says that since the ratio of the perimeters of two polygons is $\frac{1}{2}$, the area of the smaller polygon must be one half the area of the larger polygon. What is wrong with this statement? Explain.

16. Compare and Contrast How is the relationship between the areas of two congruent figures different from the relationship between the areas of two similar figures?

More Practice and Problem-Solving Exercises

B Apply

The scale factor of two similar polygons is given. Find the ratio of their perimeters and the ratio of their areas.

17. 3 : 1   **18.** 2 : 5   **19.** $\frac{2}{3}$ **20.** $\frac{7}{4}$ **21.** 6 : 1

22. The area of a regular decagon is 50 cm^2. What is the area of a regular decagon with sides four times the sides of the smaller decagon?

   A 200 cm^2 **B** 500 cm^2 **C** 800 cm^2 **D** 2000 cm^2

23. Error Analysis A reporter used the graphic below to show that the number of houses with more than two televisions had doubled in the past few years. Explain why this graphic is misleading.

24. **Think About a Plan** Two similar rectangles have areas 27 in.^{2} and 48 in.^{2}. The length of one side of the larger rectangle is 16 in. What are the dimensions of both rectangles?
   - How does the ratio of the areas of the similar rectangles compare to their scale factor?
   - How can you use the dimensions of the larger rectangle to find the dimensions of the smaller rectangle?

25. The longer sides of a parallelogram are 5 m. The longer sides of a similar parallelogram are 15 m. The area of the smaller parallelogram is 28 m^2. What is the area of the larger parallelogram?

Algebra Find the values of x and y when the smaller triangle shown here has the given area.

26. 3 cm^2 27. 6 cm^2 28. 12 cm^2

29. 16 cm^2 30. 24 cm^2 31. 48 cm^2

STEM 32. **Medicine** For some medical imaging, the scale of the image is 3 : 1. That means that if an image is 3 cm long, the corresponding length on the person's body is 1 cm. Find the actual area of a lesion if its image has area 2.7 cm^2.

33. In △RST, $RS = 20$ m, $ST = 25$ m, and $RT = 40$ m.
   a. **Open-Ended** Choose a convenient scale. Then use a ruler and compass to draw △$R'S'T' \sim$ △RST.
   b. **Constructions** Construct an altitude of △$R'S'T'$ and measure its length. Find the area of △$R'S'T'$.
   c. **Estimation** Estimate the area of △RST.

Compare the blue figure to the red figure. Find the ratios of (a) their perimeters and (b) their areas.

34.

35.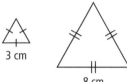

36.

37. a. Find the area of a regular hexagon with sides 2 cm long. Leave your answer in simplest radical form.
   b. Use your answer to part (a) and Theorem 10 to find the areas of the regular hexagons shown at the right.

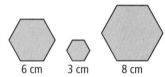

38. **Writing** The enrollment at an elementary school is going to increase from 200 students to 395 students. A parents' group is planning to increase the 100 ft-by-200 ft playground area to a larger area that is 200 ft by 400 ft. What would you tell the parents' group when they asked your opinion about whether the new playground will be large enough?

STEM **39. a. Surveying** A surveyor measured one side and two angles of a field, as shown in the diagram. Use a ruler and a protractor to draw a similar triangle.

    b. Measure the sides and altitude of your triangle and find its perimeter and area.

    Ⓒ **c. Estimation** Estimate the perimeter and area of the field.

40. Gardening You have a triangular garden that you want to expand. The larger garden will be similar to the smaller garden, and the ratio of the side lengths will be 5 : 8. If you can grow 8 pea plants per square foot, and you were able to grow 55 pea plants in the smaller garden, how many pea plants can you grow in the larger garden?

41. Design You would like to build a rectangular skateboarding platform in your yard similar to the one in the park, but on a smaller scale. The length of the platform in the park is 20 ft, and the area is 192 ft^2. The length of the platform you are building in your yard is 15 ft. What will the area of the new skateboarding platform be after it is built?

Ⓒ **Challenge**

Reasoning Complete each statement with *always*, *sometimes*, or *never*. Justify your answers.

42. Two similar rectangles with the same perimeter are _?_ congruent.

43. Two rectangles with the same area are _?_ similar.

44. Two rectangles with the same area and different perimeters are _?_ similar.

45. Similar figures _?_ have the same area.

8-4 Geometric Probability

G.MG.1 Use geometric shapes, their measures, and their properties to describe objects . . .

Objective To use segment and area models to find the probabilities of events

 Solve It! Write your solution to the Solve It in the space below.

In the Solve It, you found a probability involving a coin. In this lesson you will find probabilities based on lengths and areas. The probability of an event, written *P*(event), is the likelihood that the event will occur.

When the possible outcomes are equally likely, the theoretical probability of an event is the ratio of the number of favorable outcomes to the number of possible outcomes.

$$P(\text{event}) = \frac{\text{number of favorable outcomes}}{\text{number of possible outcomes}}$$

Recall that a probability can be expressed as a fraction, a decimal, or a percent.

Essential Understanding You can use geometric models to solve certain types of probability problems.

In **geometric probability**, points on a segment or in a region of a plane represent outcomes. The geometric probability of an event is a ratio that involves geometric measures such as length or area.

take note

Key Concept Probability and Length

Point *S* on $\overline{AD}$ is chosen at random. The probability that *S* is on $\overline{BC}$ is the ratio of the length of $\overline{BC}$ to the length of $\overline{AD}$.

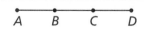

$$P(S \text{ on } \overline{BC}) = \frac{BC}{AD}$$

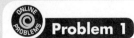 **Problem 1** Using Segments to Find Probability

Got It? Use the diagram below. Point *H* on $\overline{ST}$ is selected at random. What is the probability that *H* lies on $\overline{SR}$?

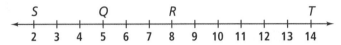

S   Q   R   T

2   3   4   5   6   7   8   9   10   11   12   13   14

Ⓐ Practice A point on $\overline{AK}$ is chosen at random. Find the probability that the point lies on the given segment.

A   B   C   D   E   F   G   H   I   J   K

0   1   2   3   4   5   6   7   8   9   10

1. $\overline{DJ}$ **2.** $\overline{AK}$

Problem 2 Using Segments to Find Probability

Got It? **Transportation** A commuter train runs every 25 min. If a commuter arrives at the station at a random time, what is the probability that a commuter will have to wait no more than 5 min for the train?

Think

What segment represents a wait of 5 minutes or less?

3. Traffic Lights The cycle of the traffic light on Main Street at the intersection of Main Street and Commercial Street is 40 seconds green, 5 seconds yellow, and 30 seconds red. If you reach the intersection at a random time, what is the probability that the light is red?

4. Communication Your friend is supposed to call you between 3 P.M. and 4 P.M. At 3:20 P.M., you realize that your cell phone is off and you immediately turn it on. What is the probability that you missed your friend's call?

When the points of a region represent equally likely outcomes, you can find probabilities by comparing areas.

take note

Key Concept Probability and Area

Point S in region R is chosen at random. The probability that S is in region N is the ratio of the area of region N to the area of region R.

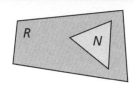

$$P(S \text{ in region } N) = \frac{\text{area of region } N}{\text{area of region } R}$$

Problem 3 Using Area to Find Probability

Got It? A triangle is inscribed in a square. Point *T* in the square is selected at random. What is the probability that *T* lies in the shaded region?

5 in.

Think

What two areas must you compare to find the probability?

Ⓐ Practice A point in the figure is chosen at random. Find the probability that the point lies in the shaded region.

5.

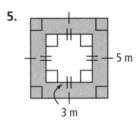

5 m

3 m

6.

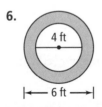

4 ft

|← 6 ft →|

 **Problem 4** **Using Area to Find Probability**

Got It?   **a.** What is the probability that an arrow hits the yellow zone in Problem 4?

©**b. Reasoning** If an arrow hits the target at a random point, is it more likely to hit the black zone or the red zone? Explain.

Ⓐ**Practice** **Target Game** A target with a diameter of 14 cm has 4 scoring zones formed by concentric circles. The diameter of the center circle is 2 cm. The width of each ring is 2 cm. A dart hits the target at a random point. Find the probability that it will hit a point in the indicated region.

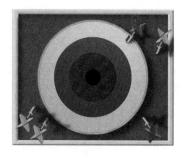

7. the center region

8. either the blue or the red region

Lesson Check

Do you know HOW?

Point T on $\overline{AD}$ is chosen at random. What is the probability that T lies on the given segment?

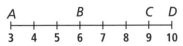

A | | B | | | | C | D
3 4 5 6 7 8 9 10

9. $\overline{AB}$ **10.** $\overline{AC}$ **11.** $\overline{BD}$ **12.** $\overline{BC}$

13. A point K in the regular hexagon is chosen at random. What is the probability that K lies in the region that is *not* shaded?

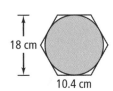

18 cm

10.4 cm

Do you UNDERSTAND?

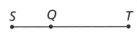

⊚ **14. Reasoning** In the figure at the right, $\frac{SQ}{QT} = \frac{1}{2}$. What is the probability that a point on $\overline{ST}$ chosen at random will lie on $\overline{QT}$? Explain.

S   Q   T

MATHEMATICAL PRACTICES

15. Error Analysis Your class needs to find the probability that a point A in the square chosen at random lies in the shaded region. Your classmate's work is shown below. What is the error? Explain.

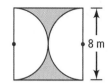

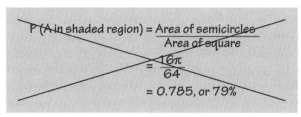

$$P(A \text{ in shaded region}) = \frac{\text{Area of semicircles}}{\text{Area of square}}$$

$$= \frac{16\pi}{64}$$

$$= 0.785, \text{ or } 79\%$$

Practice and Problem-Solving Exercises

B Apply

16. Points M and N are on $\overline{ZB}$ with M between Z and N. $ZM = 5$, $NB = 9$, and $ZB = 20$. A point on $\overline{ZB}$ is chosen at random. What is the probability that the point is on $\overline{MN}$?

17. $\overline{BZ}$ contains $\overline{MN}$, and $BZ = 20$. A point on $\overline{BZ}$ is chosen at random. The probability that the point is also on $\overline{MN}$ is 0.3, or 30%. Find MN.

18. Think About a Plan Every 20 min from 4:00 P.M. to 7:00 P.M., a commuter train crosses Boston Road. For 3 min, a gate stops cars from crossing over the tracks as the train goes by. What is the probability that a motorist randomly arriving at the train crossing during this time interval will have to stop for a train?
• How can you represent the situation visually?
• What ratio can you use to solve the problem?

19. Reasoning Suppose a point in the regular pentagon is chosen at random. What is the probability that the point is *not* in the shaded region? Explain.

20. Commuting A bus arrives at a stop every 16 min and waits 3 min before leaving. What is the probability that a person arriving at the bus stop at a random time has to wait more than 10 min for a bus to leave?

STEM **21. Astronomy** Meteorites (mostly dust-particle size) are continually bombarding Earth. The surface area of Earth is about 65.7 million mi^2. The area of the United States is about 3.7 million mi^2. What is the probability that a meteorite landing on Earth will land in the United States?

© **22. Reasoning** What is the probability that a point chosen at random on the circumference of the circle lies on $\overset{\frown}{AB}$? Explain how you know.

© **23. Writing** Describe a real-life situation in which you would use geometric probability.

Algebra Find the probability that coordinate x of a point chosen at random on $\overline{AK}$ satisfies the inequality.

24. $2 \le x \le 8$ **25.** $2x \le 8$ **26.** $5 \le 11 - 6x$

27. $\frac{1}{2}x - 5 > 0$ **28.** $2 \le 4x \le 3$ **29.** $-7 \le 1 - 2x \le 1$

30. One type of dartboard is a square of radius 10 in. You throw a dart and hit the target. What is the probability that the dart lies within $\sqrt{10}$ in. of the square's center?

© **31. Games** To win a prize at a carnival game, you must toss a quarter so that it lands entirely within a circle, as shown at the right. Assume that the center of a tossed quarter is equally likely to land at any point within the 8-in. square.
   a. What is the probability that the quarter lands entirely in the circle in one toss?
   b. Reasoning On average, how many coins must you toss to win a prize? Explain.

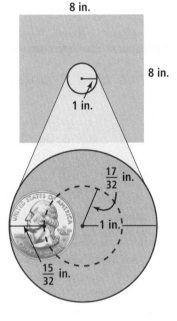

32. Traffic Patterns The traffic lights at Fourth and State Streets repeat themselves in 1-min cycles. A motorist will face a red light 60% of the time. Use this information to estimate how long the Fourth Street light is red during each 1-min cycle.

33. You have a 4-in. straw and a 6-in. straw. You want to cut the 6-in. straw into two pieces so that the three pieces form a triangle.
   a. If you cut the straw to get two 3-in. pieces, can you form a triangle?
   b. If the two pieces are 1 in. and 5 in., can you form a triangle?
   c. If you cut the straw at a random point, what is the probability that you can form a triangle?

34. Target Game Assume that a dart you throw will land on the 12 in.-by-12 in. square dartboard and is equally likely to land at any point on the board. The diameter of the center circle is 2 in., and the width of each ring is 1 in.

  a. What is the probability of hitting either the dark blue or the red region?

  b. What is the probability the dart will *not* hit the light blue region?

 **Challenge**

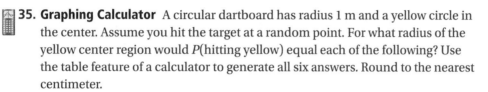 **35. Graphing Calculator** A circular dartboard has radius 1 m and a yellow circle in the center. Assume you hit the target at a random point. For what radius of the yellow center region would P(hitting yellow) equal each of the following? Use the table feature of a calculator to generate all six answers. Round to the nearest centimeter.

  a. 0.2   **b.** 0.4   **c.** 0.5

  d. 0.6   **e.** 0.8   **f.** 1.0

36. You and your friend agree to meet for lunch between 12 P.M. and 1 P.M. Each of you agrees to wait 15 min for the other before giving up and eating lunch alone. If you arrive at 12:20, what is the probability that you and your friend will eat lunch together?

8-5

Space Figures and Cross Sections

G.GMD.4 Identify the shapes of two-dimensional cross-sections of three-dimensional objects . . .

Objectives   To recognize polyhedra and their parts
To visualize cross sections of space figures

 Solve It!   Write your solution to the Solve It in the space below.

In the Solve It, you used two-dimensional nets to represent a three-dimensional object.

A **polyhedron** is a space figure, or three-dimensional figure, whose surfaces are polygons. Each polygon is a **face** of the polyhedron. An **edge** is a segment that is formed by the intersection of two faces. A **vertex** is a point where three or more edges intersect.

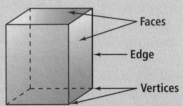

Essential Understanding   You can analyze a three-dimensional figure by using the relationships among its vertices, edges, and faces.

Problem 1 Identifying Vertices, Edges, and Faces

Got It? **a.** How many vertices, edges, and faces are in the polyhedron at the right? List them.

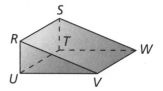

© b. Reasoning Is $\overline{TV}$ an edge? Explain why or why not.

Ⓐ Practice For each polyhedron, how many vertices, edges, and faces are there? List them.

1.

2.

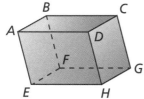

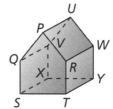

Leonhard Euler, a Swiss mathematician, discovered a relationship among the numbers of faces, vertices, and edges of any polyhedron. The result is known as Euler's Formula.

 take note

Key Concept Euler's Formula

The sum of the number of faces (F) and vertices (V) of a polyhedron is two more than the number of its edges (E).

$$F + V = E + 2$$

Problem 2 **Using Euler's Formula**

Got It? For each polyhedron, use Euler's Formula to find the missing number.

a.

faces: _____

edges: 30

vertices: 20

b.

faces: 20

edges: _____

vertices: 12

Practice **3.** For the polyhedron, use Euler's Formula to find the missing number.

faces: _____

edges: 15

vertices: 9

4. Use Euler's Formula to find the number of vertices of a polyhedron made up of 1 octagon and 8 triangles.

In two dimensions, Euler's Formula reduces to $F + V = E + 1$, where F is the number of regions formed by V vertices linked by E segments.

 **Problem 3** **Verifying Euler's Formula in Two Dimensions**

Got It? Use the solid at the right.

    a. How can you verify Euler's Formula $F + V = E + 2$ for the solid?

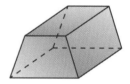

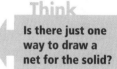

Think

Is there just one way to draw a net for the solid?

    b. Draw a net for the solid.

    c. How can you verify Euler's Formula $F + V = E + 1$ for your two-dimensional net?

Verify Euler's Formula for each polyhedron. Then draw a net for the figure and verify Euler's Formula for the two-dimensional figure.

5.

6.

A **cross section** is the intersection of a solid and a plane. You can think of a cross section as a very thin slice of the solid.

This cross section is a triangle.

Problem 4 **Describing a Cross Section**

Got It? For the solid at the right, what is the cross section formed by each of the following planes?

Think

How can you see the cross section more clearly?

  a. a horizontal plane

  b. a vertical plane that divides the solid in half

Practice Describe each cross section.

7.

8.

To draw a cross section, you can sometimes use the fact that the intersection of two planes is exactly one line.

Problem 5 **Drawing a Cross Section**

Got It? Draw the cross section formed by a horizontal plane intersecting the left and right faces of the cube. What shape is the cross section?

Practice **Visualization** Draw and describe a cross section formed by a vertical plane intersecting the cube above as follows.

9. The vertical plane intersects the front and left faces of the cube.

10. The vertical plane contains the red edges of the cube.

Lesson Check

Do you know HOW?

11. How many faces, edges, and vertices are in the solid? List them.

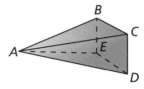

12. What is a net for the solid in Exercise 11? Verify Euler's Formula for the net.

13. What is the cross section of the cube formed by the plane containing the diagonals of a pair of opposite faces?

© 14. **Vocabulary** Suppose you built a polyhedron from two octagons and eight squares. Without using Euler's Formula, how many edges would the solid have? Explain.

© 15. **Error Analysis** Your math class is drawing polyhedrons. Which figure does not belong in the diagram below? Explain.

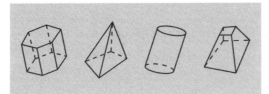

More Practice and Problem-Solving Exercises

 **Apply**

© 16. **a. Open-Ended** Sketch a polyhedron whose faces are all rectangles. Label the lengths of its edges.
   b. Use graph paper to draw two different nets for the polyhedron.

17. For the figure shown at the right, sketch each of following.
   a. a horizontal cross section
   b. a vertical cross section that contains the vertical line of symmetry

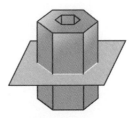

© 18. **Reasoning** Can you find a cross section of a cube that forms a triangle? Explain.

19. Reasoning Suppose the number of faces in a certain polyhedron is equal to the number of vertices. Can the polyhedron have nine edges? Explain.

Visualization Draw and describe a cross section formed by a plane intersecting the cube as follows.

20. The plane is tilted and intersects the left and right faces of the cube.

21. The plane contains the red edges of the cube.

22. The plane cuts off a corner of the cube.

Visualization A plane region that revolves completely about a line sweeps out a solid of revolution. Use the sample to help you describe the *solid of revolution* you get by revolving each region about line ℓ.

Sample: Revolve the rectangular region about the line ℓ. You get a cylinder as the solid of revolution.

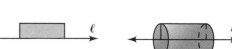

23.    **24.**    **25.**

26. Think About a Plan Some balls are made from panels that suggest polygons. A soccer ball suggests a polyhedron with 20 regular hexagons and 12 regular pentagons. How many vertices does this polyhedron have?

- How can you determine the number of edges in a solid if you know the types of polygons that form the faces?
- What relationship can you use to find the number of vertices?

Euler's Formula $F + V = E + 1$ applies to any two-dimensional network where F is the number of regions formed by V vertices linked by E edges (or paths). Verify Euler's Formula for each network shown.

27.   **28.**    **29.**

30. Platonic Solids There are five regular polyhedrons. They are called *regular* because all their faces are congruent regular polygons, and the same number of faces meet at each vertex. They are also called *Platonic solids* after the Greek philosopher Plato, who first described them in his work *Timaeus* (about 350 B.C.).

Tetrahedron

Hexahedron

Octahedron

Dodecahedron

Icosahedron

  a. Match each net below with a Platonic solid.

A.    **B.**   **C.**   **D.**   **E.**

  b. The first two Platonic solids also have more familiar names. What are they?
  c. Verify that Euler's Formula is true for the first three Platonic solids.

31. A cube has a net with area 216 in.^{2}. How long is an edge of the cube?

32. Writing Cross sections are used in medical training and research. Research and write a paragraph on how magnetic resonance imaging (MRI) is used to study cross sections of the brain.

Challenge

33. Open-Ended Draw a single solid that has the following three cross sections.

Horizontal

Vertical

Visualization Draw a plane intersecting a cube to get the cross section indicated.

34. scalene triangle   **35.** isosceles triangle   **36.** equilateral triangle

37. trapezoid   **38.** isosceles trapezoid   **39.** parallelogram

40. rhombus   **41.** pentagon   **42.** hexagon

8-6 Areas and Volumes of Similar Solids

G.MG.1 Use geometric shapes, their measures, and their properties to describe objects . . . Also
G.MG.2, G.MG.3

Objective   To compare and find the areas and volumes of similar solids

Solve It!   Write your solution to the Solve It in the space below.

Essential Understanding   You can use ratios to compare the areas and volumes of similar solids.

Similar solids have the same shape, and all their corresponding dimensions are proportional. The ratio of corresponding linear dimensions of two similar solids is the scale factor. Any two cubes are similar, as are any two spheres.

Problem 1   Identifying Similar Solids

Got It?   Are the two cylinders similar? If so, what is the scale factor of the first figure to the second figure?

ⒶPractice For Exercises 1 and 2, are the two figures similar? If so, give the scale factor of the first figure to the second figure.

1.

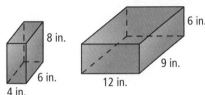

2. a cylinder and a square prism, both with 3–in. radius and 1–in. height

The two similar prisms shown here suggest two important relationships for similar solids.

The ratio of the side lengths is $1 : 2$.

The ratio of the surface areas is $22 : 88$, or $1 : 4$.

The ratio of the volumes is $6 : 48$, or $1 : 8$.

The ratio of the surface areas is the square of the scale factor. The ratio of the volumes is the cube of the scale factor. These two facts apply to all similar solids.

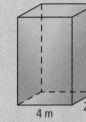

S.A. $= 22$ m²   S.A. $= 88$ m²

$V = 6$ m³ $V = 48$ m³

take note

Theorem 11   Areas and Volumes of Similar Solids

If the scale factor of two similar solids is $a : b$, then

- the ratio of their corresponding areas is $a^2 : b^2$, and

- the ratio of their volumes is $a^3 : b^3$.

 **Problem 2** Finding the Scale Factor

Got It?   **a.** What is the scale factor of two similar prisms with surface areas
144 m² and 324 m²?

b. Reasoning Are any two square prisms similar? Explain.

A.**Practice** Each pair of figures is similar. Use the given information to find the
scale factor of the smaller figure to the larger figure.

3.

$V = 216$ in.³ $V = 343$ in.³

4.

S.A. = 20π yd²   S.A. = 125π yd²

Got It? The volumes of two similar solids are 128 m^3 and 250 m^3. The surface area of the larger solid is 250 m^2. What is the surface area of the smaller solid?

Plan

How can you find the scale factor?

Practice 5. The surface areas of two similar figures are given. The volume of the larger figure is given. Find the volume of the smaller figure.

S.A. = 192 m^2

S.A. = 1728 m^2

V = 4860 m^3

6. The volumes of two similar figures are given. The surface area of the smaller figure is given. Find the surface area of the larger figure.

V = 2 yd^3

V = 250 yd^3

S.A. = 13 yd^2

You can compare the capacities and weights of similar objects. The capacity of an object is the amount of fluid the object can hold. The capacities and weights of similar objects made of the same material are proportional to their volumes.

 **Problem 4** **Using a Scale Factor to Find Capacity**

Got It? A marble paperweight shaped like a pyramid weighs 0.15 lb.
STEM How much does a similarly shaped marble paperweight weigh if each dimension is three times as large?

Think

How does weight relate to volume?

 Practice
STEM

7. Packaging A cylinder with a 4-in. diameter and a 6-in. height holds 1 lb of oatmeal. To the nearest ounce, how much oatmeal will a similar 10-in.-high cylinder hold? (*Hint*: 1 lb = 16 oz)

© **8. Compare and Contrast** A regular pentagonal prism has 9-cm base edges. A larger, similar prism of the same material has 36-cm base edges. How does each indicated measurement for the larger prism compare to the same measurement for the smaller prism?

a. the volume

b. the weight

Lesson Check

Do you know HOW?

9. Which two of the following cones are similar? What is their scale factor?

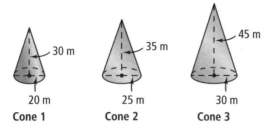

Cone 1	Cone 2	Cone 3
30 m / 20 m	35 m / 25 m	45 m / 30 m

10. The volumes of two similar containers are 115 in.^{3} and 67 in.^{3}. The surface area of the smaller container is 108 in.^{2}. What is the surface area of the larger container?

Do you UNDERSTAND?

MATHEMATICAL PRACTICES

⊚ 11. **Vocabulary** How are similar solids different from similar polygons? Explain.

12. Error Analysis Two cubes have surface areas 49 cm² and 64 cm². Your classmate tried to find the scale factor of the larger cube to the smaller cube. Explain and correct your classmate's error.

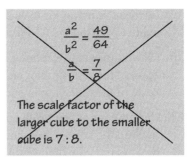

$$\frac{a^2}{b^2} = \frac{49}{64}$$

$$\frac{a}{b} = \frac{7}{8}$$

The scale factor of the larger cube to the smaller cube is 7 : 8.

More Practice and Problem-Solving Exercises

MATHEMATICAL PRACTICES

Ⓑ Apply

13. Two similar prisms have heights 4 cm and 10 cm.
    a. What is their scale factor?
    b. What is the ratio of their surface areas?
    c. What is the ratio of their volumes?

14. **Think About a Plan** A company announced that it had developed the technology to reduce the size of its atomic clock, which is used in electronic devices that transmit data. The company claims that the smaller clock will be similar to the existing clock made of the same material. The dimensions of the smaller clock will be $\frac{1}{10}$ the dimensions of the company's existing atomic clocks, and it will be $\frac{1}{100}$ the weight. Do these ratios make sense? Explain.
    • What is the scale factor of the smaller clock to the larger clock?
    • How are the weights of the two objects related to their scale factor?

15. **Reasoning** Is there a value of x for which the rectangular prisms at the right are similar? Explain.

16. The volume of a spherical balloon with radius 3.1 cm is about 125 cm³. Estimate the volume of a similar balloon with radius 6.2 cm.

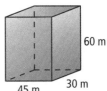

17. **Writing** Are all spheres similar? Explain.

18. **Reasoning** A carpenter is making a blanket chest based on an antique chest. Both chests have the shape of a rectangular prism. The length, width, and height of the new chest will all be 4 in. greater than the respective dimensions of the antique. Will the chests be similar? Explain.

19. Two similar pyramids have lateral areas 20 ft^2 and 45 ft^2. The volume of the smaller pyramid is 8 ft^3. Find the volume of the larger pyramid.

20. The volumes of two spheres are 729 in.^{3} and 27 in.^{3}.
 a. Find the ratio of their radii.
 b. Find the ratio of their surface areas.

21. The volumes of two similar pyramids are 1331 cm^3 and 2744 cm^3.
 a. Find the ratio of their heights.
 b. Find the ratio of their surface areas.

22. A clown's face on a balloon is 4 in. tall when the balloon holds 108 in.^{3} of air. How much air must the balloon hold for the face to be 8 in. tall?

Copy and complete the table for the similar solids.

	Similarity Ratio	Ratio of Surface Areas	
23.	1 : 2	■ : ■	■ : ■
24.	3 : 5	■ : ■	■ : ■
25.	■ : ■	49 : 81	■ : ■
26.	■ : ■	■ : ■	125 : 512

27. Literature In *Gulliver's Travels*, by Jonathan Swift, Gulliver first traveled to Lilliput. The Lilliputian average height was one twelfth of Gulliver's height.
 a. How many Lilliputian coats could be made from the material in Gulliver's coat? (*Hint*: Use the ratio of surface areas.)
 b. How many Lilliputian meals would be needed to make a meal for Gulliver? (*Hint*: Use the ratio of volumes.)

28. The trunk of an oak tree is 15 ft high. A cylindrical model of the oak tree trunk has a height of 1 foot and a surface area of about 0.838 ft^2.
 a. What is the scale factor of the cylindrical model and the oak tree trunk?
 b. Use the cylindrical model to approximate the surface area of the trunk of the oak tree. Round to the nearest tenth.

29. Design A local department store sells marbles that come in small boxes, 12 marbles to a box. You want to design a larger container, similar to the small one, that can hold more marbles. If you tripled the dimensions of the box from the department store, how many marbles would your new box hold?

30. The BTU rating needed for an air conditioner to cool a room increases proportionally with the volume of the room. An air conditioner rated at 6000 BTUs can cool a room that is 1500 cubic feet. If another room has dimensions that are each 1.2 times greater than the first room, what rating must an air conditioner have to cool the larger room?

31. Indirect Reasoning Some stories say that Paul Bunyan was ten times as tall as the average human. Assume that Paul Bunyan's bone structure was proportional to that of ordinary people.

  a. Strength of bones is proportional to the area of their cross section. How many times as strong as the average person's bones would Paul Bunyan's bones have been?

  b. Weights of objects made of like material are proportional to their volumes. How many times the average person's weight would Paul Bunyan's weight have been?

  c. Human leg bones can support about 6 times the average person's weight. Use your answers to parts (a) and (b) to explain why Paul Bunyan could not have existed with a bone structure that was proportional to that of ordinary people.

32. Square pyramids *A* and *B* are similar. In pyramid *A*, each base edge is 12 cm. In pyramid *B*, each base edge is 3 cm, and the volume is 6 cm³.

  a. Find the volume of pyramid *A*.

  b. Find the ratio of the surface area of *A* to the surface area of *B*.

  c. Find the surface area of each pyramid.

33. A cone is cut by a plane parallel to its base. The small cone on top is similar to the large cone. The ratio of the slant heights of the cones is 1 : 2. Find each ratio. (For parts (b) and (c), a *frustum* of a cone is the part that remains when the cone is cut off by a plane parallel to the base.)

  a. the surface area of the large cone to the surface area of the small cone

  b. the volume of the large cone to the volume of the small cone

  c. the surface area of the frustum to the surface area of the large cone and to the surface area of the small cone

  d. the volume of the frustum to the volume of the large cone and to the volume of the small cone

8-7 Locus: A Set of Points

G.GMD.4 . . . identify three-dimensional objects generated by rotations of two-dimensional objects.

Objective   To draw and describe a locus

Solve It!   Write your solution to the Solve It in the space below.

In the Solve It, you described the possible locations based on a certain condition. A **locus** is a set of points, all of which meet a stated condition. *Loci* is the plural of locus.

Essential Understanding You can use the description of a locus to sketch a geometric relationship.

 **Problem 1**   Describing a Locus in a Plane

Got It?   **Reasoning** If the question for part (b) of Problem 1 had asked for the locus of points in a plane 1 cm from $\overleftrightarrow{AB}$, how would the sketch change?

A Practice Sketch and describe each locus of points in a plane.

1. points equidistant from two perpendicular lines

2. midpoints of radii of a circle with radius 2 cm

You can use locus descriptions for geometric terms.

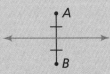

The locus of points in the interior of an angle that are equidistant from the sides of the angle is an angle bisector.

In a plane, the locus of points that are equidistant from a segment's endpoints is the perpendicular bisector of the segment.

Sometimes a locus is described by two conditions. You can draw the locus by first drawing the points that satisfy each condition. Then find their intersection.

Problem 2 **Drawing a Locus for Two Conditions**

Think

What is the locus of points in a plane that are equidistant from *X* and *Y*?

Got It? What is a sketch of the locus of points in a plane that satisfy these conditions?
- the points equidistant from two points *X* and *Y*
- the points 2 cm from the midpoint of $\overline{XY}$

Practice For Exercises 3 and 4, sketch the locus of points in a plane that satisfy the given conditions.

3. 3 cm from $\overline{GH}$ and 5 cm from *G*, where *GH* = 4.5 cm

4. equidistant from the sides of ∠*JKL* and on ⊙*C*

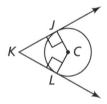

 **Problem 3** **Describing a Locus in Space**

Got It? What is each locus of points?

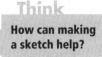Think

**How can making
a sketch help?**

    a. in a plane, the points that are equidistant from two parallel lines

    b. in space, the points that are equidistant from two parallel planes

Ⓐ Practice Describe each locus of points in space.

    5. points 3 cm from a point F

    6. points 5 mm from $\overrightarrow{PQ}$

Lesson Check

Do you know HOW?

What is a sketch and description for each locus of points in a plane?

7. points 4 cm from a point X

8. points 2 in. from $\overline{UV}$

9. points 3 mm from $\overleftrightarrow{LM}$

10. points 1 in. from a circle with radius 3 in.

Do you UNDERSTAND?

11. Vocabulary How are the words *locus* and *location* related?

12. Compare and Contrast How are the descriptions of the locus of points for each situation alike? How are they different?
- in a plane, the points equidistant from points *J* and *K*
- in space, the points equidistant from points *J* and *K*

More Practice and Problem-Solving Exercises

B Apply

Describe the locus that each light blue figure represents.

13.

14.

15.

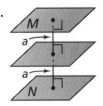

16. Open-Ended Give two examples of loci from everyday life, one in a plane and one in space.

17. Writing A classmate says that it is impossible to find a point equidistant from three collinear points. Is she correct? Explain.

18. Think About a Plan Write a locus description of the red points on the coordinate plane.

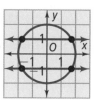

- How many conditions will be involved?
- What is the condition with respect to the origin?
- What are the conditions with respect to the *x*- and *y*-axes?

Coordinate Geometry Write an equation for the locus of points in a plane equidistant from the two given points.

19. $A(0, 2)$ and $B(2, 0)$ **20.** $P(1, 3)$ and $Q(5, 1)$ **21.** $T(2, -3)$ and $V(6, 1)$

STEM **22. Meteorology** An anemometer measures wind speed and wind direction. In an anemometer, there are three cups mounted on an axis. Consider a point on the edge of one of the cups.

a. Describe the locus that this point traces as the cup spins in the wind.
b. Suppose the distance of the point from the axis of the anemometer is 2 in. Write an equation for the locus of part (a). Use the axis as the origin.

23. Landscaping The school board plans to construct a fountain in front of the school. What are all the possible locations for a fountain such that the fountain is 8 ft from the statue and 16 ft from the flagpole?

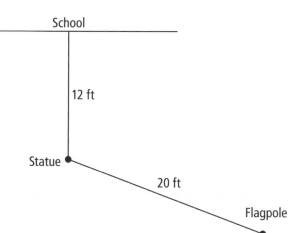

Make a drawing of each locus.

24. the path of a car as it turns to the right

25. the path of a doorknob as a door opens

26. the path of a knot in the middle of a jump-rope as it is being used

27. the path of the tip of your nose as you turn your head

28. the path of a fast-pitched softball

29. Reasoning Points *A* and *B* are 5 cm apart. Do the following loci in a plane have any points in common?

the points 3 cm from A
the points 4 cm from $\overline{AB}$

Illustrate your answer with a sketch.

Coordinate Geometry Draw each locus on the coordinate plane.

30. all points 3 units from the origin

31. all points 2 units from $(-1, 3)$

32. all points 4 units from the y-axis

33. all points 5 units from $x = 2$

34. all points equidistant from $y = 3$ and $y = -1$

35. all points equidistant from $x = 4$ and $x = 5$

36. all points equidistant from the x- and y-axes

37. all points equidistant from $x = 3$ and $y = 2$

38. a. Draw a segment to represent the base of an isosceles triangle. Locate three points that could be the vertex of the isosceles triangle.
 b. Describe the locus of possible vertices for the isosceles triangle.
 c. Writing Explain why points in the locus you described are the only possibilities for the vertex of the isosceles triangle.

39. Describe the locus of points in a plane 3 cm from the points on a circle with radius 8 cm.

40. Describe the locus of points in a plane 8 cm from the points on a circle with radius 3 cm.

41. Sketch the locus of points for the air valve on the tire of a bicycle as the bicycle moves down a straight path.

Challenge

42. In the diagram, Moesha, Jan, and Leandra are seated at uniform distances around a circular table. Copy the diagram. Shade the points on the table that are closer to Moesha than to Jan or Leandra. (Moesha is seated at the right of the table.)

Playground Equipment Think about the path of a child on each piece of playground equipment. Draw the path from (a) a top view, (b) a front view, and (c) a side view.

43. a swing

44. a straight slide

45. a corkscrew slide

46. a merry-go-round

47. a firefighters' pole

8-1 Applying Constructions

Quick Review

You can use a compass, protractor, and straightedge to apply constructions.

Example

Follow the steps to construct a line parallel to $\overline{AB}$ through point C.

A _____ B

· C

- Draw a line through C. Label the intersection of this line and $\overline{AB}$ as point D.
- Place the point of a compass on D. Draw an arc that intersects both $\overline{AB}$ and $\overline{CD}$.
- Use the same compass width. Draw an arc at C.
- Set the compass width from the intersection of $\overline{CD}$ and the first arc to the intersection of $\overline{AB}$ and the first arc.
- Place the compass at the intersection of $\overline{CD}$ and the second arc. Draw an arc. Label the intersection E.
- Draw a line through C and E.

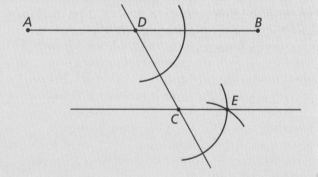

Exercises

1. Use a straightedge and compass to copy $\overline{HJ}$.

H •————————————• J

2. Copy $\overline{RT}$. Then use a straightedge and compass to construct a 30° angle on $\overline{RT}$ with vertex at R.

R •————————————• T

3. Design The shape of the triangle below is used in a local high school's logo. The school wants to use the logo on key chains to sell at a fundraiser. You need to supply the maker of the key chains with a drawing of the logo. Use a straightedge and compass to copy the triangle used in the school's logo.

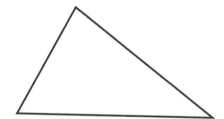

8-2 Solving Density and Design Problems

Quick Review

To find the **density** of an object, divide its mass by its volume. To find **population density,** divide the number of individuals in the population by the total area or volume that they occupy.

Example

A calcium tablet has a volume of 12 cm³ and a mass of 18.48 grams. What is the density of the calcium tablet?

$$\text{Density} = \frac{m}{V}$$

$$= \frac{18.48}{12} \qquad \text{Substitute 18.48 for } m \text{ and } 12 \text{ for } V.$$

$$= 1.54 \text{ g/cm}^3 \qquad \text{Simplify.}$$

Exercises

4. Japan has an area of 377,944 square kilometers. The population of Japan is 127,960,000. What was the population density of Japan?

5. **Gift Box** A company wants to manufacture gift boxes in the shape of rectangular prisms. Each gift box will have a volume of 84 cubic inches. The base of the rectangular prism should be twice as long as it is wide. What dimensions should the company choose for the gift boxes in order to minimize the surface area of each box?

8-3 Perimeters and Areas of Similar Figures

Quick Review

If the scale factor of two similar figures is $\frac{a}{b}$, then the ratio of their perimeters is $\frac{a}{b}$, and the ratio of their areas is $\frac{a^2}{b^2}$.

Example

If the ratio of the areas of two similar figures is $\frac{4}{9}$, what is the ratio of their perimeters?

Find the scale factor.

$$\frac{\sqrt{4}}{\sqrt{9}} = \frac{2}{3} \qquad \text{Take the square root of the ratio of areas.}$$

The ratio of the perimeters is the same as the ratio of corresponding sides, $\frac{2}{3}$.

Exercises

For each pair of similar figures, find the ratio of the area of the first figure to the area of the second.

6.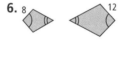

7.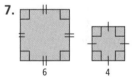

8.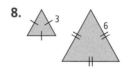

9.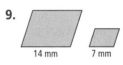

10. If the ratio of the areas of two similar hexagons is 8 : 25, what is the ratio of their perimeters?

8-4 Geometric Probability

Quick Review

Geometric probability uses geometric figures to represent occurrences of events. You can use a segment model or an area model. Compare the part that represents favorable outcomes to the whole, which represents all outcomes.

Example

A ball hits the target at a random point. What is the probability that it lands in the shaded region?

Since $\frac{1}{3}$ of the target is shaded, the probability that the ball hits the shaded region is $\frac{1}{3}$.

Exercises

A dart hits each dartboard at a random point. Find the probability that it lands in the shaded region.

11. 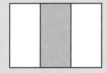   **12.**

13.   **14.**

15.

8-5 Space Figures and Cross Sections

Quick Review

A **polyhedron** is a three-dimensional figure whose surfaces are polygons. The polygons are **faces** of the polyhedron. An **edge** is a segment that is the intersection of two faces. A **vertex** is a point where three or more edges intersect. A **cross section** is the intersection of a solid and a plane.

Example

How many faces and edges does the polyhedron have?

The polyhedron has 2 triangular bases and 3 rectangular faces for a total of 5 faces.

The 2 triangles have a total of 6 edges. The 3 rectangles have a total of 12 edges. The total number of edges in the polyhedron is one half the total of 18 edges, or 9.

Exercises

Draw a net for each three-dimensional figure.

16.    **17.**

Use Euler's Formula to find the missing number.

18. $F = 5, V = 5, E = \blacksquare$ **19.** $F = 6, V = \blacksquare, E = 12$

20. How many vertices are there in a solid with 4 triangular faces and 1 square base?

21. Describe the cross section in the figure at the right.

22. Sketch a cube with an equilateral triangle cross section.

8-6 Areas and Volumes of Similar Solids

Quick Review

Similar solids have the same shape, and all their corresponding dimensions are proportional.

If the scale factor of two similar solids is $a : b$, then the ratio of their corresponding surface areas is $a^2 : b^2$, and the ratio of their volumes is $a^3 : b^3$.

Example

Is a cylinder with radius 4 in. and height 12 in. similar to a cylinder with radius 14 in. and height 35 in.? If so, give the scale factor.

$\frac{4}{14} \neq \frac{12}{35}$

The cylinders are not similar because the ratios of corresponding linear dimensions are not equal.

Exercises

23. **Open-Ended** Sketch two similar solids whose surface areas are in the ratio 16 : 25. Include dimensions.

For each pair of similar solids, find the ratio of the volume of the first figure to the volume of the second.

24.

25.

26. **Packaging** There are 12 pencils in a regular-sized box. If a jumbo box is made by tripling all the dimensions of the regular-sized box, how many pencils will the jumbo box hold?

8-7 Locus: A Set of Points

Quick Review

A **locus** is a set of points that satisfies a stated condition.

Example

Sketch and describe the locus of points in a plane equidistant from points A and B.

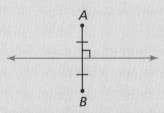

The locus is the perpendicular bisector of $\overline{AB}$.

Exercises

Describe each locus of points.

27. The set of all points in a plane that are in the interior of an angle and equidistant from the sides of the angle.

28. The set of all points in a plane that are 5 cm from a circle with radius 2 cm.

29. The set of all points in a plane at a distance 8 in. from a given line.

30. The set of all points in space that are 6 in. from $\overline{AB}$.

Pull It **All** Together

Calculating the Cost of a Gardening Project

 ASSESSMENT

Frank is at the nursery buying fencing and fertilizer for his garden. Fencing costs $5.00 per foot and fertilizer costs $.01 per square foot. Frank made the sketch below to represent the garden, which is divided into two trapezoid-shaped sections. The fencing will be placed along the seven line segments shown in the sketch, and the fertilizer will cover the entire garden.

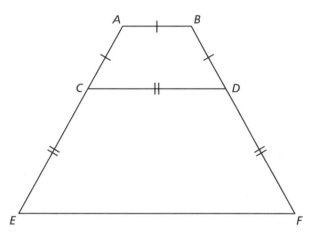

Unfortunately, Frank forgot to label his sketch with measurements, and he does not want to drive home to measure the garden again. However, Frank recalls some additional information:

- The two trapezoids are similar, with corresponding side lengths in the ratio 2 : 1.
- The total outer perimeter of the garden (not including the separation between the two sections) is 66 feet.

Task Description

Determine the total cost of the fencing and fertilizer.

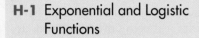

HONORS APPENDIX

The loudness of a sound we hear is based on the intensity of the associated sound wave. This sound intensity is the energy per unit time of the wave over a given area, measured in watts per square meter (W/m^2). The intensity is greatest near the source and decreases as you move away, whether the sound is rustling leaves or rock music. Because of the wide range of audible sound intensities, they are generally converted into *decibels*, which are based on logarithms. See page H29.

What you'll learn about

- Exponential Functions and Their Graphs
- The Natural Base e
- Logistic Functions and Their Graphs
- Population Models

... and why

Exponential and logistic functions model many growth patterns, including the growth of human and animal populations.

H-1 Exponential and Logistic Functions

Polynomial functions, rational functions, and power functions with rational exponents are **algebraic functions**— functions obtained by adding, subtracting, multiplying, and dividing constants and an independent variable, and raising expressions to integer powers and extracting roots. We will now explore **transcendental functions**, which go beyond, or transcend, these algebraic operations.

Just like their algebraic cousins, exponential, logistic, and logarithmic functions have wide application. Exponential functions model growth and decay over time, such as *unrestricted* population growth and the decay of radioactive substances. Logistic functions model *restricted* population growth, certain chemical reactions, and the spread of rumors and diseases. Logarithmic functions are the basis of the Richter scale of earthquake intensity, the pH acidity scale, and the decibel measurement of sound.

Exponential Functions and Their Graphs

The functions $f(x) = x^2$ and $g(x) = 2^x$ each involve a base raised to a power, but the roles are reversed:

- For $f(x) = x^2$, the base is the variable x, and the exponent is the constant 2; f is a familiar monomial and power function.
- For $g(x) = 2^x$, the base is the constant 2, and the exponent is the variable x; g is an *exponential function*. See Figure H.1.

DEFINITION Exponential Functions

Let a and b be real number constants. An **exponential function** in x is a function that can be written in the form

$$f(x) = a \cdot b^x,$$

where a is nonzero, b is positive, and $b \neq 1$. The constant a is the *initial value* of f (the value at $x = 0$), and b is the **base**.

Exponential functions are defined and continuous for all real numbers. It is important to recognize whether a function is an exponential function.

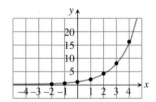

FIGURE H.1 Sketch of $g(x) = 2^x$.

EXAMPLE 1 Identifying Exponential Functions

(a) $f(x) = 3^x$ is an exponential function, with an initial value of 1 and base of 3.

(b) $g(x) = 6x^{-4}$ is *not* an exponential function because the base x is a variable and the exponent is a constant; g is a power function.

(c) $h(x) = -2 \cdot 1.5^x$ is an exponential function, with an initial value of -2 and base of 1.5.

(d) $k(x) = 7 \cdot 2^{-x}$ is an exponential function, with an initial value of 7 and base of 1/2 because $2^{-x} = (2^{-1})^x = (1/2)^x$.

(e) $q(x) = 5 \cdot 6^\pi$ is *not* an exponential function because the exponent π is a constant; q is a constant function.   *Now try Exercise 1.*

One way to evaluate an exponential function, when the inputs are rational numbers, is to use the properties of exponents.

EXAMPLE 2   **Computing Exponential Function Values for Rational Number Inputs**

For $f(x) = 2^x$,

(a) $f(4) = 2^4 = 2 \cdot 2 \cdot 2 \cdot 2 = 16$

(b) $f(0) = 2^0 = 1$

(c) $f(-3) = 2^{-3} = \dfrac{1}{2^3} = \dfrac{1}{8} = 0.125$

(d) $f\left(\dfrac{1}{2}\right) = 2^{1/2} = \sqrt{2} = 1.4142\ldots$

(e) $f\left(-\dfrac{3}{2}\right) = 2^{-3/2} = \dfrac{1}{2^{3/2}} = \dfrac{1}{\sqrt{2^3}} = \dfrac{1}{\sqrt{8}} = 0.35355\ldots$

Now try Exercise 7.

There is no way to use properties of exponents to express an exponential function's value for *irrational* inputs. For example, if $f(x) = 2^x$, $f(\pi) = 2^\pi$, but what does 2^π mean? Using properties of exponents, $2^3 = 2 \cdot 2 \cdot 2$, $2^{3.1} = 2^{31/10} = \sqrt[10]{2^{31}}$. So we can find meaning for 2^π by using successively closer *rational* approximations to π as shown in Table H.1.

Table H.1 Values of $f(x) = 2^x$ for Rational Numbers x Approaching $\pi = 3.14159265\ldots$						
x	3	3.1	3.14	3.141	3.1415	3.14159
2^x	8	8.5...	8.81...	8.821...	8.8244...	8.82496...

We can conclude that $f(\pi) = 2^\pi \approx 8.82$, which could be found directly using a grapher. The methods of calculus permit a more rigorous definition of exponential functions than we give here, a definition that allows for both rational and irrational inputs.

The way exponential functions change makes them useful in applications. This pattern of change can best be observed in tabular form.

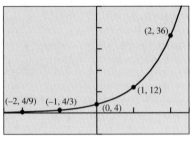

$[-2.5, 2.5]$ by $[-10, 50]$

(a)

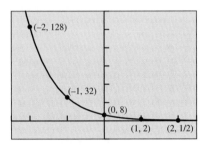

$[-2.5, 2.5]$ by $[-25, 150]$

(b)

FIGURE H.2 Graphs of (a) $g(x) = 4 \cdot 3^x$ and (b) $h(x) = 8 \cdot (1/4)^x$. (Example 3)

EXAMPLE 3 Finding an Exponential Function from Its Table of Values

Determine formulas for the exponential functions g and h whose values are given in Table H.2.

Table H.2 Values for Two Exponential Functions

x	$g(x)$	$h(x)$
-2	4/9	128
-1	4/3	32
0	4	8
1	12	2
2	36	1/2

g: $\times 3$ between each row.
h: $\times \frac{1}{4}$ between each row.

SOLUTION Because g is exponential, $g(x) = a \cdot b^x$. Because $g(0) = 4$, the initial value a is 4. Because $g(1) = 4 \cdot b^1 = 12$, the base b is 3. So,

$$g(x) = 4 \cdot 3^x.$$

Because h is exponential, $h(x) = a \cdot b^x$. Because $h(0) = 8$, the initial value a is 8. Because $h(1) = 8 \cdot b^1 = 2$, the base b is 1/4. So,

$$h(x) = 8 \cdot \left(\frac{1}{4}\right)^x.$$

Figure H.2 shows the graphs of these functions pass through the points whose coordinates are given in Table H.2.   *Now try Exercise 11.*

Table H.3 Values for a General Exponential Function $f(x) = a \cdot b^x$

x	$a \cdot b^x$
-2	ab^{-2}
-1	ab^{-1}
0	a
1	ab
2	ab^2

$\times b$ between each row.

Observe the patterns in the $g(x)$ and $h(x)$ columns of Table H.2. The $g(x)$ values increase by a factor of 3 and the $h(x)$ values decrease by a factor of 1/4, as we add 1 to x moving from one row of the table to the next. In each case, the change factor is the base of the exponential function. This pattern generalizes to all exponential functions as illustrated in Table H.3.

In Table H.3, as x increases by 1, the function value is multiplied by the base b. This relationship leads to the following *recursive formula*.

Exponential Growth and Decay

For any exponential function $f(x) = a \cdot b^x$ and any real number x,

$$f(x + 1) = b \cdot f(x).$$

If $a > 0$ and $b > 1$, the function f is increasing and is an **exponential growth function**. The base b is its **growth factor**.

If $a > 0$ and $b < 1$, f is decreasing and is an **exponential decay function**. The base b is its **decay factor**.

In Example 3, g is an exponential growth function, and h is an exponential decay function. As x increases by 1, $g(x) = 4 \cdot 3^x$ grows by a factor of 3, and $h(x) = 8 \cdot (1/4)^x$ decays by a factor of 1/4. Whenever the initial value is positive, the base of an exponential function, like the slope of a linear function, tells us whether the function is increasing or decreasing and by how much.

So far, we have focused most of our attention on the algebraic and numerical aspects of exponential functions. We now turn our attention to the graphs of these functions.

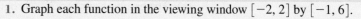

EXPLORATION 1   Graphs of Exponential Functions

1. Graph each function in the viewing window $[-2, 2]$ by $[-1, 6]$.

   (a) $y_1 = 2^x$ **(b)** $y_2 = 3^x$ **(c)** $y_3 = 4^x$ **(d)** $y_4 = 5^x$

   • Which point is common to all four graphs?

   • Analyze the functions for domain, range, continuity, increasing or decreasing behavior, symmetry, boundedness, extrema, asymptotes, and end behavior.

2. Graph each function in the viewing window $[-2, 2]$ by $[-1, 6]$.

   (a) $y_1 = \left(\dfrac{1}{2}\right)^x$ **(b)** $y_2 = \left(\dfrac{1}{3}\right)^x$

   (c) $y_3 = \left(\dfrac{1}{4}\right)^x$ **(d)** $y_4 = \left(\dfrac{1}{5}\right)^x$

   • Which point is common to all four graphs?

   • Analyze the functions for domain, range, continuity, increasing or decreasing behavior, symmetry, boundedness, extrema, asymptotes, and end behavior.

We summarize what we have learned about exponential functions with an initial value of 1.

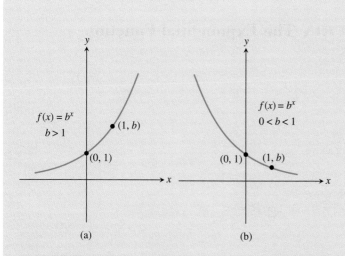

Exponential Functions $f(x) = b^x$

Domain: All reals
Range: $(0, \infty)$
Continuous
No symmetry: neither even nor odd
Bounded below, but not above
No local extrema
Horizontal asymptote: $y = 0$
No vertical asymptotes

If $b > 1$ (see Figure 3.3a), then

• f is an increasing function,
• $\displaystyle\lim_{x \to -\infty} f(x) = 0$ and $\displaystyle\lim_{x \to \infty} f(x) = \infty$.

If $0 < b < 1$ (see Figure 3.3b), then

• f is a decreasing function,
• $\displaystyle\lim_{x \to -\infty} f(x) = \infty$ and $\displaystyle\lim_{x \to \infty} f(x) = 0$.

(a)   (b)

FIGURE H.3 Graphs of $f(x) = b^x$ for (a) $b > 1$ and (b) $0 < b < 1$.

Our knowledge of translations, reflections, stretches, and shrinks, together with our knowledge of the graphs of basic exponential functions, allow us to predict the graphs of the functions in Example 4.

EXAMPLE 4 Transforming Exponential Functions

Describe how to transform the graph of $f(x) = 2^x$ into the graph of the given function. Sketch the graphs by hand and support your answer with a grapher.

(a) $g(x) = 2^{x-1}$ **(b)** $h(x) = 2^{-x}$ **(c)** $k(x) = 3 \cdot 2^x$

SOLUTION

(a) The graph of $g(x) = 2^{x-1}$ is obtained by translating the graph of $f(x) = 2^x$ by 1 unit to the right (Figure H.4a).

(b) We can obtain the graph of $h(x) = 2^{-x}$ by reflecting the graph of $f(x) = 2^x$ across the y-axis (Figure H.4b). Because $2^{-x} = (2^{-1})^x = (1/2)^x$, we can also think of h as an exponential function with an initial value of 1 and a base of 1/2.

(c) We can obtain the graph of $k(x) = 3 \cdot 2^x$ by vertically stretching the graph of $f(x) = 2^x$ by a factor of 3 (Figure H.4c). *Now try Exercise 15.*

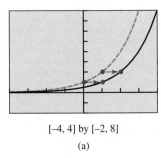
[–4, 4] by [–2, 8]
(a)

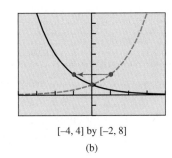
[–4, 4] by [–2, 8]
(b)

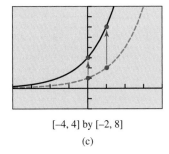
[–4, 4] by [–2, 8]
(c)

FIGURE H.4 The graph of $f(x) = 2^x$ shown with (a) $g(x) = 2^{x-1}$, (b) $h(x) = 2^{-x}$, and (c) $k(x) = 3 \cdot 2^x$. (Example 4)

The Natural Base e

The function $f(x) = e^x$ is one of the basic functions introduced in Lesson A-2, and is an exponential growth function.

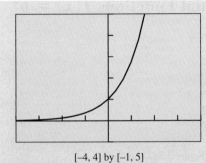
[–4, 4] by [–1, 5]

FIGURE H.5 The graph of $f(x) = e^x$.

BASIC FUNCTION The Exponential Function

$f(x) = e^x$
Domain: All reals
Range: $(0, \infty)$
Continuous
Increasing for all x
No symmetry
Bounded below, but not above
No local extrema
Horizontal asymptote: $y = 0$
No vertical asymptotes
End behavior: $\lim_{x \to -\infty} e^x = 0$ and $\lim_{x \to \infty} e^x = \infty$

Because $f(x) = e^x$ is increasing, it is an exponential growth function, so $e > 1$. But what is e, and what makes this exponential function *the* exponential function?

The letter e is the initial of the last name of Leonhard Euler (1707–1783), who introduced the notation. Because $f(x) = e^x$ has special calculus properties that simplify many calculations, e is the *natural base* of exponential functions for calculus purposes, and $f(x) = e^x$ is considered the *natural exponential function*.

DEFINITION The Natural Base e

$$e = \lim_{x \to \infty} \left(1 + \frac{1}{x} \right)^x$$

We cannot compute the irrational number e directly, but using this definition we can obtain successively closer approximations to e, as shown in Table H.4. Continuing the process in Table H.4 with a sufficiently accurate computer can show that $e \approx 2.718281828459$.

Table H.4 Approximations Approaching the Natural Base e

x	1	10	100	1000	10,000	100,000
$(1 + 1/x)^x$	2	2.5. . .	2.70. . .	2.716. . .	2.7181. . .	2.71826. . .

We are usually more interested in the exponential function $f(x) = e^x$ and variations of this function than in the irrational number e. In fact, *any* exponential function can be expressed in terms of the natural base e.

THEOREM 12 Exponential Functions and the Base e

Any exponential function $f(x) = a \cdot b^x$ can be rewritten as

$$f(x) = a \cdot e^{kx},$$

for an appropriately chosen real number constant k.

If $a > 0$ and $k > 0$, $f(x) = a \cdot e^{kx}$ is an exponential growth function. (See Figure H.6a.)

If $a > 0$ and $k < 0$, $f(x) = a \cdot e^{kx}$ is an exponential decay function. (See Figure H.6b.)

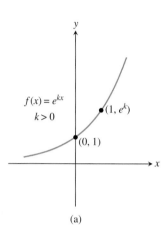

$f(x) = e^{kx}$
$k > 0$
$(1, e^k)$
$(0, 1)$

(a)

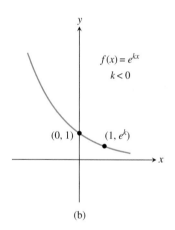

$f(x) = e^{kx}$
$k < 0$
$(0, 1)$ $(1, e^k)$

(b)

FIGURE H.6 Graphs of $f(x) = e^{kx}$ for (a) $k > 0$ and (b) $k < 0$.

In Lesson H-3 we will develop some mathematics so that, for any positive number $b \neq 1$, we can easily find the value of k such that $e^{kx} = b^x$. In the meantime, we can use graphical and numerical methods to approximate k, as you will discover in Exploration 2.

EXPLORATION 2   Choosing k so that $e^{kx} = 2^x$

1. Graph $f(x) = 2^x$ in the viewing window $[-4, 4]$ by $[-2, 8]$.

2. One at a time, overlay the graphs of $g(x) = e^{kx}$ for $k = 0.4, 0.5, 0.6, 0.7,$ and 0.8. For which of these values of k does the graph of g most closely match the graph of f?

3. Using tables, find the 3-decimal-place value of k for which the values of g most closely approximate the values of f.

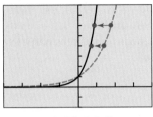

[–4, 4] by [–2, 8]

(a)

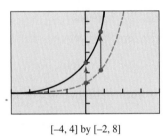

[–4, 4] by [–2, 8]

(b)

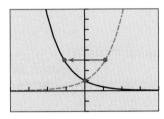

[–4, 4] by [–2, 8]

(c)

FIGURE H.7 The graph of $f(x) = e^x$ shown with (a) $g(x) = e^{2x}$, (b) $h(x) = e^{-x}$, and (c) $k(x) = 3e^x$. (Example 5)

Aliases for Logistic Growth

Logistic growth is also known as *restricted, inhibited,* or *constrained exponential growth.*

EXAMPLE 5 Transforming Exponential Functions

Describe how to transform the graph of $f(x) = e^x$ into the graph of the given function. Sketch the graphs by hand and support your answer with a grapher.

(a) $g(x) = e^{2x}$ **(b)** $h(x) = e^{-x}$ **(c)** $k(x) = 3e^x$

SOLUTION

(a) The graph of $g(x) = e^{2x}$ is obtained by horizontally shrinking the graph of $f(x) = e^x$ by a factor of 2 (Figure H.7a).

(b) We can obtain the graph of $h(x) = e^{-x}$ by reflecting the graph of $f(x) = e^x$ across the *y*-axis (Figure H.7b).

(c) We can obtain the graph of $k(x) = 3e^x$ by vertically stretching the graph of $f(x) = e^x$ by a factor of 3 (Figure H.7c).   *Now try Exercise 21.*

Logistic Functions and Their Graphs

Exponential growth is *unrestricted.* An exponential growth function increases at an ever-increasing rate and is not bounded above. In many growth situations, however, there is a limit to the possible growth. A plant can only grow so tall. The number of goldfish in an aquarium is limited by the size of the aquarium. In such situations the growth often begins in an exponential manner, but the growth eventually slows and the graph levels out. The associated growth function is bounded both below and above by horizontal asymptotes.

DEFINITION Logistic Growth Functions

Let a, b, c, and k be positive constants, with $b < 1$. A **logistic growth function** in x is a function that can be written in the form

$$f(x) = \frac{c}{1 + a \cdot b^x} \text{ or } f(x) = \frac{c}{1 + a \cdot e^{-kx}}$$

where the constant c is the **limit to growth**.

If $b > 1$ or $k < 0$, these formulas yield **logistic decay functions.** Unless otherwise stated, all *logistic functions* in this book will be logistic growth functions.

By setting $a = c = k = 1$, we obtain the **logistic function**

$$f(x) = \frac{1}{1 + e^{-x}}.$$

This function, though related to the exponential function e^x, *cannot* be obtained from e^x by translations, reflections, and horizontal and vertical stretches and shrinks. So we give the logistic function a formal introduction:

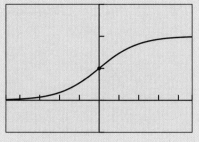

[–4.7, 4.7] by [–0.5, 1.5]

FIGURE H.8 The graph of
$f(x) = 1/(1 + e^{-x})$.

BASIC FUNCTION The Logistic Function

$$f(x) = \frac{1}{1 + e^{-x}}$$

Domain: All reals
Range: $(0, 1)$
Continuous
Increasing for all x
Symmetric about $(0, 1/2)$, but neither even nor odd
Bounded below and above
No local extrema
Horizontal asymptotes: $y = 0$ and $y = 1$
No vertical asymptotes
End behavior: $\lim\limits_{x \to -\infty} f(x) = 0$ and $\lim\limits_{x \to \infty} f(x) = 1$

All logistic growth functions have graphs much like the basic logistic function. Their end behavior is always described by the equations

$$\lim_{x \to -\infty} f(x) = 0 \text{ and } \lim_{x \to \infty} f(x) = c,$$

where c is the limit to growth (see Exercise 67). All logistic functions are bounded by their horizontal asymptotes, $y = 0$ and $y = c$, and have a range of $(0, c)$. Although every logistic function is symmetric about the point of its graph with y- coordinate $c/2$, this point of symmetry is usually not the y-intercept, as we can see in Example 6.

EXAMPLE 6 Graphing Logistic Growth Functions

Graph the function. Find the y-intercept and the horizontal asymptotes.

(a) $f(x) = \dfrac{8}{1 + 3 \cdot 0.7^x}$ **(b)** $g(x) = \dfrac{20}{1 + 2e^{-3x}}$

SOLUTION

(a) The graph of $f(x) = 8/(1 + 3 \cdot 0.7^x)$ is shown in Figure H.9a. The y-intercept is

$$f(0) = \frac{8}{1 + 3 \cdot 0.7^0} = \frac{8}{1 + 3} = 2.$$

Because the limit to growth is 8, the horizontal asymptotes are $y = 0$ and $y = 8$.

(b) The graph of $g(x) = 20/(1 + 2e^{-3x})$ is shown in Figure H.9b. The y-intercept is

$$g(0) = \frac{20}{1 + 2e^{-3 \cdot 0}} = \frac{20}{1 + 2} = 20/3 \approx 6.67.$$

Because the limit to growth is 20, the horizontal asymptotes are $y = 0$ and $y = 20$.

Now try Exercise 41.

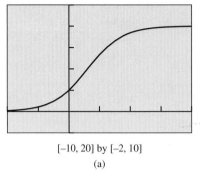

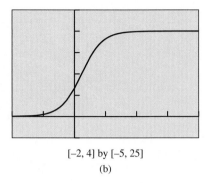

[–10, 20] by [–2, 10]

(a)

[–2, 4] by [–5, 25]

(b)

FIGURE H.9 The graphs of (a) $f(x) = 8/(1 + 3 \cdot 0.7^x)$ and (b) $g(x) = 20/(1 + 2e^{-3x})$. (Example 6)

Population Models

Exponential and logistic functions have many applications. One area where both types of functions are used is in modeling population. Between 1990 and 2000, both Phoenix and San Antonio passed the 1 million mark. With its Silicon Valley industries, San Jose, California, appears to be the next U.S. city destined to surpass 1 million residents. When a city's population is growing rapidly, as in the case of San Jose, exponential growth is a reasonable model.

EXAMPLE 7 Modeling San Jose's Population

Using the data in Table H.5 and assuming the growth is exponential, when will the population of San Jose, California, surpass 1 million persons?

SOLUTION

Model Let $P(t)$ be the population of San Jose t years after July 1, 2000. (See margin note.) Because P is exponential, $P(t) = P_0 \cdot b^t$, where P_0 is the initial (2000) population of 898,759. From Table H.5 we see that $P(7) = 898759b^7 = 939899$. So,

$$b = \sqrt[7]{\frac{939,899}{898,759}} \approx 1.0064$$

and $P(t) = 898,759 \cdot 1.0064^t$.

Solve Graphically Figure H.10 shows that this population model intersects $y = 1,000,000$ when the independent variable is about 16.73.

Interpret Because 16.73 yr after mid-2000 is in the first half of 2017, according to this model the population of San Jose will surpass the 1 million mark in early 2017.

Now try Exercise 51.

Table H.5 The Population of San Jose, California

Year	Population
2000	898,759
2007	939,899

Source: U.S. Census Bureau.

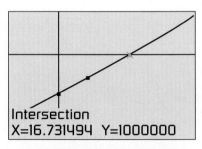

Intersection
X=16.731494 Y=1000000

[–10, 30] by [800 000, 1 100 000]

FIGURE H.10 A population model for San Jose, California. (Example 7)

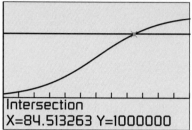

Intersection
X=84.513263 Y=1000000

[0, 120] by [−500 000, 1 500 000]

FIGURE H.11 A population model for Dallas, Texas. (Example 8)

While San Jose's population is soaring, in other major cities, such as Dallas, the population growth is slowing. The once sprawling Dallas is now *constrained* by its neighboring cities. *A logistic function is often an appropriate model for restricted growth*, such as the growth that Dallas is experiencing.

EXAMPLE 8 Modeling Dallas's Population

Based on recent census data, a logistic model for the population of Dallas, t years after 1900, is as follows:

$$P(t) = \frac{1,301,642}{1 + 21.602e^{-0.05054t}}$$

According to this model, when was the population 1 million?

SOLUTION Figure H.11 shows that the population model intersects $y = 1,000,000$ when the independent variable is about 84.51. Because 84.51 yr after mid-1900 is at the beginning of 1985, if Dallas's population has followed this logistic model, its population was 1 million then.   *Now try Exercise 55.*

  LESSON H-1 EXERCISES

Exercise numbers with a gray background indicate problems that the authors have designed to be solved *without a calculator.*

In Exercises 1–6, which of the following are exponential functions? For those that are exponential functions, state the initial value and the base. For those that are not, explain why not.

1. $y = x^8$

2. $y = 3^x$

3. $y = 5^x$

4. $y = 4^2$

5. $y = x^{\sqrt{x}}$

6. $y = x^{1.3}$

In Exercises 7–10, compute the exact value of the function for the given x-value without using a calculator.

7. $f(x) = 3 \cdot 5^x$ for $x = 0$

8. $f(x) = 6 \cdot 3^x$ for $x = -2$

9. $f(x) = -2 \cdot 3^x$ for $x = 1/3$

10. $f(x) = 8 \cdot 4^x$ for $x = -3/2$

In Exercises 11 and 12, determine a formula for the exponential function whose values are given in Table H.6.

11. $f(x)$

12. $g(x)$

Table H.6 Values for Two Exponential Functions

x	$f(x)$	$g(x)$
−2	6	108
−1	3	36
0	3/2	12
1	3/4	4
2	3/8	4/3

In Exercises 13 and 14, determine a formula for the exponential function whose graph is shown in the figure.

13. $f(x)$

14. $g(x)$

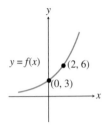

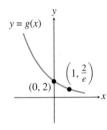

In Exercises 15–24, describe how to transform the graph of f into the graph of g. Sketch the graphs by hand and support your answer with a grapher.

15. $f(x) = 2^x$, $g(x) = 2^{x-3}$

16. $f(x) = 3^x$, $g(x) = 3^{x+4}$

17. $f(x) = 4^x$, $g(x) = 4^{-x}$

18. $f(x) = 2^x$, $g(x) = 2^{5-x}$

19. $f(x) = 0.5^x$, $g(x) = 3 \cdot 0.5^x + 4$

20. $f(x) = 0.6^x$, $g(x) = 2 \cdot 0.6^{3x}$

21. $f(x) = e^x$, $g(x) = e^{-2x}$

22. $f(x) = e^x$, $g(x) = -e^{-3x}$

23. $f(x) = e^x$, $g(x) = 2e^{3-3x}$

24. $f(x) = e^x$, $g(x) = 3e^{2x} - 1$

In Exercises 25–30, **(a)** match the given function with its graph. **(b) Writing to Learn** Explain how to make the choice without using a grapher.

25. $y = 3^x$

26. $y = 2^{-x}$

27. $y = -2^x$

28. $y = -0.5^x$

29. $y = 3^{-x} - 2$

30. $y = 1.5^x - 2$

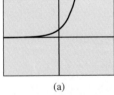

(a)

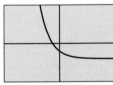

(b)

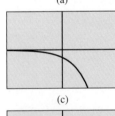

(c)

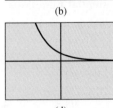

(d)

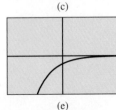

(e)

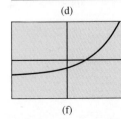

(f)

In Exercises 31–34, state whether the function is an exponential growth function or exponential decay function, and describe its end behavior using limits.

31. $f(x) = 3^{-2x}$

32. $f(x) = \left(\dfrac{1}{e}\right)^x$

33. $f(x) = 0.5^x$

34. $f(x) = 0.75^{-x}$

In Exercises 35–38, solve the inequality graphically.

35. $9^x < 4^x$

36. $6^{-x} > 8^{-x}$

37. $\left(\dfrac{1}{4}\right)^x > \left(\dfrac{1}{3}\right)^x$

38. $\left(\dfrac{1}{3}\right)^x < \left(\dfrac{1}{2}\right)^x$

Group Activity In Exercises 39 and 40, use the properties of exponents to prove that two of the given three exponential functions are identical. Support graphically.

39. (a) $y_1 = 3^{2x+4}$

(b) $y_2 = 3^{2x} + 4$

(c) $y_3 = 9^{x+2}$

40. (a) $y_1 = 4^{3x-2}$

(b) $y_2 = 2(2^{3x-2})$

(c) $y_3 = 2^{3x-1}$

In Exercises 41–44, use a grapher to graph the function. Find the y-intercept and the horizontal asymptotes.

41. $f(x) = \dfrac{12}{1 + 2 \cdot 0.8^x}$

42. $f(x) = \dfrac{18}{1 + 5 \cdot 0.2^x}$

43. $f(x) = \dfrac{16}{1 + 3e^{-2x}}$

44. $g(x) = \dfrac{9}{1 + 2e^{-x}}$

In Exercises 45–50, graph the function and analyze it for domain, range, continuity, increasing or decreasing behavior, symmetry, boundedness, extrema, asymptotes, and end behavior.

45. $f(x) = 3 \cdot 2^x$

46. $f(x) = 4 \cdot 0.5^x$

47. $f(x) = 4 \cdot e^{3x}$

48. $f(x) = 5 \cdot e^{-x}$

49. $f(x) = \dfrac{5}{1 + 4 \cdot e^{-2x}}$

50. $f(x) = \dfrac{6}{1 + 2 \cdot e^{-x}}$

51. Population Growth Using the midyear data in Table H.7 and assuming the growth is exponential, when did the population of Austin surpass 800,000 persons?

Table H.7 Populations of Two Major U.S. Cities

City	1990 Population	2000 Population
Austin, Texas	465,622	656,562
Columbus, Ohio	632,910	711,265

Source: World Almanac and Book of Facts 2005.

52. Population Growth Using the data in Table H.7 and assuming the growth is exponential, when would the population of Columbus surpass 800,000 persons?

53. Population Growth Using the data in Table H.7 and assuming the growth is exponential, when were the populations of Austin and Columbus equal?

54. Population Growth Using the data in Table H.7 and assuming the growth is exponential, which city—Austin or Columbus—would reach a population of 1 million first, and in what year?

55. Population Growth Using 20th-century U.S. census data, the population of Ohio can be modeled by

$$P(t) = \frac{12.79}{1 + 2.402e^{-0.0309x}},$$

where P is the population in millions and t is the number of years since April 1, 1900. Based on this model, when was the population of Ohio 10 million?

56. Population Growth Using 20th-century U.S. census data, the population of New York state can be modeled by

$$P(t) = \frac{19.875}{1 + 57.993e^{-0.035005t}},$$

where P is the population in millions and t is the number of years since 1800. Based on this model,

(a) What was the population of New York in 1850?

(b) What will New York state's population be in 2015?

(c) What is New York's *maximum sustainable population* (limit to growth)?

57. Bacteria Growth The number B of bacteria in a petri dish culture after t hours is given by

$$B = 100e^{0.693t}.$$

(a) What was the initial number of bacteria present?

(b) How many bacteria are present after 6 hours?

58. Carbon Dating The amount C in grams of carbon-14 present in a certain substance after t years is given by

$$C = 20e^{-0.0001216t}.$$

(a) What was the initial amount of carbon-14 present?

(b) How much is left after 10,400 years? When will the amount left be 10 g?

Explorations

59. Graph each function and analyze it for domain, range, increasing or decreasing behavior, boundedness, extrema, asymptotes, and end behavior.

(a) $f(x) = x \cdot e^x$　　　**(b)** $g(x) = \dfrac{e^{-x}}{x}$

60. Use the properties of exponents to solve each equation. Support graphically.

(a) $2^x = 4^2$　　　**(b)** $3^x = 27$

(c) $8^{x/2} = 4^{x+1}$　　　**(d)** $9^x = 3^{x+1}$

Extending the Ideas

61. Writing to Learn Table H.8 gives function values for $y = f(x)$ and $y = g(x)$. Also, three different graphs are shown.

Table H.8 Data for Two Functions

x	$f(x)$	$g(x)$
1.0	5.50	7.40
1.5	5.35	6.97
2.0	5.25	6.44
2.5	5.17	5.76
3.0	5.13	4.90
3.5	5.09	3.82
4.0	5.06	2.44
4.5	5.05	0.71

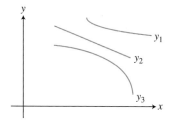

(a) Which curve of those shown in the graph most closely resembles the graph of $y = f(x)$? Explain your choice.

(b) Which curve most closely resembles the graph of $y = g(x)$? Explain your choice.

62. Writing to Learn Let $f(x) = 2^x$. Explain why the graph of $f(ax + b)$ can be obtained by applying one transformation to the graph of $y = c^x$ for an appropriate value of c. What is c?

Exercises 63–66 refer to the expression $f(a, b, c) = a \cdot b^c$. For example, if $a = 2$, $b = 3$, and $c = x$, the expression is $f(2, 3, x) = 2 \cdot 3^x$, an exponential function.

63. If $b = x$, state conditions on a and c under which the expression $f(a, b, c)$ is a quadratic power function.

64. If $b = x$, state conditions on a and c under which the expression $f(a, b, c)$ is a decreasing linear function.

65. If $c = x$, state conditions on a and b under which the expression $f(a, b, c)$ is an increasing exponential function.

66. If $c = x$, state conditions on a and b under which the expression $f(a, b, c)$ is a decreasing exponential function.

67. Prove that $\displaystyle\lim_{x \to -\infty} \frac{c}{1 + a \cdot b^x} = 0$ and $\displaystyle\lim_{x \to \infty} \frac{c}{1 + a \cdot b^x} = c,$ for constants a, b, and c, with $a > 0$, $0 < b < 1$, and $c > 0$.

What you'll learn about

- Constant Percentage Rate and Exponential Functions
- Exponential Growth and Decay Models
- Using Regression to Model Population
- Other Logistic Models

... and why

Exponential functions model many types of unrestricted growth; logistic functions model restricted growth, including the spread of disease and the spread of rumors.

Constant Percentage Rate and Exponential Functions

Suppose that a population is changing at a **constant percentage rate r**, where r is the percent rate of change expressed in decimal form. Then the population follows the pattern shown.

Time in Years	Population
0	$P(0) = P_0 = $ initial population
1	$P(1) = P_0 + P_0 r = P_0(1 + r)$
2	$P(2) = P(1) \cdot (1 + r) = P_0(1 + r)^2$
3	$P(3) = P(2) \cdot (1 + r) = P_0(1 + r)^3$
$\vdots$	$\vdots$
t	$P(t) = P_0(1 + r)^t$

So, in this case, the population is an exponential function of time.

Exponential Population Model

If a population P is changing at a constant percentage rate r each year, then

$$P(t) = P_0(1 + r)^t,$$

where P_0 is the initial population, r is expressed as a decimal, and t is time in years.

If $r > 0$, then $P(t)$ is an exponential growth function, and its *growth factor* is the base of the exponential function, $1 + r$.

On the other hand, if $r < 0$, the base $1 + r < 1$, $P(t)$ is an exponential decay function, and $1 + r$ is the *decay factor* for the population.

EXAMPLE 1 Finding Growth and Decay Rates

Tell whether the population model is an exponential growth function or exponential decay function, and find the constant percentage rate of growth or decay.

(a) San Jose: $P(t) = 898,759 \cdot 1.0064^t$

(b) Detroit: $P(t) = 1,203,368 \cdot 0.9858^t$

SOLUTION

(a) Because $1 + r = 1.0064$, $r = 0.0064 > 0$. So, P is an exponential growth function with a growth rate of 0.64%.

(b) Because $1 + r = 0.9858$, $r = -0.0142 < 0$. So, P is an exponential decay function with a decay rate of 1.42%.   *Now try Exercise 1.*

EXAMPLE 2 Finding an Exponential Function

Determine the exponential function with initial value $= 12$, increasing at a rate of 8% per year.

SOLUTION Because $P_0 = 12$ and $r = 8\% = 0.08$, the function is $P(t) = 12(1 + 0.08)^t$ or $P(t) = 12 \cdot 1.08^t$. We could write this as $f(x) = 12 \cdot 1.08^x$, where x represents time.   *Now try Exercise 7.*

Exponential Growth and Decay Models

Exponential growth and decay models are used for populations of animals, bacteria, and even radioactive atoms. Exponential growth and decay apply to any situation where the growth is proportional to the current size of the quantity of interest. Such situations are frequently encountered in biology, chemistry, business, and the social sciences.

Exponential growth models can be developed in terms of the time it takes a quantity to double. On the flip side, exponential decay models can be developed in terms of the time it takes for a quantity to be halved. Examples 3 through 5 use these strategies.

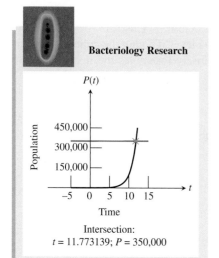

Bacteriology Research

Intersection:
$t = 11.773139; P = 350,000$

FIGURE H.12 Rapid growth of a bacteria population. (Example 3)

EXAMPLE 3 Modeling Bacteria Growth

Suppose a culture of 100 bacteria is put into a petri dish and the culture doubles every hour. Predict when the number of bacteria will be 350,000.

SOLUTION

Model

$$200 = 100 \cdot 2 \quad \text{Total bacteria after 1 hr}$$
$$400 = 100 \cdot 2^2 \quad \text{Total bacteria after 2 hr}$$
$$800 = 100 \cdot 2^3 \quad \text{Total bacteria after 3 hr}$$
$$\vdots$$
$$P(t) = 100 \cdot 2^t \quad \text{Total bacteria after } t \text{ hr}$$

So the function $P(t) = 100 \cdot 2^t$ represents the bacteria population t hr after it is placed in the petri dish.

Solve Graphically Figure H.12 shows that the population function intersects $y = 350,000$ when $t \approx 11.77$.

Interpret The population of the bacteria in the petri dish will be 350,000 in about 11 hr and 46 min.   *Now try Exercise 15.*

Exponential decay functions model the amount of a radioactive substance present in a sample. The number of atoms of a specific element that change from a radioactive state to a nonradioactive state is a fixed fraction per unit time. The process is called **radioactive decay**, and the time it takes for half of a sample to change its state is the **half-life** of the radioactive substance.

EXAMPLE 4 Modeling Radioactive Decay

Suppose the half-life of a certain radioactive substance is 20 days and there are 5 g (grams) present initially. Find the time when there will be 1 g of the substance remaining.

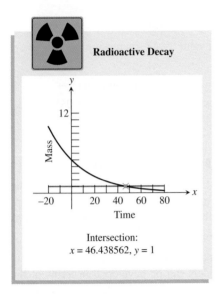

FIGURE H.13 Radioactive decay. (Example 4)

Model If t is the time in days, the number of half-lives will be $t/20$.

$$\frac{5}{2} = 5\left(\frac{1}{2}\right)^{20/20} \qquad \text{Grams after 20 days}$$

$$\frac{5}{4} = 5\left(\frac{1}{2}\right)^{40/20} \qquad \text{Grams after } 2(20) = 40 \text{ days}$$

$$\vdots$$

$$f(t) = 5\left(\frac{1}{2}\right)^{t/20} \qquad \text{Grams after } t \text{ days}$$

Thus the function $f(t) = 5 \cdot 0.5^{t/20}$ models the mass in grams of the radioactive substance at time t.

Solve Graphically Figure H.13 shows that the graph of $f(t) = 5 \cdot 0.5^{t/20}$ intersects $y = 1$ when $t \approx 46.44$.

Interpret There will be 1 g of the radioactive substance left after approximately 46.44 days, or about 46 days, 11 hr. *Now try Exercise 33.*

Scientists have established that atmospheric pressure at sea level is 14.7 lb/in.^{2}, and the pressure is reduced by half for each 3.6 mi above sea level. For example, the pressure 3.6 mi above sea level is $(1/2)(14.7) = 7.35$ lb/in.^{2}. This rule for atmospheric pressure holds for altitudes up to 50 mi above sea level. Though the context is different, the mathematics of atmospheric pressure closely resembles the mathematics of radioactive decay.

EXAMPLE 5 Determining Altitude from Atmospheric Pressure

Find the altitude above sea level at which the atmospheric pressure is 4 lb/in.^{2}.

SOLUTION

Model

$$7.35 = 14.7 \cdot 0.5^{3.6/3.6} \qquad \text{Pressure at 3.6 mi}$$

$$3.675 = 14.7 \cdot 0.5^{7.2/3.6} \qquad \text{Pressure at } 2(3.6) = 7.2 \text{ mi}$$

$$\vdots$$

$$P(h) = 14.7 \cdot 0.5^{h/3.6} \qquad \text{Pressure at } h \text{ mi}$$

So $P(h) = 14.7 \cdot 0.5^{h/3.6}$ models the atmospheric pressure P (in pounds per square inch) as a function of the height h (in miles above sea level). We must find the value of h that satisfies the equation

$$14.7 \cdot 0.5^{h/3.6} = 4.$$

Solve Graphically Figure H.14 shows that the graph of $P(h) = 14.7 \cdot 0.5^{h/3.6}$ intersects $y = 4$ when $h \approx 6.76$.

Interpret The atmospheric pressure is 4 lb/in.^{2} at an altitude of approximately 6.76 mi above sea level. *Now try Exercise 41.*

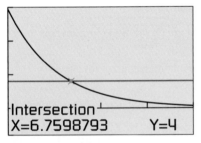

[0, 20] by [−4, 15]

FIGURE H.14 A model for atmospheric pressure. (Example 5)

Using Regression to Model Population

So far, our models have been given to us or developed algebraically. We now use exponential and logistic regression to build models from population data.

Due to the post–World War II baby boom and other factors, exponential growth is not a perfect model for the U.S. population. It does, however, provide a means to make approximate predictions, as illustrated in Example 6.

Table H.9 U.S. Population (in millions)

Year	Population
1900	76.2
1910	92.2
1920	106.0
1930	123.2
1940	132.2
1950	151.3
1960	179.3
1970	203.3
1980	226.5
1990	248.7
2000	281.4
2007	301.6

Source: World Almanac and Book of Facts 2009.

EXAMPLE 6 Modeling U.S. Population Using Exponential Regression

Use the 1900–2000 data in Table H.9 and exponential regression to predict the U.S. population for 2007. Compare the result with the listed value for 2007.

SOLUTION

Model

Let $P(t)$ be the population (in millions) of the United States t years after 1900. Figure H.15a shows a scatter plot of the data. Using exponential regression, we find a model for the 1990–2000 data:

$$P(t) = 80.5514 \cdot 1.01289^t$$

Figure H.15b shows the scatter plot of the data with a graph of the population model just found. You can see that the curve fits the data fairly well. The coefficient of determination is $r^2 \approx 0.995$, indicating a close fit and supporting the visual evidence.

Solve Graphically

To predict the 2007 U.S. population we substitute $t = 107$ into the regression model. Figure H.15c reports that $P(107) = 80.5514 \cdot 1.01289^{107} \approx 317.1$.

Interpret

The model predicts the U.S. population was 317.1 million in 2007. The actual population was 301.6 million. We overestimated by 15.5 million, a 5.1% error.

Now try Exercise 43.

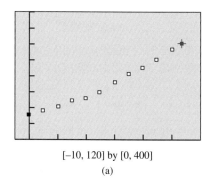

[–10, 120] by [0, 400]

(a)

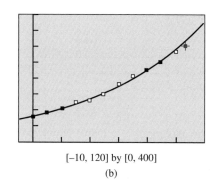

[–10, 120] by [0, 400]

(b)

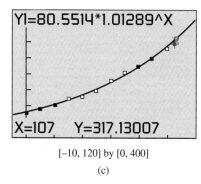

[–10, 120] by [0, 400]

(c)

FIGURE H.15 Scatter plots and graphs for Example 6. The red "+" depicts the data point for 2007. The blue "×" in (c) represents the model's prediction for 2007.

Exponential growth is unrestricted, but population growth often is not. For many populations, the growth begins exponentially, but eventually slows and approaches a limit to growth called the **maximum sustainable population**.

In Lesson H-1 we modeled Dallas's population with a logistic function. We now use logistic regression to do the same for the populations of Florida and Pennsylvania. As the data in Table H.10 suggest, Florida had rapid growth in the second half of the 20th century, whereas Pennsylvania appears to be approaching its maximum sustainable population.

Table H.10 Populations of Two U.S. States (in millions)

Year	Florida	Pennsylvania
1900	0.5	6.3
1910	0.8	7.7
1920	1.0	8.7
1930	1.5	9.6
1940	1.9	9.9
1950	2.8	10.5
1960	5.0	11.3
1970	6.8	11.8
1980	9.7	11.9
1990	12.9	11.9
2000	16.0	12.3

Source: U.S. Census Bureau.

EXAMPLE 7 Modeling Two States' Populations Using Logistic Regression

Use the data in Table H.10 and logistic regression to predict the maximum sustainable populations for Florida and Pennsylvania. Graph the logistic models and interpret their significance.

SOLUTION Let $F(t)$ and $P(t)$ be the populations (in millions) of Florida and Pennsylvania, respectively, t years *after 1800*. Figure H.16a shows a scatter plot of the data for both states; the data for Florida is shown in black, and for Pennsylvania, in red. Using logistic regression, we obtain the models for the two states:

$$F(t) = \frac{28.021}{1 + 9018.63e^{-0.047015t}} \quad \text{and} \quad P(t) = \frac{12.579}{1 + 29.0003e^{-0.034315t}}$$

Figure H.16b shows the scatter plots of the data with graphs of the two population models. You can see that the curves fit the data fairly well. From the numerators of the models we see that

$$\lim_{t \to \infty} F(t) = 28.021 \quad \text{and} \quad \lim_{t \to \infty} P(t) = 12.579.$$

So the maximum sustainable population for Florida is about 28.0 million, and for Pennsylvania is about 12.6 million.

Figure H.16c shows a three-century span for the two states. Pennsylvania had rapid growth in the 19th century and first half of the 20th century, and is now approaching its limit to growth. Florida, on the other hand, is currently experiencing extremely rapid growth but should be approaching its maximum sustainable population by the end of the 21st century. *Now try Exercise 50.*

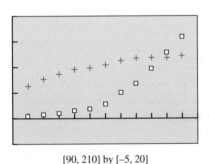

[90, 210] by [−5, 20]

(a)

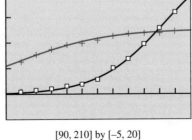

[90, 210] by [−5, 20]

(b)

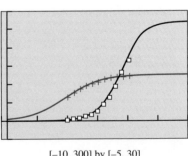

[−10, 300] by [−5, 30]

(c)

FIGURE H.16 Scatter plots and graphs for Example 7.

Other Logistic Models

In Example 3, the bacteria cannot continue to grow exponentially forever because they cannot grow beyond the confines of the petri dish. In Example 7, though Florida's population is booming now, it will eventually level off, just as Pennsylvania's has done. Sunflowers and many other plants grow to a natural height following a logistic pattern. Chemical acid-base titration curves are logistic. Yeast cultures grow logistically. Contagious diseases and even rumors spread according to logistic models.

EXAMPLE 8 Modeling a Rumor

Watauga High School has 1200 students. Bob, Carol, Ted, and Alice start a rumor, which spreads logistically so that $S(t) = 1200/(1 + 39 \cdot e^{-0.9t})$ models the number of students who have heard the rumor by the end of Day t.

(a) How many students have heard the rumor by the end of Day 0?

(b) How long does it take for 1000 students to hear the rumor?

SOLUTION

(a) $S(0) = \dfrac{1200}{1 + 39 \cdot e^{-0.9 \cdot 0}} = \dfrac{1200}{1 + 39} = 30$. So, 30 students have heard the rumor by the end of Day 0.

(b) We need to solve $\dfrac{1200}{1 + 39e^{-0.9t}} = 1000$.

Figure H.17 shows that the graph of $S(t) = 1200/(1 + 39 \cdot e^{-0.9t})$ intersects $y = 1000$ when $t \approx 5.86$. So toward the end of Day 6 the rumor has reached the ears of 1000 students. *Now try Exercise 45.*

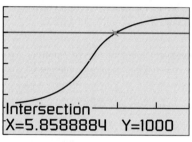

[0, 10] by [−400, 1400]

FIGURE H.17 The spread of a rumor. (Example 8)

LESSON H-2 EXERCISES

Exercise numbers with a gray background indicate problems that the authors have designed to be solved *without a calculator*.

In Exercises 1–6, tell whether the function is an exponential growth function or exponential decay function, and find the constant percentage rate of growth or decay.

1. $P(t) = 3.5 \cdot 1.09^t$

2. $P(t) = 4.3 \cdot 1.018^t$

3. $f(x) = 78{,}963 \cdot 0.968^x$

4. $f(x) = 5607 \cdot 0.9968^x$

5. $g(t) = 247 \cdot 2^t$

6. $g(t) = 43 \cdot 0.05^t$

In Exercises 7–18, determine the exponential function that satisfies the given conditions.

7. Initial value = 5, increasing at a rate of 17% per year

8. Initial value = 52, increasing at a rate of 2.3% per day

9. Initial value = 16, decreasing at a rate of 50% per month

10. Initial value = 5, decreasing at a rate of 0.59% per week

11. Initial population = 28,900, decreasing at a rate of 2.6% per year

12. Initial population = 502,000, increasing at a rate of 1.7% per year

13. Initial height = 18 cm, growing at a rate of 5.2% per week

14. Initial mass = 15 g, decreasing at a rate of 4.6% per day

15. Initial mass = 0.6 g, doubling every 3 days

16. Initial population = 250, doubling every 7.5 hours

17. Initial mass = 592 g, halving once every 6 years

18. Initial mass = 17 g, halving once every 32 hours

In Exercises 19 and 20, determine a formula for the exponential function whose values are given in Table H.11.

19. $f(x)$ 20. $g(x)$

Table H.11 Values for Two Exponential Functions

x	$f(x)$	$g(x)$
−2	1.472	−9.0625
−1	1.84	−7.25
0	2.3	−5.8
1	2.875	−4.64
2	3.59375	−3.7123

In Exercises 21 and 22, determine a formula for the exponential function whose graph is shown in the figure.

21.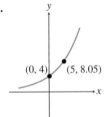

22.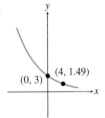

In Exercises 23–26, find the logistic function that satisfies the given conditions.

23. Initial value = 10, limit to growth = 40, passing through $(1, 20)$.

24. Initial value = 12, limit to growth = 60, passing through $(1, 24)$.

25. Initial population = 16, maximum sustainable population = 128, passing through $(5, 32)$.

26. Initial height = 5, limit to growth = 30, passing through $(3, 15)$.

In Exercises 27 and 28, determine a formula for the logistic function whose graph is shown in the figure.

27.   28.

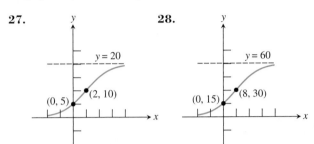

29. **Exponential Growth** The 2000 population of Jacksonville, Florida, was 736,000 and was increasing at the rate of 1.49% each year. At that rate, when will the population be 1 million?

30. **Exponential Growth** The 2000 population of Las Vegas, Nevada, was 478,000 and is increasing at the rate of 6.28% each year. At that rate, when will the population be 1 million?

31. **Exponential Growth** The population of Smallville in the year 1890 was 6250. Assume the population increased at a rate of 2.75% per year.

(a) Estimate the population in 1915 and 1940.

(b) Predict when the population reached 50,000.

32. **Exponential Growth** The population of River City in the year 1910 was 4200. Assume the population increased at a rate of 2.25% per year.

(a) Estimate the population in 1930 and 1945.

(b) Predict when the population reached 20,000.

33. **Radioactive Decay** The half-life of a certain radioactive substance is 14 days. There are 6.6 g present initially.

(a) Express the amount of substance remaining as a function of time t.

(b) When will there be less than 1 g remaining?

34. **Radioactive Decay** The half-life of a certain radioactive substance is 65 days. There are 3.5 g present initially.

(a) Express the amount of substance remaining as a function of time t.

(b) When will there be less than 1 g remaining?

35. **Writing to Learn** Without using formulas or graphs, compare and contrast exponential functions and linear functions.

36. **Writing to Learn** Without using formulas or graphs, compare and contrast exponential functions and logistic functions.

37. Writing to Learn Using the population model that is graphed in the figure, explain why the time it takes the population to double (doubling time) is independent of the population size.

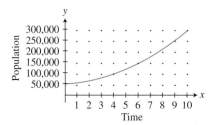

38. Writing to Learn Explain why the half-life of a radioactive substance is independent of the initial amount of the substance that is present.

39. Bacteria Growth The number B of bacteria in a petri dish culture after t hours is given by

$$B = 100e^{0.693t}.$$

When will the number of bacteria be 200? Estimate the doubling time of the bacteria.

40. Radiocarbon Dating The amount C in grams of carbon-14 present in a certain substance after t years is given by

$$C = 20e^{-0.0001216t}.$$

Estimate the half-life of carbon-14.

41. Atmospheric Pressure Determine the atmospheric pressure outside an aircraft flying at 52,800 ft (10 mi above sea level).

42. Atmospheric Pressure Find the altitude above sea level at which the atmospheric pressure is 2.5 lb/in.^{2}.

43. Population Modeling Use the 1950–2000 data in Table H.12 and exponential regression to predict Los Angeles's population for 2007. Compare the result with the listed value for 2007. [*Hint:* Let 1900 be $t = 0$.]

44. Population Modeling Use the 1950–2000 data in Table H.12 and exponential regression to predict Phoenix's population for 2007. Compare the result with the listed value for 2007. Repeat these steps using 1960–2000 data to create the model. [*Hint:* Let 1900 be $t = 0$.]

Table H.12 Populations of Two U.S. Cities (in thousands)

Year	Los Angeles	Phoenix
1950	1970	107
1960	2479	439
1970	2812	584
1980	2969	790
1990	3485	983
2000	3695	1321
2007	3834	1552

Source: World Almanac and Book of Facts 2002, 2009.

45. Spread of Flu The number of students infected with flu at Springfield High School after t days is modeled by the function

$$P(t) = \frac{800}{1 + 49e^{-0.2t}}.$$

(a) What was the initial number of infected students?

(b) When will the number of infected students be 200?

(c) The school will close when 300 of the 800-student body are infected. When will the school close?

46. Population of Deer The population of deer after t years in Cedar State Park is modeled by the function

$$P(t) = \frac{1001}{1 + 90e^{-0.2t}}.$$

(a) What was the initial population of deer?

(b) When will the number of deer be 600?

(c) What is the maximum number of deer possible in the park?

47. Population Growth Using all of the data in Table H.9, compute a logistic regression model, and use it to predict the U.S. population in 2010.

48. Population Growth Using the data in Table H.13, confirm the model used in Example 8 of Lesson H-1.

Table H.13 Population of Dallas, Texas

Year	Population
1950	434,462
1960	679,684
1970	844,401
1980	904,599
1990	1,006,877
2000	1,188,589

Source: U.S. Census Bureau.

49. Population Growth Using the data in Table H.14, confirm the model used in Exercise 56 of Lesson H-1.

Table H.14 Populations of Two U.S. States (in millions)

Year	Arizona	New York
1900	0.1	7.3
1910	0.2	9.1
1920	0.3	10.3
1930	0.4	12.6
1940	0.5	13.5
1950	0.7	14.8
1960	1.3	16.8
1970	1.8	18.2
1980	2.7	17.6
1990	3.7	18.0
2000	5.1	19.0

Source: U.S. Census Bureau.

50. Population Growth Using the data in Table H.14, compute a logistic regression model for Arizona's population for t years since 1800. Based on your model and the New York population model from Exercise 56 of Lesson H-1, will the population of Arizona ever surpass that of New York? If so, when?

Explorations

51. Population Growth (a) Use the 1900–1990 data in Table H.9 and *logistic* regression to predict the U.S. population for 2000.

(b) **Writing to Learn** Compare the prediction with the value listed in the table for 2000.

(c) Noting the results of Example 6, which model—exponential or logistic—makes the better prediction in this case?

52. Population Growth Use all of the data in Tables H.9 and H.15.

(a) Based on exponential growth models, will Mexico's population surpass that of the United States, and if so, when?

(b) Based on logistic growth models, will Mexico's population surpass that of the United States, and if so, when?

(c) What are the maximum sustainable populations for the two countries?

(d) **Writing to Learn** Which model—exponential or logistic—is more valid in this case? Justify your choice.

Table H.15 Population of Mexico (in millions)

Year	Population
1900	13.6
1950	25.8
1960	34.9
1970	48.2
1980	66.8
1990	88.1
2001	101.9
2025	130.2
2050	154.0

Sources: 1992 Statesman's Yearbook and World Almanac and Book of Facts 2002.

Extending the Ideas

53. The **hyperbolic sine function** is defined by $\sinh(x) = (e^x - e^{-x})/2$. Prove that sinh is an odd function.

54. The **hyperbolic cosine function** is defined by $\cosh(x) = (e^x + e^{-x})/2$. Prove that cosh is an even function.

55. The **hyperbolic tangent function** is defined by $\tanh(x) = (e^x - e^{-x})/(e^x + e^{-x})$.

(a) Prove that $\tanh(x) = \sinh(x)/\cosh(x)$.
(b) Prove that tanh is an odd function.
(c) Prove that $f(x) = 1 + \tanh(x)$ is a logistic function.

H-3 Logarithmic Functions and Their Graphs

Inverses of Exponential Functions

If a function passes the *horizontal line test*, then the inverse of the function is also a function. Figure H.18 shows that an exponential function $f(x) = b^x$ would pass the horizontal line test. So it has an inverse that is a function. This inverse is the **logarithmic function with base b**, denoted $\log_b(x)$, or more simply as $\log_b x$. That is, if $f(x) = b^x$ with $b > 0$ and $b \neq 1$, then $f^{-1}(x) = \log_b x$. See Figure H.19.

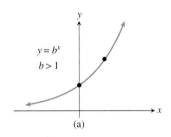
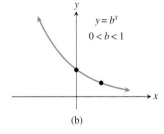

FIGURE H.18 Exponential functions are either (a) increasing or (b) decreasing.

An immediate and useful consequence of this definition is the link between an exponential equation and its logarithmic counterpart.

Changing Between Logarithmic and Exponential Form

If $x > 0$ and $0 < b \neq 1$, then

$$y = \log_b(x) \quad \text{if and only if} \quad b^y = x.$$

This linking statement says that *a logarithm is an exponent*. Because logarithms are exponents, we can evaluate simple logarithmic expressions using our understanding of exponents.

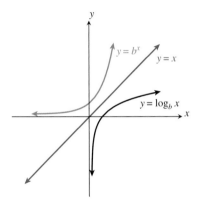

FIGURE H.19 Because logarithmic functions are inverses of exponential functions, we can obtain the graph of a logarithmic function by the mirror or rotational methods.

EXAMPLE 1 Evaluating Logarithms

(a) $\log_2 8 = 3$ because $2^3 = 8$.

(b) $\log_3 \sqrt{3} = 1/2$ because $3^{1/2} = \sqrt{3}$.

(c) $\log_5 \dfrac{1}{25} = -2$ because $5^{-2} = \dfrac{1}{5^2} = \dfrac{1}{25}$.

(d) $\log_4 1 = 0$ because $4^0 = 1$.

(e) $\log_7 7 = 1$ because $7^1 = 7$.

Now try Exercise 1.

We can generalize the relationships observed in Example 1.

Basic Properties of Logarithms

For $0 < b \neq 1$, $x > 0$, and any real number y,

- $\log_b 1 = 0$ because $b^0 = 1$.
- $\log_b b = 1$ because $b^1 = b$.
- $\log_b b^y = y$ because $b^y = b^y$.
- $b^{\log_b x} = x$ because $\log_b x = \log_b x$.

These properties give us efficient ways to evaluate simple logarithms and some exponential expressions. The first two parts of Example 2 are the same as the first two parts of Example 1.

EXAMPLE 2 Evaluating Logarithmic and Exponential Expressions

(a) $\log_2 8 = \log_2 2^3 = 3$.

(b) $\log_3 \sqrt{3} = \log_3 3^{1/2} = 1/2$.

(c) $6^{\log_6 11} \doteq 11$.   *Now try Exercise 5.*

Logarithmic functions are inverses of exponential functions. So the inputs and outputs are switched. Table H.16 illustrates this relationship for $f(x) = 2^x$ and $f^{-1}(x) = \log_2 x$.

Table H.16 An Exponential Function and Its Inverse

x	$f(x) = 2^x$	x	$f^{-1}(x) = \log_2 x$
−3	1/8	1/8	−3
−2	1/4	1/4	−2
−1	1/2	1/2	−1
0	1	1	0
1	2	2	1
2	4	4	2
3	8	8	3

This relationship can be used to produce both tables and graphs for logarithmic functions, as you will discover in Exploration 1.

EXPLORATION 1   Comparing Exponential and Logarithmic Functions

1. Set your grapher to Parametric mode and Simultaneous graphing mode.

   Set X1T = T and Y1T = 2^T.

   Set X2T = 2^T and Y2T = T.

   Creating Tables. Set TblStart = −3 and ΔTbl = 1. Use the Table feature of your grapher to obtain the decimal form of both parts of Table 3.16. Be sure to scroll to the right to see X2T and Y2T.

   Drawing Graphs. Set Tmin = −6, Tmax = 6, and Tstep = 0.5. Set the (x, y) window to $[-6, 6]$ by $[-4, 4]$. Use the Graph feature to obtain the simultaneous graphs of $f(x) = 2^x$ and $f^{-1}(x) = \log_2 x$. Use the Trace feature to explore the numerical relationships within the graphs.

2. *Graphing in Function mode.* Graph $y = 2^x$ in the same window. Then use the "draw inverse" command to draw the graph of $y = \log_2 x$.

Common Logarithms—Base 10

Logarithms with base 10 are called **common logarithms**. Because of their connection to our base-ten number system, the metric system, and scientific notation, common logarithms are especially useful. We often drop the subscript of 10 for the base when using common logarithms. The common logarithmic function $\log_{10} x = \log x$ is the inverse of the exponential function $f(x) = 10^x$. So

$$y = \log x \quad \text{if and only if} \quad 10^y = x.$$

Applying this relationship, we can obtain other relationships for logarithms with base 10.

> ### Basic Properties of Common Logarithms
>
> Let x and y be real numbers with $x > 0$.
>
> - $\log 1 = 0$ because $10^0 = 1$.
> - $\log 10 = 1$ because $10^1 = 10$.
> - $\log 10^y = y$ because $10^y = 10^y$.
> - $10^{\log x} = x$ because $\log x = \log x$.

Some Words of Warning

In Figure H.20, notice we used "10^Ans" instead of "10^1.537819095" to check log (34.5). This is because graphers generally store more digits than they display and so we can obtain a more accurate check. Even so, because log (34.5) is an irrational number, a grapher cannot produce its exact value, so checks like those shown in Figure H.20 may not always work out so perfectly.

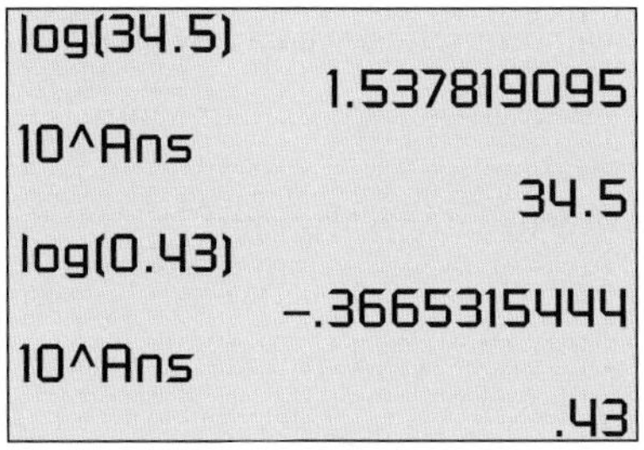

```
log(34.5)
            1.537819095
10^Ans
                   34.5
log(0.43)
            -.3665315444
10^Ans
                    .43
```

FIGURE H.20 Doing and checking common logarithmic computations. (Example 4)

Using the definition of common logarithm or these basic properties, we can evaluate expressions involving a base of 10.

EXAMPLE 3 Evaluating Logarithmic and Exponential Expressions—Base 10

(a) $\log 100 = \log_{10} 100 = 2$ because $10^2 = 100$.

(b) $\log \sqrt[5]{10} = \log 10^{1/5} = \dfrac{1}{5}$.

(c) $\log \dfrac{1}{1000} = \log \dfrac{1}{10^3} = \log 10^{-3} = -3$.

(d) $10^{\log 6} = 6$.   *Now try Exercise 7.*

Common logarithms can be evaluated by using the $\boxed{\text{LOG}}$ key on a calculator, as illustrated in Example 4.

EXAMPLE 4 Evaluating Common Logarithms with a Calculator

Use a calculator to evaluate the logarithmic expression if it is defined, and check your result by evaluating the corresponding exponential expression.

(a) $\log 34.5 = 1.537\ldots$ because $10^{1.537\ldots} = 34.5$.

(b) $\log 0.43 = -0.366\ldots$ because $10^{-0.366\ldots} = 0.43$.

See Figure H.20.

(c) $\log(-3)$ is undefined because there is no real number y such that $10^y = -3$. A grapher will yield either an error message or a complex-number answer for entries such as $\log(-3)$. We shall restrict the domain of logarithmic functions to the set of positive real numbers and ignore such complex-number answers.

Now try Exercise 25.

Changing from logarithmic form to exponential form sometimes is enough to solve an equation involving logarithmic functions.

EXAMPLE 5 Solving Simple Logarithmic Equations

Solve each equation by changing it to exponential form.

(a) $\log x = 3$ (b) $\log_2 x = 5$

SOLUTION

(a) Changing to exponential form, $x = 10^3 = 1000$.

(b) Changing to exponential form, $x = 2^5 = 32$.   *Now try Exercise 33.*

Natural Logarithms—Base e

Because of their special calculus properties, logarithms with the natural base e are used in many situations. Logarithms with base e are **natural logarithms**. We often use the special abbreviation "ln" (without a subscript) to denote a natural logarithm. Thus, the natural logarithmic function $\log_e x = \ln x$. It is the inverse of the exponential function $f(x) = e^x$. So

$$y = \ln x \quad \text{if and only if} \quad e^y = x.$$

Applying this relationship, we can obtain other fundamental relationships for logarithms with the natural base e.

Basic Properties of Natural Logarithms

Let x and y be real numbers with $x > 0$.

- $\ln 1 = 0$ because $e^0 = 1$.
- $\ln e = 1$ because $e^1 = e$.
- $\ln e^y = y$ because $e^y = e^y$.
- $e^{\ln x} = x$ because $\ln x = \ln x$.

Using the definition of natural logarithm or these basic properties, we can evaluate expressions involving the natural base e.

EXAMPLE 6 Evaluating Logarithmic and Exponential Expressions—Base e

(a) $\ln \sqrt{e} = \log_e \sqrt{e} = 1/2$ because $e^{1/2} = \sqrt{e}$.

(b) $\ln e^5 = \log_e e^5 = 5$.

(c) $e^{\ln 4} = 4$.   *Now try Exercise 13.*

Natural logarithms can be evaluated by using the $\boxed{\text{LN}}$ key on a calculator, as illustrated in Example 7.

EXAMPLE 7 Evaluating Natural Logarithms with a Calculator

Use a calculator to evaluate the logarithmic expression, if it is defined, and check your result by evaluating the corresponding exponential expression.

(a) $\ln 23.5 = 3.157\ldots$ because $e^{3.157\ldots} = 23.5$.

(b) $\ln 0.48 = -0.733\ldots$ because $e^{-0.733\ldots} = 0.48$.

See Figure H.21.

(c) $\ln(-5)$ is undefined because there is no real number y such that $e^y = -5$. A grapher will yield either an error message or a complex-number answer for entries such as $\ln(-5)$. We will continue to restrict the domain of logarithmic functions to the set of positive real numbers and ignore such complex-number answers.   *Now try Exercise 29.*

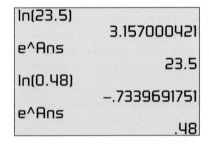

FIGURE H.21 Doing and checking natural logarithmic computations. (Example 7)

Graphs of Logarithmic Functions

The natural logarithmic function $f(x) = \ln x$ is one of the basic functions. We now list its properties.

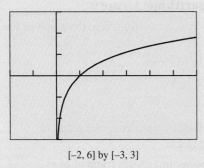

[-2, 6] by [-3, 3]

FIGURE H.22

BASIC FUNCTION The Natural Logarithmic Function

$f(x) = \ln x$
Domain: $(0, \infty)$
Range: All reals
Continuous on $(0, \infty)$
Increasing on $(0, \infty)$
No symmetry
Not bounded above or below
No local extrema
No horizontal asymptotes
Vertical asymptote: $x = 0$
End behavior: $\lim\limits_{x \to \infty} \ln x = \infty$

Any logarithmic function $g(x) = \log_b x$ with $b > 1$ has the same domain, range, continuity, increasing behavior, lack of symmetry, and other general behavior as $f(x) = \ln x$. It is rare that we are interested in logarithmic functions $g(x) = \log_b x$ with $0 < b < 1$. So, the graph and behavior of $f(x) = \ln x$ are typical of logarithmic functions.

We now consider the graphs of the common and natural logarithmic functions and their geometric transformations. To understand the graphs of $y = \log x$ and $y = \ln x$, we can compare each to the graph of its inverse, $y = 10^x$ and $y = e^x$, respectively. Figure H.23a shows that the graphs of $y = \ln x$ and $y = e^x$ are reflections of each other across the line $y = x$. Similarly, Figure H.23b shows that the graphs of $y = \log x$ and $y = 10^x$ are reflections of each other across this same line.

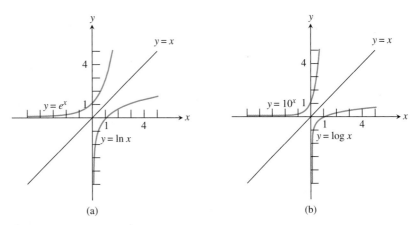

(a)   (b)

FIGURE H.23 Two pairs of inverse functions.

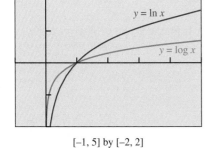

[-1, 5] by [-2, 2]

FIGURE H.24 The graphs of the common and natural logarithmic functions.

From Figure H.24 we can see that the graphs of $y = \log x$ and $y = \ln x$ have much in common. Figure H.24 also shows how they differ.

The geometric transformations previously studied, together with our knowledge of the graphs of $y = \ln x$ and $y = \log x$, allow us to predict the graphs of the functions in Example 8.

EXAMPLE 8 Transforming Logarithmic Graphs

Describe how to transform the graph of $y = \ln x$ or $y = \log x$ into the graph of the given function.

(a) $g(x) = \ln (x + 2)$ **(b)** $h(x) = \ln (3 - x)$

(c) $g(x) = 3 \log x$ **(d)** $h(x) = 1 + \log x$

SOLUTION

(a) The graph of $g(x) = \ln (x + 2)$ is obtained by translating the graph of $y = \ln (x)$ 2 units to the left. See Figure H.25a.

(b) $h(x) = \ln (3 - x) = \ln [-(x - 3)]$. So we obtain the graph of $h(x) = \ln (3 - x)$ from the graph of $y = \ln x$ by applying, in order, a reflection across the y-axis followed by a translation 3 units to the right. See Figure H.25b.

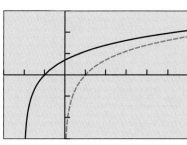

[–3, 6] by [–3, 3]

(a)

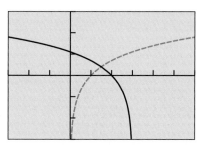

[–3, 6] by [–3, 3]

(b)

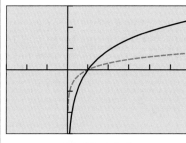

[–3, 6] by [–3, 3]

(c)

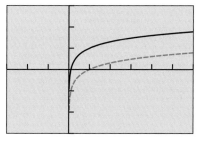

[–3, 6] by [–3, 3]

(d)

FIGURE H.25 Transforming $y = \ln x$ to obtain (a) $g(x) = \ln (x + 2)$ and (b) $h(x) = \ln (3 - x)$; and $y = \log x$ to obtain (c) $g(x) = 3 \log x$ and (d) $h(x) = 1 + \log x$. (Example 8)

(c) The graph of $g(x) = 3 \log x$ is obtained by vertically stretching the graph of $f(x) = \log x$ by a factor of 3. See Figure H.25c.

(d) We can obtain the graph of $h(x) = 1 + \log x$ from the graph of $f(x) = \log x$ by a translation 1 unit up. See Figure H.25d. *Now try Exercise 41.*

Sound Intensity

Sound intensity is the energy per unit time of a sound wave over a given area, and is measured in watts per square meter (W/m^2).

Measuring Sound Using Decibels

Table H.17 lists assorted sounds. Notice that a jet at takeoff is 100 trillion times as loud as a soft whisper. Because the range of audible sound intensities is so great, common logarithms (powers of 10) are used to compare how loud sounds are.

Table H.17 Approximate Intensities of Selected Sounds

Sound	Intensity (W/m^2)
Hearing threshold	10^{-12}
Soft whisper at 5 m	10^{-11}
City traffic	10^{-5}
Subway train	10^{-2}
Pain threshold	10^{0}
Jet at takeoff	10^{3}

Source: Adapted from R. W. Reading, Exploring Physics: Concepts and Applications. Belmont, CA: Wadsworth, 1984.

Bel Is for Bell

The original unit for sound intensity level was the *bel* (B), which proved to be inconveniently large. So the decibel, one-tenth of a bel, has replaced it. The bel was named in honor of Scottish-born American Alexander Graham Bell (1847–1922), inventor of the telephone.

DEFINITION Decibels

The level of sound intensity in **decibels** (dB) is

$$\beta = 10 \log(I/I_0),$$

where β (beta) is the number of decibels, I is the sound intensity in W/m^2, and $I_0 = 10^{-12}$ W/m^2 is the threshold of human hearing (the quietest audible sound intensity).

Appendix Opener Problem (from page H1)

Problem: How loud is a train inside a subway tunnel?

Solution: Based on the data in Table H.17,

$$\beta = 10 \log(I/I_0)$$
$$= 10 \log(10^{-2}/10^{-12})$$
$$= 10 \log(10^{10})$$
$$= 10 \cdot 10 = 100$$

So the sound intensity level inside the subway tunnel is 100 dB.

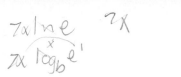 

LESSON H-3 EXERCISES

Exercise numbers with a gray background indicate problems that the authors have designed to be solved *without a calculator.*

In Exercises 1–18, evaluate the logarithmic expression without using a calculator.

1. $\log_4 4$

2. $\log_6 1$

3. $\log_2 32$

4. $\log_3 81$

5. $\log_5 \sqrt[3]{25}$

6. $\log_6 \dfrac{1}{\sqrt[5]{36}}$

7. $\log 10^3$

8. $\log 10{,}000$

9. $\log 100{,}000$

10. $\log 10^{-4}$

11. $\log \sqrt[3]{10}$

12. $\log \dfrac{1}{\sqrt{1000}}$

13. $\ln e^3$

14. $\ln e^{-4}$

15. $\ln \dfrac{1}{e}$

16. $\ln 1$

17. $\ln \sqrt[4]{e}$

18. $\ln \dfrac{1}{\sqrt{e^7}}$

In Exercises 19–24, evaluate the expression without using a calculator.

19. $7^{\log_7 3}$

20. $5^{\log_5 8}$

21. $10^{\log (0.5)}$

22. $10^{\log 14}$

23. $e^{\ln 6}$

24. $e^{\ln(1/5)}$

In Exercises 25–32, use a calculator to evaluate the logarithmic expression if it is defined, and check your result by evaluating the corresponding exponential expression.

25. $\log 9.43$

26. $\log 0.908$

27. $\log (-14)$

28. $\log (-5.14)$

29. $\ln 4.05$

30. $\ln 0.733$

31. $\ln (-0.49)$

32. $\ln (-3.3)$

In Exercises 33–36, solve the equation by changing it to exponential form.

33. $\log x = 2$

34. $\log x = 4$

35. $\log x = -1$

36. $\log x = -3$

In Exercises 37–40, match the function with its graph.

37. $f(x) = \log (1 - x)$

38. $f(x) = \log (x + 1)$

39. $f(x) = -\ln (x - 3)$

40. $f(x) = -\ln (4 - x)$

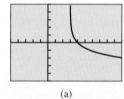

(a)

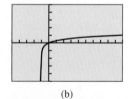

(b)

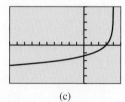

(c)

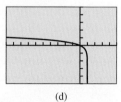

(d)

In Exercises 41–46, describe how to transform the graph of $y = \ln x$ into the graph of the given function. Sketch the graph by hand and support your sketch with a grapher.

41. $f(x) = \ln (x + 3)$

42. $f(x) = \ln (x) + 2$

43. $f(x) = \ln (-x) + 3$

44. $f(x) = \ln (-x) - 2$

45. $f(x) = \ln (2 - x)$

46. $f(x) = \ln (5 - x)$

In Exercises 47–52, describe how to transform the graph of $y = \log x$ into the graph of the given function. Sketch the graph by hand and support with a grapher.

47. $f(x) = -1 + \log (x)$

48. $f(x) = \log (x - 3)$

49. $f(x) = -2 \log (-x)$

50. $f(x) = -3 \log (-x)$

51. $f(x) = 2 \log (3 - x) - 1$

52. $f(x) = -3 \log (1 - x) + 1$

In Exercises 53–58, graph the function, and analyze it for domain, range, continuity, increasing or decreasing behavior, boundedness, extrema, symmetry, asymptotes, and end behavior.

53. $f(x) = \log (x - 2)$

54. $f(x) = \ln (x + 1)$

55. $f(x) = -\ln (x - 1)$

56. $f(x) = -\log (x + 2)$

57. $f(x) = 3 \log (x) - 1$

58. $f(x) = 5 \ln (2 - x) - 3$

59. Sound Intensity Use the data in Table H.17 to compute the sound intensity in decibels for **(a)** a soft whisper, **(b)** city traffic, and **(c)** a jet at takeoff.

60. Light Absorption The Beer-Lambert Law of Absorption applied to Lake Erie states that the light intensity I (in lumens), at a depth of x feet, satisfies the equation

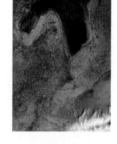

$$\log \dfrac{I}{12} = -0.00235x.$$

Find the intensity of the light at a depth of 30 ft.

61. Population Growth Using the data in Table H.18, compute a logarithmic regression model, and use it to predict when the population of San Antonio will be 1,500,000.

Table H.18 Population of San Antonio

Year	Population
1970	654,153
1980	785,940
1990	935,933
2000	1,151,305

Source: World Alamanac and Book of Facts 2005.

62. Population Decay   Using the data in Table H.19, compute a logarithmic regression model, and use it to predict when the population of Milwaukee will be 500,000.

 Table H.19 Population of Milwaukee

Year	Population
1970	717,372
1980	636,297
1990	628,088
2000	596,974

Source: World Alamanac and Book of Facts 2005.

Explorations

63. Writing to Learn Parametric Graphing   In the manner of Exploration 1, make tables and graphs for $f(x) = 3^x$ and its inverse $f^{-1}(x) = \log_3 x$. Write a comparative analysis of the two functions regarding domain, range, intercepts, and asymptotes.

64. Writing to Learn Parametric Graphing   In the manner of Exploration 1, make tables and graphs for $f(x) = 5^x$ and its inverse $f^{-1}(x) = \log_5 x$. Write a comparative analysis of the two functions regarding domain, range, intercepts, and asymptotes.

65. Group Activity Parametric Graphing   In the manner of Exploration 1, find the number $b > 1$ such that the graphs of $f(x) = b^x$ and its inverse $f^{-1}(x) = \log_b x$ have exactly one point of intersection. What is the one point that is in common to the two graphs?

66. Writing to Learn   Explain why zero is not in the domain of the logarithmic functions $f(x) = \log_3 x$ and $g(x) = \log_5 x$.

Extending the Ideas

67. Describe how to transform the graph of $f(x) = \ln x$ into the graph of $g(x) = \log_{1/e} x$.

68. Describe how to transform the graph of $f(x) = \log x$ into the graph of $g(x) = \log_{0.1} x$.

H-4 Properties of Logarithmic Functions

What you'll learn about
- Properties of Logarithms
- Change of Base
- Graphs of Logarithmic Functions with Base b
- Re-expressing Data

... and why
The applications of logarithms are based on their many special properties, so learn them well.

Properties of Logarithms

Logarithms have special algebraic traits that historically made them indispensable for calculations and that still make them valuable in many areas of application and modeling. In Lesson H-3 we learned about the inverse relationship between exponents and logarithms and how to apply some basic properties of logarithms. We now delve deeper into the nature of logarithms to prepare for equation solving and modeling.

Properties of Logarithms

Let b, R, and S be positive real numbers with $b \neq 1$, and c any real number.

- **Product rule:** $\quad \log_b (RS) = \log_b R + \log_b S$

- **Quotient rule:** $\quad \log_b \dfrac{R}{S} = \log_b R - \log_b S$

- **Power rule:** $\quad \log_b R^c = c \log_b R$

Properties of Exponents

Let b, x, and y be real numbers with $b > 0$.

1. $b^x \cdot b^y = b^{x+y}$

2. $\dfrac{b^x}{b^y} = b^{x-y}$

3. $(b^x)^y = b^{xy}$

The properties of exponents in the margin are the basis for these three properties of logarithms. For instance, the first exponent property listed in the margin is used to verify the product rule.

EXAMPLE 1 Proving the Product Rule for Logarithms

Prove $\log_b (RS) = \log_b R + \log_b S$.

SOLUTION Let $x = \log_b R$ and $y = \log_b S$. The corresponding exponential statements are $b^x = R$ and $b^y = S$. Therefore,

$$RS = b^x \cdot b^y$$
$$= b^{x+y} \qquad \text{First property of exponents}$$
$$\log_b (RS) = x + y \qquad \text{Change to logarithmic form.}$$
$$= \log_b R + \log_b S \qquad \text{Use the definitions of } x \text{ and } y.$$

Now try Exercise 37.

```
log(2)
                .30103
log(4)
                .60206
log(8)
                .90309
■
```

FIGURE H.26 An arithmetic pattern of logarithms. (Exploration 1)

EXPLORATION 1 Exploring the Arithmetic of Logarithms

Use the 5-decimal-place approximations shown in Figure H.26 to support the properties of logarithms numerically.

1. Product $\quad \log (2 \cdot 4) = \log 2 + \log 4$

2. Quotient $\quad \log \left(\dfrac{8}{2} \right) = \log 8 - \log 2$

3. Power $\quad \log 2^3 = 3 \log 2$

Now evaluate the common logs of other positive integers using the information given in Figure H.26 and without using your calculator.

4. Use the fact that $5 = 10/2$ to evaluate log 5.

5. Use the fact that 16, 32, and 64 are powers of 2 to evaluate log 16, log 32, and log 64.

6. Evaluate log 25, log 40, and log 50.

List all of the positive integers less than 100 whose common logs can be evaluated knowing only log 2 and the properties of logarithms and without using a calculator.

When we solve equations algebraically that involve logarithms, we often have to rewrite expressions using properties of logarithms. Sometimes we need to expand as far as possible, and other times we condense as much as possible. The next three examples illustrate how properties of logarithms can be used to change the form of expressions involving logarithms.

EXAMPLE 2 **Expanding the Logarithm of a Product**

Assuming x and y are positive, use properties of logarithms to write $\log (8xy^4)$ as a sum of logarithms or multiples of logarithms.

SOLUTION
$$\begin{aligned} \log (8xy^4) &= \log 8 + \log x + \log y^4 \qquad \text{Product rule} \\ &= \log 2^3 + \log x + \log y^4 \qquad 8 = 2^3 \\ &= 3 \log 2 + \log x + 4 \log y \qquad \text{Power rule} \end{aligned}$$

Now try Exercise 1.

EXAMPLE 3 **Expanding the Logarithm of a Quotient**

Assuming x is positive, use properties of logarithms to write $\ln (\sqrt{x^2 + 5}/x)$ as a sum or difference of logarithms or multiples of logarithms.

SOLUTION
$$\begin{aligned} \ln \frac{\sqrt{x^2 + 5}}{x} &= \ln \frac{(x^2 + 5)^{1/2}}{x} \\ &= \ln (x^2 + 5)^{1/2} - \ln x \qquad \text{Quotient rule} \\ &= \frac{1}{2} \ln (x^2 + 5) - \ln x \qquad \text{Power rule} \end{aligned}$$

Now try Exercise 9.

EXAMPLE 4 **Condensing a Logarithmic Expression**

Assuming x and y are positive, write $\ln x^5 - 2 \ln (xy)$ as a single logarithm.

SOLUTION
$$\begin{aligned} \ln x^5 - 2 \ln (xy) &= \ln x^5 - \ln (xy)^2 \qquad \text{Power rule} \\ &= \ln x^5 - \ln (x^2 y^2) \\ &= \ln \frac{x^5}{x^2 y^2} \qquad \text{Quotient rule} \\ &= \ln \frac{x^3}{y^2} \end{aligned}$$

Now try Exercise 13.

As we have seen, logarithms have some surprising properties. It is easy to overgeneralize and fall into misconceptions about logarithms. Exploration 2 should help you discern what is true and false about logarithmic relationships.

EXPLORATION 2 **Discovering Relationships and Nonrelationships**

Of the eight relationships suggested here, four are *true* and four are *false* (using values of x within the domains of both sides of the equations). Thinking about the properties of logarithms, make a prediction about the truth of each statement. Then test each with some specific numerical values for x. Finally, compare the graphs of the two sides of the equation.

1. $\ln (x + 2) = \ln x + \ln 2$ 2. $\log_3 (7x) = 7 \log_3 x$

3. $\log_2 (5x) = \log_2 5 + \log_2 x$ 4. $\ln \dfrac{x}{5} = \ln x - \ln 5$

5. $\log \dfrac{x}{4} = \dfrac{\log x}{\log 4}$ 6. $\log_4 x^3 = 3 \log_4 x$

7. $\log_5 x^2 = (\log_5 x)(\log_5 x)$ 8. $\log |4x| = \log 4 + \log |x|$

Which four are true, and which four are false?

Change of Base

When working with a logarithmic expression with an undesirable base, it is possible to change the expression into a quotient of logarithms with a different base. For example, it is hard to evaluate $\log_4 7$ because 7 is not a simple power of 4 and there is no $\boxed{\log_4}$ key on a calculator or grapher.

We can work around this problem with some algebraic trickery. First let $y = \log_4 7$. Then

$$
\begin{aligned}
4^y &= 7 && \text{Switch to exponential form.} \\
\ln 4^y &= \ln 7 && \text{Apply ln.} \\
y\ln 4 &= \ln 7 && \text{Power rule} \\
y &= \frac{\ln 7}{\ln 4} && \text{Divide by ln 4.}
\end{aligned}
$$

Using a grapher (Figure H.27), we see that

$$
\log_4 7 = \frac{\ln 7}{\ln 4} = 1.4036\ldots
$$

We generalize this useful trickery as the change-of-base formula:

FIGURE H.27 Evaluating and checking $\log_4 7$.

```
ln(7)/ln(4)
            1.403677461
4^Ans
                      7
```

Change-of-Base Formula for Logarithms

For positive real numbers a, b, and x with $a \neq 1$ and $b \neq 1$,

$$
\log_b x = \frac{\log_a x}{\log_a b}.
$$

Calculators and graphers generally have two logarithm keys—$\boxed{\text{LOG}}$ and $\boxed{\text{LN}}$—which correspond to the bases 10 and e, respectively. So we often use the change-of-base formula in one of the following two forms:

$$\log_b x = \frac{\log x}{\log b} \quad \text{or} \quad \log_b x = \frac{\ln x}{\ln b}$$

These two forms are useful in evaluating logarithms and graphing logarithmic functions.

EXAMPLE 5 **Evaluating Logarithms by Changing the Base**

(a) $\log_3 16 = \dfrac{\ln 16}{\ln 3} = 2.523\ldots \approx 2.52$

(b) $\log_6 10 = \dfrac{\log 10}{\log 6} = \dfrac{1}{\log 6} = 1.285\ldots \approx 1.29$

(c) $\log_{1/2} 2 = \dfrac{\ln 2}{\ln (1/2)} = \dfrac{\ln 2}{\ln 1 - \ln 2} = \dfrac{\ln 2}{-\ln 2} = -1$ *Now try Exercise 23.*

Graphs of Logarithmic Functions with Base *b*

Σ Using the change-of-base formula we can rewrite any logarithmic function $g(x) = \log_b x$ as

$$g(x) = \frac{\ln x}{\ln b} = \frac{1}{\ln b}\ln x.$$

Therefore, every logarithmic function is a constant multiple of the natural logarithmic function $f(x) = \ln x$. If the base is $b > 1$, the graph of $g(x) = \log_b x$ is a vertical stretch or shrink of the graph of $f(x) = \ln x$ by the factor $1/\ln b$. If $0 < b < 1$, a reflection across the x-axis is required as well.

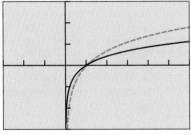

[−3, 6] by [−3, 3]
(a)

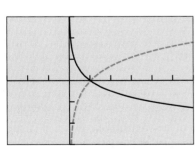

[−3, 6] by [−3, 3]
(b)

FIGURE H.28 Transforming $f(x) = \ln x$ to obtain (a) $g(x) = \log_5 x$ and (b) $h(x) = \log_{1/4} x$. (Example 6)

EXAMPLE 6 **Graphing Logarithmic Functions**

Describe how to transform the graph of $f(x) = \ln x$ into the graph of the given function. Sketch the graph by hand and support your answer with a grapher.

(a) $g(x) = \log_5 x$ **(b)** $h(x) = \log_{1/4} x$

SOLUTION

(a) Because $g(x) = \log_5 x = \ln x/\ln 5$, its graph is obtained by vertically shrinking the graph of $f(x) = \ln x$ by a factor of $1/\ln 5 \approx 0.62$. See Figure H.28a.

(b) $h(x) = \log_{1/4} x = \dfrac{\ln x}{\ln 1/4} = \dfrac{\ln x}{\ln 1 - \ln 4} = \dfrac{\ln x}{-\ln 4} = -\dfrac{1}{\ln 4}\ln x$. We can obtain the graph of h from the graph of $f(x) = \ln x$ by applying, in either order, a reflection across the x-axis and a vertical shrink by a factor of $1/\ln 4 \approx 0.72$. See Figure H.28b.   *Now try Exercise 39.*

We can generalize Example 6b in the following way: If $b > 1$, then $0 < 1/b < 1$ and

$$\log_{1/b} x = -\log_b x.$$

So when given a function like $h(x) = \log_{1/4} x$, with a base between 0 and 1, we can immediately rewrite it as $h(x) = -\log_4 x$. Because we can so readily change the base of logarithms with bases between 0 and 1, such logarithms are rarely encountered or used. Instead, we work with logarithms that have bases $b > 1$, which behave much like natural and common logarithms, as we now summarize.

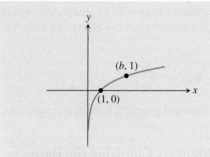

Logarithmic Functions $f(x) = \log_b x$, with $b > 1$

$(b, 1)$

$(1, 0)$

Domain: $(0, \infty)$
Range: All reals
Continuous
Increasing on its domain
No symmetry: neither even nor odd
Not bounded above or below
No local extrema
No horizontal asymptotes
Vertical asymptote: $x = 0$
End behavior: $\lim\limits_{x \to \infty} \log_b x = \infty$

FIGURE H.29 $f(x) = \log_b x, b > 1$.

Astronomically Speaking

An astronomical unit (AU) is the average distance between the Earth and the Sun, about 149.6 million kilometers (149.6 Gm).

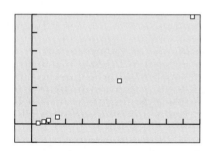

[−1, 10] by [−5, 30]
(a)

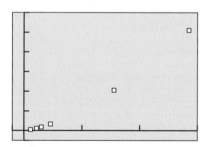

[−100, 1500] by [−1000, 12 000]
(b)

FIGURE H.30 Scatter plots of planetary data.

Re-expressing Data

When seeking a model for a set of data, it is often helpful to transform the data by applying a function to one or both of the variables in the data set. We did this already when we treated the years 1900–2000 as 0–100. Such a transformation of a data set is a **re-expression** of the data.

Kepler's Third Law states that the square of the orbit period T for each planet is proportional to the cube of its average distance a from the Sun. If we re-express Kepler planetary data using Earth-based units, the constant of proportion becomes 1 and the "is proportional to" in Kepler's Third Law becomes "equals." We can do this by dividing the "average distance" column by 149.6 Gm/AU and the "period of orbit" column by 365.2 days/yr. The re-expressed data are shown in Table H.20.

Table H.20 Average Distances and Orbit Periods for the Six Innermost Planets

Planet	Average Distance from Sun (AU)	Period of Orbit (yr)
Mercury	0.3870	0.2410
Venus	0.7233	0.6161
Earth	1.000	1.000
Mars	1.523	1.881
Jupiter	5.203	11.86
Saturn	9.539	29.46

Source: Re-expression of data from: Shupe, et al., *National Geographic Atlas of the World* (rev. 6th ed.). Washington, DC: National Geographic Society, 1992, plate 116.

Notice that the pattern in the scatter plot of these re-expressed data, shown in Figure H.30a, is essentially the same as the pattern in the plot of the original data, shown in Figure H.30b. What we have done is to make the numerical values of the data more convenient and to guarantee that our plot contains the ordered pair (1, 1) for Earth, which could potentially simplify our model. What we have *not* done and still wish to do is to clarify the relationship between the variables a (distance from the Sun) and T (orbit period).

Logarithms can be used to re-express data and help us clarify relationships and uncover hidden patterns. For the planetary data, if we plot $(\ln a, \ln T)$ pairs instead of (a, T) pairs, the pattern is much clearer. In Example 7, we carry out this re-expression of the data and then use an algebraic *tour de force* to obtain Kepler's Third Law.

EXAMPLE 7 Establishing Kepler's Third Law Using Logarithmic Re-expression

Re-express the (a, T) data pairs in Table H.20 as $(\ln a, \ln T)$ pairs. Find a linear regression model for the $(\ln a, \ln T)$ pairs. Rewrite the linear regression in terms of a and T, and rewrite the equation in a form with no logs or fractional exponents.

SOLUTION

Model

We use grapher list operations to obtain the $(\ln a, \ln T)$ pairs (see Figure H.31a). We make a scatter plot of the re-expressed data in Figure H.31b. The $(\ln a, \ln T)$ pairs appear to lie along a straight line.

L2	L3	L4
.241	−.9493	−1.423
.6161	−.3239	−.4843
1	0	0
1.881	.42068	.6318
11.86	1.6492	2.4732
29.46	2.2554	3.383
------	------	------

L4 = ln(L2)

(a)

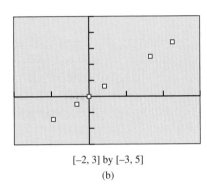

[−2, 3] by [−3, 5]

(b)

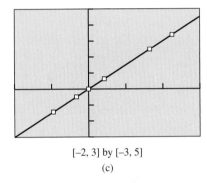

[−2, 3] by [−3, 5]

(c)

FIGURE H.31 Scatter plot and graphs for Example 7.

We let $y = \ln T$ and $x = \ln a$. Then using linear regression, we obtain the following model:

$$y = 1.49950x + 0.00070 \approx 1.5x.$$

Figure H.31c shows the scatter plot for the $(x, y) = (\ln a, \ln T)$ pairs together with a graph of $y = 1.5x$. You can see that the line fits the re-expressed data remarkably well.

Remodel

Returning to the original variables a and T, we obtain:

$$\ln T = 1.5 \cdot \ln a \qquad \text{y = 1.5x}$$

$$\frac{\ln T}{\ln a} = 1.5 \qquad \text{Divide by ln a.}$$

$$\log_a T = \frac{3}{2} \qquad \text{Change of base}$$

$$T = a^{3/2} \qquad \text{Switch to exponential form.}$$

$$T^2 = a^3 \qquad \text{Square both sides.}$$

Interpret

This is Kepler's Third Law!

Now try Exercise 59.

Exercise numbers with a gray background indicate problems that the authors have designed to be solved *without a calculator*.

In Exercises 1–12, assuming x and y are positive, use properties of logarithms to write the expression as a sum or difference of logarithms or multiples of logarithms.

1. $\ln 8x$

2. $\ln 9y$

3. $\log \dfrac{3}{x}$

4. $\log \dfrac{2}{y}$

5. $\log_2 y^5$

6. $\log_2 x^{-2}$

7. $\log x^3 y^2$

8. $\log xy^3$

9. $\ln \dfrac{x^2}{y^3}$

10. $\log 1000x^4$

11. $\log \sqrt[4]{\dfrac{x}{y}}$

12. $\ln \dfrac{\sqrt[3]{x}}{\sqrt[3]{y}}$

In Exercises 13–22, assuming x, y, and z are positive, use properties of logarithms to write the expression as a single logarithm.

13. $\log x + \log y$

14. $\log x + \log 5$

15. $\ln y - \ln 3$

16. $\ln x - \ln y$

17. $\dfrac{1}{3} \log x$

18. $\dfrac{1}{5} \log z$

19. $2 \ln x + 3 \ln y$

20. $4 \log y - \log z$

21. $4 \log (xy) - 3 \log (yz)$

22. $3 \ln (x^3 y) + 2 \ln (yz^2)$

In Exercises 23–28, use the change-of-base formula and your calculator to evaluate the logarithm.

23. $\log_2 7$

24. $\log_5 19$

25. $\log_8 175$

26. $\log_{12} 259$

27. $\log_{0.5} 12$

28. $\log_{0.2} 29$

In Exercises 29–32, write the expression using only natural logarithms.

29. $\log_3 x$ $x \log 3$

30. $\log_7 x$

31. $\log_2 (a + b)$

32. $\log_5 (c - d)$

In Exercises 33–36, write the expression using only common logarithms.

33. $\log_2 x$

34. $\log_4 x$

35. $\log_{1/2} (x + y)$

36. $\log_{1/3} (x - y)$

37. Prove the quotient rule of logarithms.

38. Prove the power rule of logarithms.

In Exercises 39–42, describe how to transform the graph of $g(x) = \ln x$ into the graph of the given function. Sketch the graph by hand and support with a grapher.

39. $f(x) = \log_4 x$

40. $f(x) = \log_7 x$

41. $f(x) = \log_{1/3} x$

42. $f(x) = \log_{1/5} x$

In Exercises 43–46, match the function with its graph. Identify the window dimensions, Xscl, and Yscl of the graph.

43. $f(x) = \log_4 (2 - x)$

44. $f(x) = \log_6 (x - 3)$

45. $f(x) = \log_{0.5} (x - 2)$

46. $f(x) = \log_{0.7} (3 - x)$

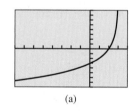

(a)

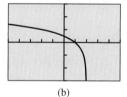

(b)

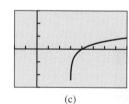

(c)

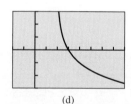

(d)

In Exercises 47–50, graph the function, and analyze it for domain, range, continuity, increasing or decreasing behavior, asymptotes, and end behavior.

47. $f(x) = \log_2 (8x)$

48. $f(x) = \log_{1/3} (9x)$

49. $f(x) = \log (x^2)$

50. $f(x) = \ln (x^3)$

51. Sound Intensity Compute the sound intensity level in decibels for each sound listed in Table H.21.

 Table H.21 Approximate Intensities for Selected Sounds

Sound	Intensity (Watts/m²)
(a) Hearing threshold	10^{-12}
(b) Rustling leaves	10^{-11}
(c) Conversation	10^{-6}
(d) School cafeteria	10^{-4}
(e) Jack hammer	10^{-2}
(f) Pain threshold	1

Sources: J. J. Dwyer, College Physics. Belmont, CA: Wadsworth, 1984; and E. Connally et al., Functions Modeling Change. New York: Wiley, 2000.

52. Earthquake Intensity The **Richter scale** magnitude R of an earthquake is based on the features of the associated seismic wave and is measured by

$$R = \log (a/T) + B,$$

where a is the amplitude in μm (micrometers), T is the period in seconds, and B accounts for the weakening of the seismic wave due to the distance from the epicenter. Compute the earthquake magnitude R for each set of values.

(a) $a = 250$, $T = 2$, and $B = 4.25$

(b) $a = 300$, $T = 4$, and $B = 3.5$

53. Light Intensity in Lake Erie The relationship between intensity I of light (in lumens) at a depth of x feet in Lake Erie is given by

$$\log \frac{I}{12} = -0.00235x.$$

What is the intensity at a depth of 40 ft?

54. Light Intensity in Lake Superior The relationship between intensity I of light (in lumens) at a depth of x feet in Lake Superior is given by

$$\log \frac{I}{12} = -0.0125x.$$

What is the intensity at a depth of 10 ft?

55. Writing to Learn Use the change-of-base formula to explain how we know that the graph of $f(x) = \log_3 x$ can be obtained by applying a transformation to the graph of $g(x) = \ln x$.

56. Writing to Learn Use the change-of-base formula to explain how the graph of $f(x) = \log_{0.8} x$ can be obtained by applying transformations to the graph of $g(x) = \log x$.

Explorations

57. (a) Compute the power regression model for the following data.

x	4	6.5	8.5	10
y	2816	31,908	122,019	275,000

(b) Predict the y-value associated with $x = 7.1$ using the power regression model.

(c) Re-express the data in terms of their natural logarithms and make a scatter plot of $(\ln x, \ln y)$.

(d) Compute the linear regression model $(\ln y) = a(\ln x) + b$ for $(\ln x, \ln y)$.

(e) Confirm that $y = e^b \cdot x^a$ is the power regression model found in (a).

58. (a) Compute the power regression model for the following data.

x	2	3	4.8	7.7
y	7.48	7.14	6.81	6.41

(b) Predict the y-value associated with $x = 9.2$ using the power regression model.

(c) Re-express the data in terms of their natural logarithms and make a scatter plot of $(\ln x, \ln y)$.

(d) Compute the linear regression model $(\ln y) = a(\ln x) + b$ for $(\ln x, \ln y)$.

(e) Confirm that $y = e^b \cdot x^a$ is the power regression model found in (a).

59. Keeping Warm

Scientists have found the pulse rate r of mammals to be a power function of their body weight w.

(a) Re-express the data in Table H.22 in terms of their *common* logarithms and make a scatter plot of $(\log w, \log r)$.

(b) Compute the linear regression model $(\log r) = a(\log w) + b$ for $(\log w, \log r)$.

(c) Superimpose the regression curve on the scatter plot.

(d) Use the regression equation to predict the pulse rate for a 450-kg horse. Is the result close to the 38 beats/min reported by A. J. Clark in 1927?

(e) **Writing to Learn**   Why can we use either common or natural logarithms to re-express data that fit a power regression model?

Table H.22 Weight and Pulse Rate of Selected Mammals

Mammal	Body Weight (kg)	Pulse Rate (beats/min)
Rat	0.2	420
Guinea pig	0.3	300
Rabbit	2	205
Small dog	5	120
Large dog	30	85
Sheep	50	70
Human	70	72

Source: A. J. Clark, *Comparative Physiology of the Heart.*
New York: Macmillan, 1927.

60. Let $a = \log 2$ and $b = \log 3$. Then, for example, $\log 6 = a + b$ and $\log 15 = 1 - a + b$. List all of the positive integers less than 100 whose common logs can be written as expressions involving a or b or both. (*Hint:* See Exploration 1 on page H32.)

Extending the Ideas

61. Solve $\ln x > \sqrt[3]{x}$.

62. Solve $1.2^x \le \log_{1.2} x$.

63. Group Activity   Work in groups of three. Have each group member graph and compare the domains for one pair of functions.

(a) $f(x) = 2 \ln x + \ln (x - 3)$ and $g(x) = \ln x^2(x - 3)$

(b) $f(x) = \ln (x + 5) - \ln (x - 5)$ and $g(x) = \ln \dfrac{x + 5}{x - 5}$

(c) $f(x) = \log (x + 3)^2$ and $g(x) = 2 \log (x + 3)$

Writing to Learn   After discussing your findings, write a brief group report that includes your overall conclusions and insights.

64. Prove the change-of-base formula for logarithms.

65. Prove that $f(x) = \log x/\ln x$ is a constant function with restricted domain by finding the exact value of the constant $\log x/\ln x$ expressed as a common logarithm.

66. Graph $f(x) = \ln (\ln (x))$, and analyze it for domain, range, continuity, increasing or decreasing behavior, symmetry, asymptotes, end behavior, and invertibility.

H-5 Equation Solving and Modeling

What you'll learn about

• Solving Exponential Equations

• Solving Logarithmic Equations

• Orders of Magnitude and Logarithmic Models

• Newton's Law of Cooling

• Logarithmic Re-expression

... and why

The Richter scale, pH, and Newton's Law of Cooling are among the most important uses of logarithmic and exponential functions.

Solving Exponential Equations

Some logarithmic equations can be solved by changing to exponential form, as we saw in Example 5 of Lesson H-3. For other equations, the properties of exponents or the properties of logarithms are used. A property of both exponential and logarithmic functions that is often helpful for solving equations is that they are one-to-one functions.

One-to-One Properties

For any exponential function $f(x) = b^x$,

• If $b^u = b^v$, then $u = v$.

For any logarithmic function $f(x) = \log_b x$,

• If $\log_b u = \log_b v$, then $u = v$.

Example 1 shows how the one-to-oneness of exponential functions can be used. Examples 3 and 4 use the one-to-one property of logarithms.

> **EXAMPLE 1** Solving an Exponential Equation Algebraically
>
> Solve $20(1/2)^{x/3} = 5$.
>
> **SOLUTION**
>
> $$20\left(\frac{1}{2}\right)^{x/3} = 5$$
>
> $$\left(\frac{1}{2}\right)^{x/3} = \frac{1}{4} \qquad \text{Divide by 20.}$$
>
> $$\left(\frac{1}{2}\right)^{x/3} = \left(\frac{1}{2}\right)^2 \qquad \frac{1}{4} = \left(\frac{1}{2}\right)^2$$
>
> $$\frac{x}{3} = 2 \qquad \text{One-to-one property}$$
>
> $$x = 6 \qquad \text{Multiply by 3.} \qquad \textbf{\textit{Now try Exercise 1.}}$$

The equation in Example 2 involves a difference of two exponential functions, which makes it difficult to solve algebraically. So we start with a graphical approach.

> **EXAMPLE 2** Solving an Exponential Equation
>
> Solve $(e^x - e^{-x})/2 = 5$.
>
> **SOLUTION**
>
> **Solve Graphically** Figure H.32 shows that the graphs of $y = (e^x - e^{-x})/2$ and $y = 5$ intersect when $x \approx 2.31$.
>
> **Confirm Algebraically** The algebraic approach involves some ingenuity. If we multiply each side of the original equation by $2e^x$ and rearrange the terms, we can obtain a quadratic equation in e^x:
>
> $$\frac{e^x - e^{-x}}{2} = 5$$
>
> $$e^{2x} - e^0 = 10e^x \qquad \text{Multiply by } 2e^x.$$
>
> $$(e^x)^2 - 10(e^x) - 1 = 0 \qquad \text{Subtract } 10e^x. \qquad \textit{(continued)}$$

Intersection
X=2.3124383 Y=5

[–4, 4] by [–10, 10]

FIGURE H.32 $y = (e^x - e^{-x})/2$ and $y = 5$. (Example 2)

If we let $w = e^x$, this equation becomes $w^2 - 10w - 1 = 0$, and the quadratic formula gives

$$w = e^x = \frac{10 \pm \sqrt{104}}{2} = 5 \pm \sqrt{26}.$$

Because e^x is always positive, we reject the possibility that e^x has the negative value $5 - \sqrt{26}$. Therefore,

$$e^x = 5 + \sqrt{26}$$
$$x = \ln(5 + \sqrt{26}) \qquad \text{Convert to logarithmic form.}$$
$$x = 2.312\ldots \approx 2.31 \qquad \text{Approximate with a grapher.}$$

Now try Exercise 31.

Solving Logarithmic Equations

When logarithmic equations are solved algebraically, it is important to keep track of the domain of each expression in the equation as it is being solved. A particular algebraic method may introduce extraneous solutions, or worse yet, *lose* some valid solutions, as illustrated in Example 3.

EXAMPLE 3 Solving a Logarithmic Equation

Solve $\log x^2 = 2$.

SOLUTION

Method 1 Use the one-to-one property of logarithms.

$$\log x^2 = 2$$
$$\log x^2 = \log 10^2 \qquad y = \log 10^y$$
$$x^2 = 10^2 \qquad \text{One-to-one property}$$
$$x^2 = 100 \qquad 10^2 = 100$$
$$x = 10 \quad \text{or} \quad x = -10$$

Method 2 Change the equation from logarithmic to exponential form.

$$\log x^2 = 2$$
$$x^2 = 10^2 \qquad \text{Change to exponential form.}$$
$$x^2 = 100 \qquad 10^2 = 100$$
$$x = 10 \quad \text{or} \quad x = -10$$

Method 3 (Incorrect) Use the power rule of logarithms.

$$\log x^2 = 2$$
$$2 \log x = 2 \qquad \text{Power rule, incorrectly applied}$$
$$\log x = 1 \qquad \text{Divide by 2.}$$
$$x = 10 \qquad \text{Change to exponential form.}$$

Support Graphically

Figure H.33 shows that the graphs of $f(x) = \log x^2$ and $y = 2$ intersect when $x = -10$. From the symmetry of the graphs due to f being an even function, we can see that $x = 10$ is also a solution.

Interpret

Methods 1 and 2 are correct. Method 3 fails because the domain of $\log x^2$ is all nonzero real numbers, but the domain of $\log x$ is only the positive real numbers. The correct solution includes both 10 and -10 because both of these x-values make the original equation true.

Now try Exercise 25.

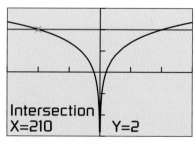

Intersection
X=210   Y=2

[-15, 15] by [-3, 3]

FIGURE H.33 Graphs of $f(x) = \log x^2$ and $y = 2$. (Example 3)

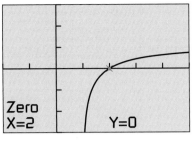

[-2, 5] by [-3, 3]

FIGURE H.34 The zero of
$f(x) = \ln(3x - 2) + \ln(x - 1) - 2\ln x$ is
$x = 2$. (Example 4)

Method 3 above violates an easily overlooked condition of the power rule $\log_b R^c = c \log_a R$, namely, that the rule holds *if R is positive*. In the expression $\log x^2$, x plays the role of R, and x can be -10, which is *not* positive. Because algebraic manipulation of a logarithmic equation can produce expressions with different domains, a graphical solution is often less prone to error.

EXAMPLE 4 Solving a Logarithmic Equation

Solve $\ln(3x - 2) + \ln(x - 1) = 2 \ln x$.

SOLUTION To use the x-intercept method, we rewrite the equation as

$$\ln(3x - 2) + \ln(x - 1) - 2 \ln x = 0,$$

and graph

$$f(x) = \ln(3x - 2) + \ln(x - 1) - 2 \ln x,$$

as shown in Figure H.34. The x-intercept is $x = 2$, which is the solution to the equation. *Now try Exercise 35.*

---

log(5.79*10^10)
                10.76267856
log(5.9*10^12)
                12.77085201

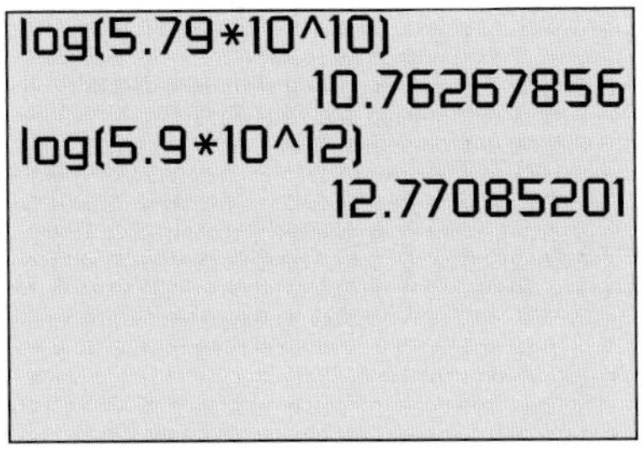

FIGURE H.35 Pluto is two orders of magnitude farther from the Sun than Mercury.

Orders of Magnitude and Logarithmic Models

When comparing quantities, their sizes sometimes span a wide range. This is why scientific notation was developed.

For instance, the planet Mercury is 57.9 billion meters from the Sun; whereas Pluto is 5900 billion meters from the Sun, roughly 100 times farther! In scientific notation, Mercury is 5.79×10^{10} m from the Sun, and Pluto is 5.9×10^{12} m from the Sun. Pluto's distance is 2 powers of ten greater than Mercury's distance. From Figure H.35, we see that the difference in the common logs of these two distances is about 2. The common logarithm of a positive quantity is its **order of magnitude**. So we say, Pluto's distance from the Sun is 2 orders of magnitude greater than Mercury's.

Orders of magnitude can be used to compare any like quantities:

- A kilometer is 3 orders of magnitude longer than a meter.
- A dollar is 2 orders of magnitude greater than a penny.
- A horse weighing 400 kg is 4 orders of magnitude heavier than a mouse weighing 40 g.
- New York City with 8 million people is 6 orders of magnitude bigger than Earmuff Junction with a population of 8.

EXPLORATION 1 Comparing Scientific Notation and Common Logarithms

1. Using a calculator compute $\log(4 \cdot 10)$, $\log(4 \cdot 10^2)$, $\log(4 \cdot 10^3)$, ..., $\log(4 \cdot 10^{10})$.

2. What is the pattern in the integer parts of these numbers?

3. What is the pattern of their decimal parts?

4. How many orders of magnitude greater is $4 \cdot 10^{10}$ than $4 \cdot 10$?

Orders of magnitude have many applications. For a sound or noise, the *bel*, mentioned in Lesson H-3, measures the order of magnitude of its intensity compared to the threshold of hearing. For instance, a sound of 3 bels or 30 dB (decibels) has a sound intensity 3 orders of magnitude above the threshold of hearing.

Orders of magnitude are also used to compare the severity of earthquakes and the acidity of chemical solutions. We now turn our attention to these two applications.

As mentioned in Exercise 52 of Lesson H-4, the *Richter scale* magnitude R of an earthquake is

$$R = \log \frac{a}{T} + B,$$

where a is the amplitude in micrometers (μm) of the vertical ground motion at the receiving station, T is the period of the associated seismic wave in seconds, and B accounts for the weakening of the seismic wave with increasing distance from the epicenter of the earthquake.

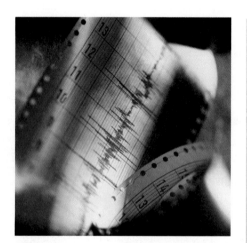

EXAMPLE 5 Comparing Earthquake Intensities

How many times more severe was the 2001 earthquake in Gujarat, India ($R_1 = 7.9$) than the 1999 earthquake in Athens, Greece ($R_2 = 5.9$)?

SOLUTION

Model

The severity of an earthquake is measured by the associated amplitude. Let a_1 be the amplitude for the Gujarat earthquake and a_2 be the amplitude for the Athens earthquake. Then

$$R_1 = \log \frac{a_1}{T} + B = 7.9$$

$$R_2 = \log \frac{a_2}{T} + B = 5.9$$

Solve Algebraically We seek the ratio of severities a_1/a_2:

$$\left(\log \frac{a_1}{T} + B \right) - \left(\log \frac{a_2}{T} + B \right) = R_1 - R_2$$

$$\log \frac{a_1}{T} - \log \frac{a_2}{T} = 7.9 - 5.9 \qquad B - B = 0$$

$$\log \frac{a_1}{a_2} = 2 \qquad \text{Quotient rule}$$

$$\frac{a_1}{a_2} = 10^2 = 100$$

Interpret

A Richter scale difference of 2 corresponds to an amplitude ratio of 2 powers of 10, or $10^2 = 100$. So the Gujarat quake was 100 times as severe as the Athens quake.

Now try Exercise 45.

In chemistry, the acidity of a water-based solution is measured by the concentration of hydrogen ions in the solution (in moles per liter). The hydrogen-ion concentration is written $[H^+]$. Because such concentrations usually involve *negative* powers of ten, *negative* orders of magnitude are used to compare acidity levels. The measure of acidity used is **pH**, the opposite of the common log of the hydrogen-ion concentration:

$$\text{pH} = -\log [H^+]$$

More acidic solutions have higher hydrogen-ion concentrations and lower pH values.

EXAMPLE 6 Comparing Chemical Acidity

Some especially sour vinegar has a pH of 2.4, and a box of Leg and Sickle baking soda has a pH of 8.4.

(a) What are their hydrogen-ion concentrations?

(b) How many times greater is the hydrogen-ion concentration of the vinegar than that of the baking soda?

(c) By how many orders of magnitude do the concentrations differ?

SOLUTION

(a) Vinegar: $-\log[H^+] = 2.4$

$\log[H^+] = -2.4$

$[H^+] = 10^{-2.4} \approx 3.98 \times 10^{-3}$ moles per liter

Baking soda: $-\log[H^+] = 8.4$

$\log[H^+] = -8.4$

$[H^+] = 10^{-8.4} \approx 3.98 \times 10^{-9}$ moles per liter

(b) $\dfrac{[H^+]\text{ of vinegar}}{[H^+]\text{ of baking soda}} = \dfrac{10^{-2.4}}{10^{-8.4}} = 10^{(-2.4)-(-8.4)} = 10^6$

(c) The hydrogen-ion concentration of the vinegar is 6 orders of magnitude greater than that of the Leg and Sickle baking soda, exactly the difference in their pH values. *Now try Exercise 47.*

Newton's Law of Cooling

An object that has been heated will cool to the temperature of the medium in which it is placed, such as the surrounding air or water. The temperature T of the object at time t can be modeled by

$$T(t) = T_m + (t_0 - T_m)e^{-kt}$$

for an appropriate value of k, where

$T_m = $ the temperature of the surrounding medium,

$T_0 = $ initial temperature of the object.

This model assumes that the surrounding medium, although taking heat from the object, essentially maintains a constant temperature. In honor of English mathematician and physicist Isaac Newton (1643–1727), this model is called **Newton's Law of Cooling**.

EXAMPLE 7 Applying Newton's Law of Cooling

A hard-boiled egg at temperature 96°C is placed in 16°C water to cool. Four minutes later the temperature of the egg is 45°C. Use Newton's Law of Cooling to determine when the egg will be 20°C.

SOLUTION

Model Because $T_0 = 96$ and $T_m = 16$, $T_0 - T_m = 80$ and

$$T(t) = T_m + (T_0 - T_m)e^{-kt} = 16 + 80e^{-kt}. \qquad \textit{(continued)}$$

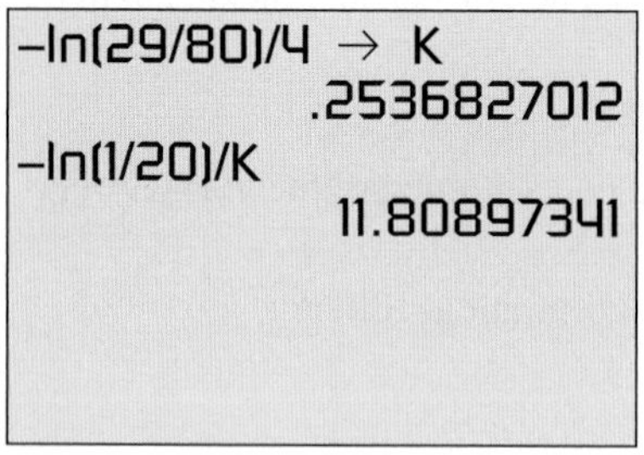

```
-ln(29/80)/4 → K
            .2536827012
-ln(1/20)/K
            11.80897341
```

FIGURE H.36 Storing and using the constant k.

To find the value of k we use the fact that $T = 45$ when $t = 4$.

$$45 = 16 + 80e^{-4k}$$

$$\frac{29}{80} = e^{-4k} \qquad \text{Subtract 16, then divide by 80.}$$

$$\ln\frac{29}{80} = -4k \qquad \text{Change to logarithmic form.}$$

$$k = -\frac{\ln(29/80)}{4} \qquad \text{Divide by } -4.$$

$$k = 0.253\ldots$$

We save this k-value because it is part of our model. (See Figure H.36.)

Solve Algebraically To find t when $T = 20°C$, we solve the equation:

$$20 = 16 + 80e^{-kt}$$

$$\frac{4}{80} = e^{-kt} \qquad \text{Subtract 16, then divide by 80.}$$

$$\ln\frac{4}{80} = -kt \qquad \text{Change to logarithmic form.}$$

$$t = -\frac{\ln(4/80)}{k} \approx 11.81 \qquad \text{See Figure 3.36.}$$

Interpret The temperature of the egg will be 20°C after about 11.81 min (11 min 49 sec). *Now try Exercise 49.*

We can rewrite Newton's Law of Cooling in the following form:

$$T(t) - T_m = (T_0 - T_m)e^{-kt}$$

We use this form of Newton's Law of Cooling when modeling temperature using data gathered from an actual experiment. Because the difference $T - T_m$ is an exponential function of time t, we can use exponential regression on $T - T_m$ versus t to obtain a model, as illustrated in Example 8.

EXAMPLE 8 Modeling with Newton's Law of Cooling

In an experiment, a temperature probe connected to a Calculator-Based-Laboratory™ device was removed from a cup of hot coffee and placed in a glass of cold water. The first two columns of Table H.23 show the resulting data for time t (in seconds since the probe was placed in the water) and temperature T (in °C). In the third column, the temperature data have been *re-expressed* by subtracting the temperature of the water, which was 4.5°C.

(a) Estimate the temperature of the coffee.

(b) Estimate the time when the temperature probe reading was 40°C.

SOLUTION

Model Figure H.37a shows a scatter plot of the re-expressed temperature data. Using exponential regression, we obtain the following model:

$$T(t) - 4.5 = 61.656 \times 0.92770^t$$

Figure H.37b shows the graph of this model with the scatter plot of the data. You can see that the curve fits the data fairly well.

Table H.23 Temperature Data from a CBL™ Experiment

Time t	Temp T	$T - T_m$
2	64.8	60.3
5	49.0	44.5
10	31.4	26.9
15	22.0	17.5
20	16.5	12.0
25	14.2	9.7
30	12.0	7.5

(continued)

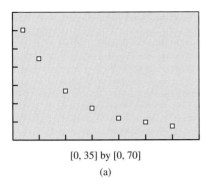

[0, 35] by [0, 70]

(a)

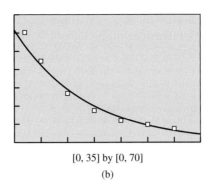

[0, 35] by [0, 70]

(b)

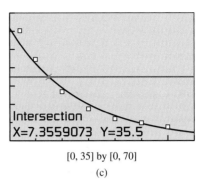

Intersection
X=7.3559073 Y=35.5

[0, 35] by [0, 70]

(c)

FIGURE H.37 Scatter plot and graphs for Example 8.

(a) Solve Algebraically From the model we see that $T_0 - T_m \approx 61.656$. So

$$T_0 \approx 61.656 + T_m = 61.656 + 4.5 \approx 66.16$$

(b) Solve Graphically Figure 3.37c shows that the graph of $T(t) - 4.5 = 61.656 \times 0.92770^t$ intersects $y = 40 - 4.5 = 35.5$ when $t \approx 7.36$.

Interpret The temperature of the coffee was roughly 66.2°C, and the probe reading was 40°C about 7.4 sec after it was placed in the water.   *Now try Exercise 51.*

Logarithmic Re-expression

In Example 7 of Lesson H.4 we learned that data pairs (x, y) that fit a power model have a linear relationship when re-expressed as $(\ln x, \ln y)$ pairs. We now illustrate that data pairs (x, y) that fit a logarithmic or exponential regression model can also be *linearized* through *logarithmic re-expression*.

Regression Models Related by Logarithmic Re-expression

- **Linear regression:** $y = ax + b$
- **Natural logarithmic regression:** $y = a + b \ln x$
- **Exponential Regression:** $y = a \cdot b^x$
- **Power regression:** $y = a \cdot x^b$

When we examine a scatter plot of data pairs (x, y), we can ask whether one of these four regression models could be the best choice. If the data plot appears to be linear, a linear regression may be the best choice. But when it is visually evident that the data plot is not linear, the best choice may be a natural logarithmic, exponential, or power regression.

Knowing the shapes of logarithmic, exponential, and power function graphs helps us choose an appropriate model. In addition, it is often helpful to re-express the (x, y) data pairs as $(\ln x, y)$, $(x, \ln y)$, or $(\ln x, \ln y)$ and create scatter plots of the re-expressed data. If any of the scatter plots appear to be linear, then we have a likely choice for an appropriate model. See page H49.

The three regression models can be justified algebraically. We give the justification for exponential regression, and leave the other two justifications as exercises.

$$v = ax + b$$
$$\ln y = ax + b$$
$$y = e^{ax+b} \qquad \text{Change to exponential form.}$$
$$y = e^{ax} \cdot e^b \qquad \text{Use the laws of exponents.}$$
$$y = e^b \cdot (e^a)^x$$
$$y = c \cdot d^x \qquad \text{Let } c = e^b \text{ and } d = e^a.$$

Example 9 illustrates how knowledge about the shapes of logarithmic, exponential, and power function graphs is used in combination with logarithmic re-expression to choose a curve of best fit.

Three Types of Logarithmic Re-expression

1. Natural Logarithmic Regression Re-expressed: $(x, y) \rightarrow (\ln x, y)$

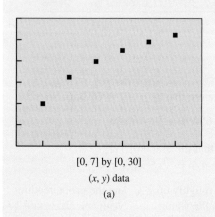

[0, 7] by [0, 30]

(x, y) data

(a)

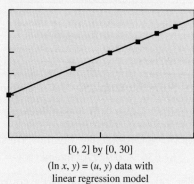

[0, 2] by [0, 30]

$(\ln x, y) = (u, y)$ data with
linear regression model
$y = au + b$

(b)

Conclusion:

$y = a \ln x + b$ is the logarithmic regression model for the (x, y) data.

2. Exponential Regression Re-expressed: $(x, y) \rightarrow (x, \ln y)$

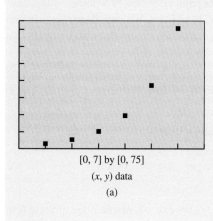

[0, 7] by [0, 75]

(x, y) data

(a)

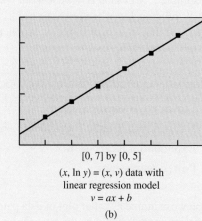

[0, 7] by [0, 5]

$(x, \ln y) = (x, v)$ data with
linear regression model
$v = ax + b$

(b)

Conclusion:

$y = c(d^x)$, where $c = e^b$ and $d = e^a$, is the exponential regression model for the (x, y) data.

3. Power Regression Re-expressed: $(x, y) \rightarrow (\ln x, \ln y)$

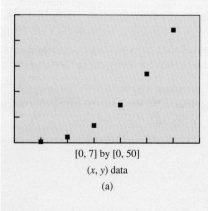

[0, 7] by [0, 50]

(x, y) data

(a)

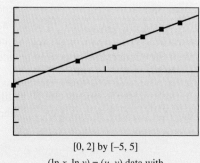

[0, 2] by [–5, 5]

$(\ln x, \ln y) = (u, v)$ data with
linear regression model
$v = au + b$

(b)

Conclusion:

$y = c(x^a)$, where $c = e^b$, is the power regression model for the (x, y) data.

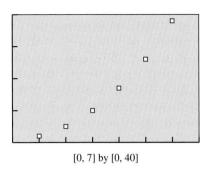

[0, 7] by [0, 40]

FIGURE H.38 A scatter plot of the original data of Example 9.

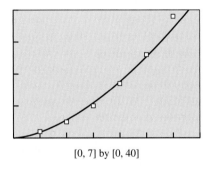

[0, 7] by [0, 40]

FIGURE H.40 A power regression model fits the data of Example 9.

EXAMPLE 9 **Selecting a Regression Model**

Decide whether these data can be best modeled by logarithmic, exponential, or power regression. Find the appropriate regression model.

x	1	2	3	4	5	6
y	2	5	10	17	26	38

SOLUTION The shape of the data plot in Figure H.38 suggests that the data could be modeled by an exponential or power function, but not a logarithmic function.

Figure H.39a shows the $(x, \ln y)$ plot, and Figure H.39b shows the $(\ln x, \ln y)$ plot. Of these two plots, the $(\ln x, \ln y)$ plot appears to be more linear, so we find the power regression model for the original data.

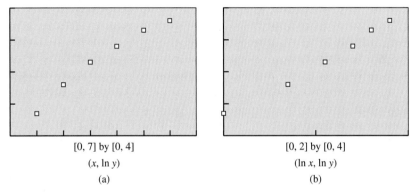

[0, 7] by [0, 4]

$(x, \ln y)$

(a)

[0, 2] by [0, 4]

$(\ln x, \ln y)$

(b)

FIGURE H.39 Two logarithmic re-expressions of the data of Example 9.

Figure H.40 shows the scatter plot of the original (x, y) data with the graph of the power regression model $y = 1.7910x^{1.6472}$ superimposed.

Now try Exercise 55.

Exercise numbers with a gray background indicate problems that the authors have designed to be solved *without a calculator*.

In Exercises 1–10, find the exact solution algebraically, and check it by substituting into the original equation.

1. $36\left(\dfrac{1}{3}\right)^{x/5} = 4$

2. $32\left(\dfrac{1}{4}\right)^{x/3} = 2$

3. $2 \cdot 5^{x/4} = 250$

4. $3 \cdot 4^{x/2} = 96$

5. $2(10^{-x/3}) = 20$

6. $3(5^{-x/4}) = 15$

7. $\log x = 4$

8. $\log_2 x = 5$

9. $\log_4 (x - 5) = -1$

10. $\log_4 (1 - x) = 1$

In Exercises 11–18, solve each equation algebraically. Obtain a numerical approximation for your solution and check it by substituting into the original equation.

11. $1.06^x = 4.1$

12. $0.98^x = 1.6$

13. $50e^{0.035x} = 200$

14. $80e^{0.045x} = 240$

15. $3 + 2e^{-x} = 6$

16. $7 - 3e^{-x} = 2$

17. $3 \ln (x - 3) + 4 = 5$

18. $3 - \log (x + 2) = 5$

In Exercises 19–24, state the domain of each function. Then match the function with its graph. (Each graph shown has a window of $[-4.7, 4.7]$ by $[-3.1, 3.1]$).

19. $f(x) = \log [x(x + 1)]$

20. $g(x) = \log x + \log (x + 1)$

21. $f(x) = \ln \dfrac{x}{x + 1}$

22. $g(x) = \ln x - \ln (x + 1)$

23. $f(x) = 2 \ln x$

24. $g(x) = \ln x^2$

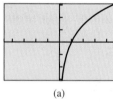
(a)

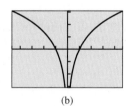
(b)

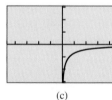
(c)

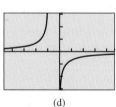
(d)

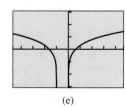
(e)

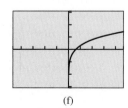
(f)

In Exercises 25–38, solve each equation by the method of your choice. Support your solution by a second method.

25. $\log x^2 = 6$

26. $\ln x^2 = 4$

27. $\log x^4 = 2$

28. $\ln x^6 = 12$

29. $\dfrac{2^x - 2^{-x}}{3} = 4$

30. $\dfrac{2^x + 2^{-x}}{2} = 3$

31. $\dfrac{e^x + e^{-x}}{2} = 4$

32. $2e^{2x} + 5e^x - 3 = 0$

33. $\dfrac{500}{1 + 25e^{0.3x}} = 200$

34. $\dfrac{400}{1 + 95e^{-0.6x}} = 150$

35. $\dfrac{1}{2} \ln (x + 3) - \ln x = 0$

36. $\log x - \dfrac{1}{2} \log (x + 4) = 1$

37. $\ln (x - 3) + \ln (x + 4) = 3 \ln 2$

38. $\log (x - 2) + \log (x + 5) = 2 \log 3$

In Exercises 39–44, determine by how many orders of magnitude the quantities differ.

39. A \$100 bill and a dime

40. A canary weighing 20 g and a hen weighing 2 kg

41. An earthquake rated 7 on the Richter scale and one rated 5.5

42. Lemon juice with pH = 2.3 and beer with pH = 4.1

43. The sound intensities of a riveter at 95 dB and ordinary conversation at 65 dB

44. The sound intensities of city traffic at 70 dB and rustling leaves at 10 dB

45. Comparing Earthquakes How many times more severe was the 1978 Mexico City earthquake ($R = 7.9$) than the 1994 Los Angeles earthquake ($R = 6.6$)?

46. Comparing Earthquakes How many times more severe was the 1995 Kobe, Japan, earthquake ($R = 7.2$) than the 1994 Los Angeles earthquake ($R = 6.6$)?

47. Chemical Acidity The pH of carbonated water is 3.9 and the pH of household ammonia is 11.9.

(a) What are their hydrogen-ion concentrations?

(b) How many times greater is the hydrogen-ion concentration of carbonated water than that of ammonia?

(c) By how many orders of magnitude do the concentrations differ?

48. Chemical Acidity Stomach acid has a pH of about 2.0, and blood has a pH of 7.4.

(a) What are their hydrogen-ion concentrations?

(b) How many times greater is the hydrogen-ion concentration of stomach acid than that of blood?

(c) By how many orders of magnitude do the concentrations differ?

49. Newton's Law of Cooling A cup of coffee has cooled from 92°C to 50°C after 12 min in a room at 22°C. How long will the cup take to cool to 30°C?

50. Newton's Law of Cooling A cake is removed from an oven at 350°F and cools to 120°F after 20 min in a room at 65°F. How long will the cake take to cool to 90°F?

51. Newton's Law of Cooling Experiment A thermometer is removed from a cup of coffee and placed in water with a temperature (T_m) of 10°C. The data in Table H.24 were collected over the next 30 sec.

Table H.24 Experimental Data

Time t	Temp T	$T - T_m$
2	80.47	70.47
5	69.39	59.39
10	49.66	39.66
15	35.26	25.26
20	28.15	18.15
25	23.56	13.56
30	20.62	10.62

(a) Draw a scatter plot of the data $T - T_m$.

(b) Find an exponential regression equation for the $T - T_m$ data. Superimpose its graph on the scatter plot.

(c) Estimate the thermometer reading when it was removed from the coffee.

52. Newton's Law of Cooling Experiment A thermometer was removed from a cup of hot chocolate and placed in a saline solution with temperature $T_m = 0$°C. The data in Table H.25 were collected over the next 30 sec.

(a) Draw a scatter plot of the data $T - T_m$.

(b) Find an exponential regression equation for the $T - T_m$ data. Superimpose its graph on the scatter plot.

(c) Estimate the thermometer reading when it was removed from the hot chocolate.

Table H.25 Experimental Data

Time t	Temp T	$T - T_m$
2	74.68	74.68
5	61.99	61.99
10	34.89	34.89
15	21.95	21.95
20	15.36	15.36
25	11.89	11.89
30	10.02	10.02

53. Penicillin Use The use of penicillin became so widespread in the 1980s in Hungary that it became practically useless against common sinus and ear infections. Now the use of more effective antibiotics has caused a decline in penicillin resistance. The bar graph shows the use of penicillin in Hungary for selected years.

(a) From the bar graph we read the data pairs to be approximately $(1, 11)$, $(8, 6)$, $(15, 4.8)$, $(16, 4)$, and $(17, 2.5)$, using $t = 1$ for 1976, $t = 8$ for 1983, and so on. Complete a scatter plot for these data.

(b) **Writing to Learn** Discuss whether the bar graph shown or the scatter plot that you completed best represents the data and why.

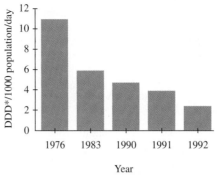

Nationwide Consumption of Penicillin

*Defined Daily Dose
Source: Science, vol. 264, April 15, 1994, American Association for the Advancement of Science.

54. Writing to Learn Which regression model would you use for the data in Exercise 53? Discuss various options, and explain why you chose the model you did. Support your writing with tables and graphs as needed.

Writing to Learn In Exercises 55–58, tables of (x, y) data pairs are given. Determine whether a linear, logarithmic, exponential, or power regression equation is the best model for the data. Explain your choice. Support your writing with tables and graphs as needed.

55.

x	1	2	3	4
y	3	4.4	5.2	5.8

56.

x	1	2	3	4
y	6	18	54	162

57.

x	1	2	3	4
y	3	6	12	24

58.

x	1	2	3	4
y	5	7	9	11

Explorations

In Exercises 59 and 60, use the data in Table H.26. Determine whether a linear, logarithmic, exponential, power, or logistic regression equation is the best model for the data. Explain your choice. Support your writing with tables and graphs as needed.

Table H.26 Populations of Two U.S. States (in thousands)

Year	Alaska	Hawaii
1900	63.6	154
1910	64.4	192
1920	55.0	256
1930	59.2	368
1940	72.5	423
1950	128.6	500
1960	226.2	633
1970	302.6	770
1980	401.9	965
1990	550.0	1108
2000	626.9	1212

Source: U.S. Census Bureau.

59. Writing to Learn Modeling Population Which regression equation is the best model for Alaska's population?

60. Writing to Learn Modeling Population Which regression equation is the best model for Hawaii's population?

61. Group Activity Normal Distribution The function

$$f(x) = k \cdot e^{-cx^2},$$

where c and k are positive constants, is a bell-shaped curve that is useful in probability and statistics.

(a) Graph f for $c = 1$ and $k = 0.1, 0.5, 1, 2, 10$. Explain the effect of changing k.

(b) Graph f for $k = 1$ and $c = 0.1, 0.5, 1, 2, 10$. Explain the effect of changing c.

Extending the Ideas

62. Writing to Learn Prove if $u/v = 10^n$ for $u > 0$ and $v > 0$, then $\log u - \log v = n$. Explain how this result relates to powers of ten and orders of magnitude.

63. Potential Energy The potential energy E (the energy stored for use at a later time) between two ions in a certain molecular structure is modeled by the function

$$E = -\frac{5.6}{r} + 10e^{-r/3}$$

where r is the distance separating the nuclei.

(a) **Writing to Learn** Graph this function in the window $[-10, 10]$ by $[-10, 30]$, and explain which portion of the graph does not represent this potential energy situation.

(b) Identify a viewing window that shows that portion of the graph (with $r \le 10$) which represents this situation, and find the maximum value for E.

64. In Example 8, the Newton's Law of Cooling model was

$$T(t) - T_m = (T_0 - T_m)e^{-kt} = 61.656 \times 0.92770^t.$$

Determine the value of k.

65. Justify the conclusion made about natural logarithmic regression on page H48.

66. Justify the conclusion made about power regression on page H48.

In Exercises 67–72, solve the equation or inequality.

67. $e^x + x = 5$

68. $e^{2x} - 8x + 1 = 0$

69. $e^x < 5 + \ln x$

70. $\ln |x| - e^{2x} \ge 3$

71. $2 \log x - 4 \log 3 > 0$

72. $2 \log (x + 1) - 2 \log 6 < 0$

H-6 Trigonometry Extended: The Circular Functions

What you'll learn about

- Trigonometric Functions of Any Angle
- Trigonometric Functions of Real Numbers
- Periodic Functions
- The 16-Point Unit Circle

... and why

Extending trigonometric functions beyond triangle ratios opens up a new world of applications.

Trigonometric Functions of Any Angle

We now extend the definitions of the six basic trigonometric functions beyond triangles so that we do not have to restrict our attention to acute angles, or even to positive angles.

In geometry we think of an angle as a union of two rays with a common vertex. Trigonometry takes a more dynamic view by thinking of an angle in terms of a rotating ray. The beginning position of the ray, the **initial side**, is rotated about its endpoint, called the **vertex**. The final position is called the **terminal side**. The **measure of an angle** is a number that describes the amount of rotation from the initial side to the terminal side of the angle. **Positive angles** are generated by counterclockwise rotations and **negative angles** are generated by clockwise rotations. Figure H.41 shows an angle of measure α, where α is a positive number.

Terminal side

α

Initial side

FIGURE H.41 An angle with positive measure α.

To bring the power of coordinate geometry into the picture (literally), we usually place an angle in **standard position** in the Cartesian plane, with the vertex of the angle at the origin and its initial side lying along the positive x-axis. Figure H.42 shows two angles in standard position, one with positive measure α and the other with negative measure β.

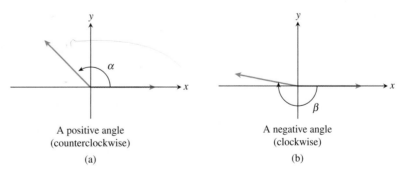

A positive angle
(counterclockwise)

(a)

A negative angle
(clockwise)

(b)

FIGURE H.42 Two angles in standard position. In (a) the counterclockwise rotation generates an angle with positive measure α. In (b) the clockwise rotation generates an angle with negative measure β.

Two angles in this expanded angle-measurement system can have the same initial side and the same terminal side, yet have different measures. We call such angles **coterminal angles**. (See Figure H.43 on the next page.) For example, angles of $90°$, $450°$, and $-270°$ are all coterminal, as are angles of π radians, 3π radians, and -99π radians. In fact, angles are coterminal whenever they differ by an integer multiple of 360 degrees or by an integer multiple of 2π radians.

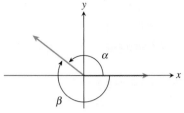

Positive and negative
coterminal angles

(a)

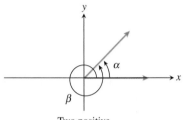

Two positive
coterminal angles

(b)

FIGURE H.43 Coterminal angles. In (a) a positive angle and a negative angle are coterminal, while in (b) both coterminal angles are positive.

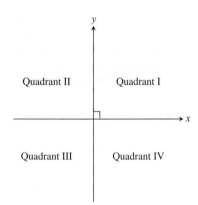

FIGURE H.45 The four quadrants of the Cartesian plane. Both *x* and *y* are positive in QI (Quadrant I). Quadrants, like Super Bowls, are invariably designated by Roman numerals.

EXAMPLE 1 Finding Coterminal Angles

Find and draw a positive angle and a negative angle that are coterminal with the given angle.

(a) 30°   **(b)** −150°   **(c)** $\dfrac{2\pi}{3}$ radians

SOLUTION There are infinitely many possible solutions; we will show two for each angle.

(a) Add 360°:   30° + 360° = 390°

Subtract 360°:   30° − 360° = −330°

Figure H.44 shows these two angles, which are coterminal with the 30° angle.

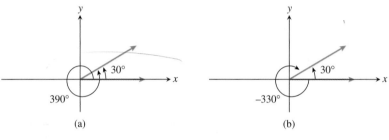

FIGURE H.44 Two angles coterminal with 30°. (Example 1a)

(b) Add 360°:   −150° + 360° = 210°

Subtract 720°:   −150° − 720° = −870°

We leave it to you to draw the coterminal angles.

(c) Add 2π: $\dfrac{2\pi}{3} + 2\pi = \dfrac{2\pi}{3} + \dfrac{6\pi}{3} = \dfrac{8\pi}{3}$

Subtract 2π: $\dfrac{2\pi}{3} - 2\pi = \dfrac{2\pi}{3} - \dfrac{6\pi}{3} = -\dfrac{4\pi}{3}$

Again, we leave it to you to draw the coterminal angles.

Now try Exercise 1.

Extending the definitions of the six basic trigonometric functions so that they can apply to any angle is surprisingly easy, but first you need to see how our current definitions relate to the (x, y) coordinates in the Cartesian plane. We start in the first quadrant (see Figure H.45), where the angles are all acute. Work through Exploration 1 before moving on.

EXPLORATION 1 Investigating First Quadrant Trigonometry

Let $P(x, y)$ be any point in the first quadrant (QI), and let r be the distance from P to the origin. (See Figure H.46.)

1. Use the acute angle definition of the sine function (sin θ = length of opposite side/length of hypotenuse) to prove that sin $\theta = y/r$.

2. Express cos θ in terms of x and r.

3. Express tan θ in terms of x and y.

4. Express the remaining three basic trigonometric functions in terms of x, y, and r.

If you have successfully completed Exploration 1, you should have no trouble verifying the solution to Example 2, which we show without the details.

EXAMPLE 2 Evaluating Trig Functions Determined by a Point in QI

Let θ be the acute angle in standard position whose terminal side contains the point $(5, 3)$. Find the six trigonometric functions of θ.

SOLUTION The distance from $(5, 3)$ to the origin is $\sqrt{34}$.

So $\sin \theta = \dfrac{3}{\sqrt{34}}$ or $\dfrac{3\sqrt{34}}{34}$ $\qquad \csc \theta = \dfrac{\sqrt{34}}{3}$

$\cos \theta = \dfrac{5}{\sqrt{34}}$ or $\dfrac{5\sqrt{34}}{34}$ $\qquad \sec \theta = \dfrac{\sqrt{34}}{5}$

$\tan \theta = \dfrac{3}{5}$ $\qquad \cot \theta = \dfrac{5}{3}$ $\qquad$ *Now try Exercise 5.*

Now we have an easy way to extend the trigonometric functions to any angle: Use the same definitions in terms of x, y, and r—*whether or not x and y are positive.* Compare Example 3 to Example 2.

EXAMPLE 3 Evaluating Trig Functions Determined by a Point Not in QI

Let θ be any angle in standard position whose terminal side contains the point $(-5, 3)$. Find the six trigonometric functions of θ.

SOLUTION The distance from $(-5, 3)$ to the origin is $\sqrt{34}$.

So $\sin \theta = \dfrac{3}{\sqrt{34}}$ or $\dfrac{3\sqrt{34}}{34}$ $\qquad \csc \theta = \dfrac{\sqrt{34}}{3}$

$\cos \theta = \dfrac{-5}{\sqrt{34}}$ or $\dfrac{-5\sqrt{34}}{34}$ $\qquad \sec \theta = \dfrac{\sqrt{34}}{-5}$

$\tan \theta = \dfrac{3}{-5} = -0.6$ $\qquad \cot \theta = \dfrac{-5}{3}$ $\qquad$ *Now try Exercise 11.*

Notice in Example 3 that θ is *any* angle in standard position whose terminal side contains the point $(-5, 3)$. There are infinitely many coterminal angles that could play the role of θ, some of them positive and some of them negative. The values of the six trigonometric functions would be the same for all of them.

We are now ready to state the formal definition.

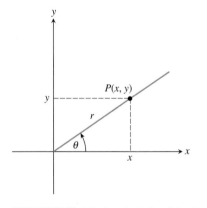

FIGURE H.46 A point $P(x, y)$ in Quadrant I determines an acute angle θ. The number r denotes the distance from P to the origin. (Exploration 1)

DEFINITION Trigonometric Functions of any Angle

Let θ be any angle in standard position and let $P(x, y)$ be any point on the terminal side of the angle (except the origin). Let r denote the distance from $P(x, y)$ to the origin, i.e., let $r = \sqrt{x^2 + y^2}$. (See Figure H.47.) Then

$$\sin \theta = \frac{y}{r} \qquad\qquad \csc \theta = \frac{r}{y} \, (y \neq 0)$$

$$\cos \theta = \frac{x}{r} \qquad\qquad \sec \theta = \frac{r}{x} \, (x \neq 0)$$

$$\tan \theta = \frac{y}{x} \, (x \neq 0) \qquad \cot \theta = \frac{x}{y} \, (y \neq 0)$$

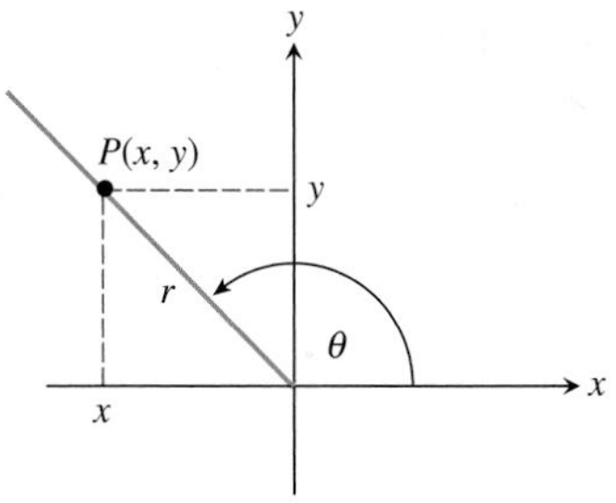

FIGURE H.47 Defining the six trig functions of θ.

Examples 2 and 3 both began with a point $P(x, y)$ rather than an angle θ. Indeed, the point gave us so much information about the trigonometric ratios that we were able to compute them all without ever finding θ. So what do we do if we start with an angle θ in standard position and we want to evaluate the trigonometric functions? We try to find a point (x, y) on its terminal side. We illustrate this process with Example 4.

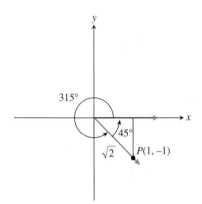

FIGURE H.48 An angle of 315° in standard position determines a 45°–45°–90° *reference triangle.* (Example 4)

EXAMPLE 4 Evaluating the Trig Functions of 315°

Find the six trigonometric functions of 315°.

SOLUTION First we draw an angle of 315° in standard position. Without declaring a scale, pick a point P on the terminal side and connect it to the x-axis with a perpendicular segment. Notice that the triangle formed (called a **reference triangle**) is a 45°–45°–90° triangle. If we arbitrarily choose the horizontal and vertical sides of the reference triangle to be of length 1, then P has coordinates $(1, -1)$. (See Figure H.48.)

We can now use the definitions with $x = 1$, $y = -1$, and $r = \sqrt{2}$.

$$\sin 315° = \frac{-1}{\sqrt{2}} \quad \text{or} \quad -\frac{\sqrt{2}}{2} \qquad \csc 315° = \frac{\sqrt{2}}{-1} = -\sqrt{2}$$

$$\cos 315° = \frac{1}{\sqrt{2}} \quad \text{or} \quad \frac{\sqrt{2}}{2} \qquad \sec 315° = \frac{\sqrt{2}}{1} = \sqrt{2}$$

$$\tan 315° = \frac{-1}{1} = -1 \qquad \cot 315° = \frac{1}{-1} = -1$$

Now try Exercise 25.

The happy fact that the reference triangle in Example 4 was a 45°–45°–90° triangle enabled us to label a point P on the terminal side of the 315° angle and then to find the trigonometric function values. We would also be able to find P if the given angle were to produce a 30°–60°–90° reference triangle.

Evaluating Trig Functions of a Nonquadrantal Angle θ

1. Draw the angle θ in standard position, being careful to place the terminal side in the correct quadrant.

2. Without declaring a scale on either axis, label a point P (other than the origin) on the terminal side of θ.

3. Draw a perpendicular segment from P to the x-axis, determining the *reference triangle.* If this triangle is one of the triangles whose ratios you know, label the sides accordingly. If it is not, then you will need to use your calculator.

4. Use the sides of the triangle to determine the coordinates of point P, making them positive or negative according to the signs of x and y in that particular quadrant.

5. Use the coordinates of point P and the definitions to determine the six trig functions.

EXAMPLE 5 Evaluating More Trig Functions

Find the following without a calculator:

(a) $\sin (-210°)$

(b) $\tan (5\pi/3)$

(c) $\sec (-3\pi/4)$

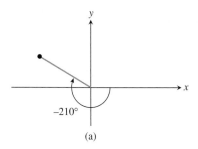

(a)

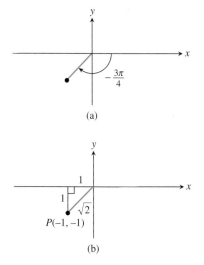

(b)

FIGURE H.49 (Example 5a)

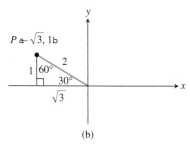

(a)

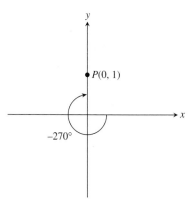

(b)

FIGURE H.51 (Example 5c)

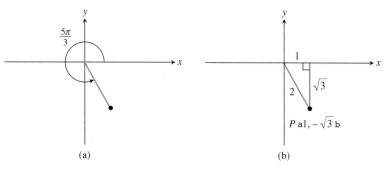

(a)   (b)

FIGURE H.50 (Example 5b)

SOLUTION

(a) An angle of $-210°$ in standard position determines a $30°$–$60°$–$90°$ reference triangle in the second quadrant (Figure H.49). We label the sides accordingly, then use the lengths of the sides to determine the point $P(-\sqrt{3}, 1)$. (Note that the x-coordinate is negative in the second quadrant.) The hypotenuse is $r = 2$. Therefore $\sin(-210°) = y/r = 1/2$.

(b) An angle of $5\pi/3$ radians in standard position determines a $30°$–$60°$–$90°$ reference triangle in the fourth quadrant (Figure H.50). We label the sides accordingly, then use the lengths of the sides to determine the point $P(1, -\sqrt{3})$. (Note that the y-coordinate is negative in the fourth quadrant.) The hypotenuse is $r = 2$. Therefore $\tan(5\pi/3) = y/x = -\sqrt{3}/1 = -\sqrt{3}$.

(c) An angle of $-3\pi/4$ radians in standard position determines a $45°$–$45°$–$90°$ reference triangle in the third quadrant. (See Figure H.51.) We label the sides accordingly, then use the lengths of the sides to determine the point $P(-1, -1)$. (Note that both coordinates are negative in the third quadrant.) The hypotenuse is $r = \sqrt{2}$. Therefore $\sec(-3\pi/4) = r/x = \sqrt{2}/-1 = -\sqrt{2}$.

Now try Exercise 29.

Angles whose terminal sides lie along one of the coordinate axes are called **quadrantal angles**, and although they do not produce reference triangles at all, it is easy to pick a point P along one of the axes.

EXAMPLE 6 **Evaluating Trig Functions of Quadrantal Angles**

Find each of the following, if it exists. If the value is undefined, write "undefined."

(a) $\sin(-270°)$

(b) $\tan 3\pi$

(c) $\sec \dfrac{11\pi}{2}$

SOLUTION

(a) In standard position, the terminal side of an angle of $-270°$ lies along the positive y-axis (Figure H.52). A convenient point P along the positive y-axis is the point for which $r = 1$, namely $(0, 1)$. Therefore

$$\sin(-270°) = \frac{y}{r} = \frac{1}{1} = 1.$$

Why Not Use a Calculator?

You might wonder why we would go through this procedure to produce values that could be found so easily with a calculator. The answer is to understand how trigonometry *works* in the coordinate plane. Ironically, technology has made these computational exercises more important than ever, since calculators have eliminated the need for the repetitive evaluations that once gave students their initial insights into the basic trig functions.

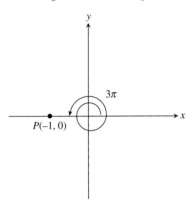

FIGURE H.53 (Example 6b)

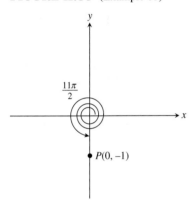

FIGURE H.54 (Example 6c)

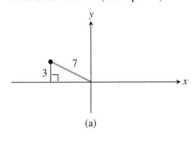

(a)

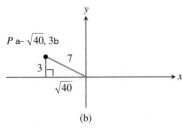

(b)

FIGURE H.55 (Example 7a)

(b) In standard position, the terminal side of an angle of 3π lies along the negative x-axis. (See Figure H.53.) A convenient point P along the negative x-axis is the point for which $r = 1$, namely $(-1, 0)$. Therefore

$$\tan 3\pi = \frac{y}{x} = \frac{0}{-1} = 0.$$

(c) In standard position, the terminal side of an angle of $11\pi/2$ lies along the negative y-axis. (See Figure H.54.) A convenient point P along the negative y-axis is the point for which $r = 1$, namely $(0, -1)$. Therefore

$$\sec \frac{11\pi}{2} = \frac{r}{x} = \frac{1}{0}.$$

Now try Exercise 41.

Another good exercise is to use information from one trigonometric ratio to produce the other five. We do not need to know the angle θ, although we do need a hint as to the location of its terminal side so that we can sketch a reference triangle in the correct quadrant (or place a quadrantal angle on the correct side of the origin). Example 7 illustrates how this is done.

EXAMPLE 7 Using One Trig Ratio to Find the Others

Find $\cos \theta$ and $\tan \theta$ by using the given information to construct a reference triangle.

(a) $\sin \theta = \dfrac{3}{7}$ and $\tan \theta < 0$

(b) $\sec \theta = 3$ and $\sin \theta > 0$

(c) $\cot \theta$ is undefined and $\sec \theta$ is negative

SOLUTION

(a) Since $\sin \theta$ is positive, the terminal side is either in QI or in QII. The added fact that $\tan \theta$ is negative means that the terminal side is in QII. We draw a reference triangle in QII with $r = 7$ and $y = 3$ (Figure H.55); then we use the Pythagorean
Theorem to find that $x = -1\sqrt{7^2 - 3^2} = -\sqrt{40}$. (Note that x is negative in QII.)
We then use the definitions to get

$$\cos \theta = \frac{-\sqrt{40}}{7} \quad \text{and} \quad \tan \theta = \frac{3}{-\sqrt{40}} \quad \text{or} \quad \frac{-3\sqrt{10}}{20}.$$

(b) Since $\sec \theta$ is positive, the terminal side is either in QI or in QIV. The added fact that $\sin \theta$ is positive means that the terminal side is in QI. We draw a reference triangle in QI with $r = 3$ and $x = 1$ (Figure H.56 on the next page); then we use the Pythagorean Theorem to find that $y = \sqrt{3^2 - 1^2} = \sqrt{8}$. (Note that y is positive in QI.)

We then use the definitions to get

$$\cos \theta = \frac{1}{3} \quad \text{and} \quad \tan \theta = \frac{\sqrt{8}}{1}.$$

(We could also have found $\cos \theta$ directly as the reciprocal of $\sec \theta$.)

(c) Since $\cot \theta$ is undefined, we conclude that $y = 0$ and that θ is a quadrantal angle on the x-axis. The added fact that $\sec \theta$ is negative means that the terminal side is along the negative x-axis. We choose the point $(-1, 0)$ on the terminal side and use the definitions to get

$$\cos \theta = -1 \quad \text{and} \quad \tan \theta = \frac{0}{-1} = 0.$$

Now try Exercise 43.

Why Not Degrees?

One could actually develop a consistent theory of trigonometric functions based on a rescaled *x*-axis with "degrees." For example, your graphing calculator will probably produce reasonable-looking graphs in degree mode. Calculus, however, uses rules that *depend* on radian measure for all trigonometric functions, so it is prudent for precalculus students to become accustomed to that now.

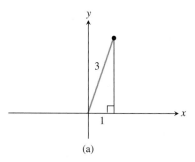

(a)

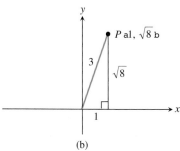

(b)

FIGURE H.56 (Example 7b)

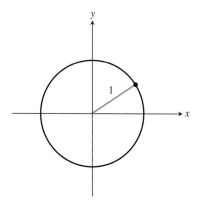

FIGURE H.57 The unit circle.

Trigonometric Functions of Real Numbers

Now that we have extended the six basic trigonometric functions to apply to any angle, we are ready to appreciate them as functions of real numbers and to study their behavior. First, we must agree to measure θ in radian mode so that the real number units of the input will match the real number units of the output.

When considering the trigonometric functions as functions of real numbers, the angles will be measured in radians.

DEFINITION Unit Circle

The unit circle is a circle of radius 1 centered at the origin (Figure H.57).

The unit circle provides an ideal connection between triangle trigonometry and the trigonometric functions. Because arc length along the unit circle corresponds exactly to radian measure, we can use the circle itself as a sort of "number line" for the input values of our functions. This involves the **wrapping function**, which associates points on the number line with points on the circle.

Figure H.58 shows how the wrapping function works. The real line is placed tangent to the unit circle at the point $(1, 0)$, the point from which we measure angles in standard position. When the line is wrapped around the unit circle in both the positive (counterclockwise) and negative (clockwise) directions, each point *t* on the real line will fall on a point of the circle that lies on the terminal side of an angle of *t* radians in standard position. Using the coordinates (x, y) of this point, we can find the six trigonometric ratios for the angle *t* just as we did in Example 7—except even more easily, since $r = 1$.

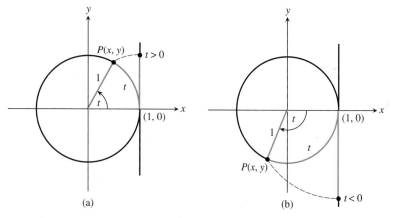

(a) (b)

FIGURE H.58 How the number line is wrapped onto the unit circle. Note that each number *t* (positive or negative) is "wrapped" to a point *P* that lies on the terminal side of an angle of *t* radians in standard position.

DEFINITION Trigonometric Functions of Real Numbers

Let *t* be any real number, and let $P(x, y)$ be the point corresponding to *t* when the number line is wrapped onto the unit circle as described above. Then

$$\sin t = y \qquad\qquad \csc t = \frac{1}{y} \,(y \neq 0)$$

$$\cos t = x \qquad\qquad \sec t = \frac{1}{x} \,(x \neq 0)$$

$$\tan t = \frac{y}{x} \,(x \neq 0) \qquad \cot t = \frac{x}{y} \,(y \neq 0)$$

Therefore, the number *t* on the number line always wraps onto the point $(\cos t, \sin t)$ on the unit circle (Figure H.59).

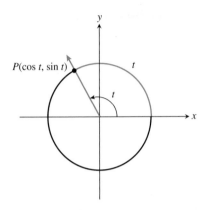

FIGURE H.59 The real number t always wraps onto the point $(\cos t, \sin t)$ on the unit circle.

Although it is still helpful to draw reference triangles inside the unit circle to see the ratios geometrically, this latest round of definitions does not invoke triangles at all. The real number t determines a point on the unit circle, and the (x, y) coordinates of the point determine the six trigonometric ratios. For this reason, the trigonometric functions when applied to real numbers are usually called the **circular functions**.

EXPLORATION 2   Exploring the Unit Circle

This works well as a group exploration. Get together in groups of two or three and explain to each other why these statements are true. Base your explanations on the unit circle (Figure H.59). Remember that $-t$ wraps the same distance as t, but in the opposite direction.

1. For any t, the value of $\cos t$ lies between -1 and 1 inclusive.

2. For any t, the value of $\sin t$ lies between -1 and 1 inclusive.

3. The values of $\cos t$ and $\cos (-t)$ are always equal to each other. (Recall that this is the check for an *even* function.)

4. The values of $\sin t$ and $\sin (-t)$ are always opposites of each other. (Recall that this is the check for an *odd* function.)

5. The values of $\sin t$ and $\sin (t + 2\pi)$ are always equal to each other. In fact, that is true of all six trig functions on their domains, and for the same reason.

6. The values of $\sin t$ and $\sin (t + \pi)$ are always opposites of each other. The same is true of $\cos t$ and $\cos (t + \pi)$.

7. The values of $\tan t$ and $\tan (t + \pi)$ are always equal to each other (unless they are both undefined).

8. The sum $(\cos t)^2 + (\sin t)^2$ always equals 1.

9. (Challenge) Can you discover a similar relationship that is not mentioned in our list of eight? There are some to be found.

Periodic Functions

Statements 5 and 7 in Exploration 2 reveal an important property of the circular functions that we need to define for future reference.

DEFINITION Periodic Function

A function $y = f(t)$ is **periodic** if there is a positive number c such that $f(t + c) = f(t)$ for all values of t in the domain of f. The smallest such number c is called the **period** of the function.

Exploration 2 suggests that the sine and cosine functions have period 2π and that the tangent function has period π. We use this periodicity later to model predictably repetitive behavior in the real world, but meanwhile we can also use it to solve little noncalculator training problems like in some of the previous examples in this section.

EXAMPLE 8   Using Periodicity

Find each of the following numbers without a calculator.

(a) $\sin \left(\dfrac{57{,}801\pi}{2} \right)$ (b) $\cos (288.45\pi) - \cos (280.45\pi)$

(c) $\tan \left(\dfrac{\pi}{4} - 99{,}999\pi \right)$

(a) $\sin\left(\dfrac{57{,}801\pi}{2}\right) = \sin\left(\dfrac{\pi}{2} + \dfrac{57{,}800\pi}{2}\right) = \sin\left(\dfrac{\pi}{2} + 28{,}900\pi\right)$

$$= \sin\left(\dfrac{\pi}{2}\right) = 1$$

Notice that $28{,}900\pi$ is just a large multiple of 2π, so $\pi/2$ and $((\pi/2) + 28{,}900\pi)$ wrap to the same point on the unit circle, namely $(0, 1)$.

(b) $\cos\,(288.45\pi) - \cos\,(280.45\pi) =$

$\cos\,(280.45\pi + 8\pi) - \cos\,(280.45\pi) = 0$

Notice that 280.45π and $(280.45\pi + 8\pi)$ wrap to the same point on the unit circle, so the cosine of one is the same as the cosine of the other.

(c) Since the period of the tangent function is π rather than 2π, $99{,}999\pi$ is a large multiple of the period of the tangent function. Therefore,

$$\tan\left(\dfrac{\pi}{4} - 99{,}999\pi\right) = \tan\left(\dfrac{\pi}{4}\right) = 1.$$

Now try Exercise 49.

We take a closer look at the properties of the six circular functions in the next two sections.

The 16-Point Unit Circle

At this point you should be able to use reference triangles and quadrantal angles to evaluate trigonometric functions for all integer multiples of 30° or 45° (equivalently, $\pi/6$ radians or $\pi/4$ radians). All of these special values wrap to the 16 special points shown on the unit circle below. Study this diagram until you are confident that you can find the coordinates of these points easily, but avoid using it as a reference when doing problems.

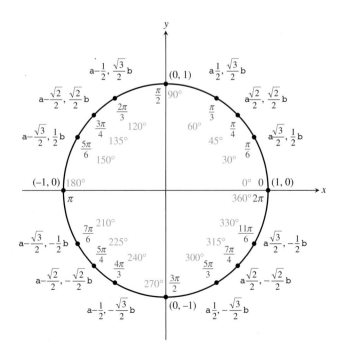

LESSON H-6 EXERCISES

Exercise numbers with a gray background indicate problems that the authors have designed to be solved *without a calculator*.

In Exercises 1 and 2, identify the one angle that is not coterminal with all the others.

1. 150°, 510°, −210°, 450°, 870°

2. $\dfrac{5\pi}{3}$, $-\dfrac{5\pi}{3}$, $\dfrac{11\pi}{3}$, $-\dfrac{7\pi}{3}$, $\dfrac{365\pi}{3}$

In Exercises 3–6, evaluate the six trigonometric functions of the angle θ.

3.
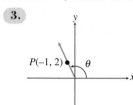

4.
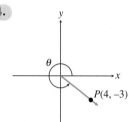

5.
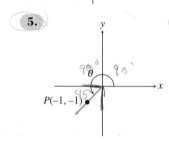

6.
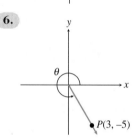

In Exercises 7–12, point P is on the terminal side of angle θ. Evaluate the six trigonometric functions for θ. If the function is undefined, write "undefined."

7. $P(3, 4)$ **8.** $P(-4, -6)$

9. $P(0, 5)$ **10.** $P(-3, 0)$

11. $P(5, -2)$ **12.** $P(22, -22)$

In Exercises 13–16, state the sign (+ or −) of **(a)** sin t, **(b)** cos t, and **(c)** tan t for values of t in the interval given.

13. $\left(0, \dfrac{\pi}{2}\right)$ **14.** $\left(\dfrac{\pi}{2}, \pi\right)$

15. $\left(\pi, \dfrac{3\pi}{2}\right)$ **16.** $\left(\dfrac{3\pi}{2}, 2\pi\right)$

In Exercises 17–20, determine the sign (+ or −) of the given value without the use of a calculator.

17. cos 143°   **18.** tan 192°

19. $\cos \dfrac{7\pi}{8}$ **20.** $\tan \dfrac{4\pi}{5}$

In Exercises 21–24, choose the point on the terminal side of θ.

21. $\theta = 45°$

   (a) $(2, 2)$ **(b)** $(1, \sqrt{3})$ **(c)** $(\sqrt{3}, 1)$

22. $\theta = \dfrac{2\pi}{3}$

   (a) $(-1, 1)$ **(b)** $(-1, \sqrt{3})$ **(c)** $(-\sqrt{3}, 1)$

23. $\theta = \dfrac{7\pi}{6}$

   (a) $(-\sqrt{3}, -1)$ **(b)** $(-1, \sqrt{3})$ **(c)** $(-\sqrt{3}, 1)$

24. $\theta = -60°$

   (a) $(-1, -1)$ **(b)** $(1, -\sqrt{3})$ **(c)** $(-\sqrt{3}, 1)$

In Exercises 25–36, evaluate without using a calculator by using ratios in a reference triangle.

25. cos 120°   **26.** tan 300°

27. $\sec \dfrac{\pi}{3}$ **28.** $\csc \dfrac{3\pi}{4}$

29. $\sin \dfrac{13\pi}{6}$ **30.** $\cos \dfrac{7\pi}{3}$

31. $\tan -\dfrac{15\pi}{4}$ **32.** $\cot \dfrac{13\pi}{4}$

33. $\cos \dfrac{23\pi}{6}$ **34.** $\cos \dfrac{17\pi}{4}$

35. $\sin \dfrac{11\pi}{3}$ **36.** $\cot \dfrac{19\pi}{6}$

In Exercises 37–42, find **(a)** sin θ, **(b)** cos θ, and **(c)** tan θ for the given quadrantal angle. If the value is undefined, write "undefined."

37. −450°   **38.** −270°

39. 7π **40.** $\dfrac{11\pi}{2}$

41. $-\dfrac{7\pi}{2}$ **42.** -4π

In Exercises 43–48, evaluate without using a calculator.

43. Find sin θ and tan θ if cos $\theta = \dfrac{2}{3}$ and cot $\theta > 0$.

44. Find cos θ and cot θ if sin $\theta = \dfrac{1}{4}$ and tan $\theta < 0$.

45. Find tan θ and sec θ if sin $\theta = -\dfrac{2}{5}$ and cos $\theta > 0$.

46. Find sin θ and cos θ if cot $\theta = \dfrac{3}{7}$ and sec $\theta < 0$.

47. Find sec θ and csc θ if cot $\theta = -\dfrac{4}{3}$ and cos $\theta < 0$.

48. Find csc θ and cot θ if tan $\theta = -\dfrac{4}{3}$ and sin $\theta > 0$.

In Exercises 49–52, evaluate by using the period of the function.

49. $\sin\left(\dfrac{\pi}{6} + 49{,}000\pi\right)$

50. $\tan\left(1{,}234{,}567\pi\right) - \tan\left(7{,}654{,}321\pi\right)$

51. $\cos\left(\dfrac{5{,}555{,}555\pi}{2}\right)$

52. $\tan\left(\dfrac{3\pi - 70{,}000\pi}{2}\right)$

53. Group Activity Use a calculator to evaluate the expressions in Exercises 49–52. Does your calculator give the correct answers? Many calculators miss all four. Give a brief explanation of what probably goes wrong.

54. Writing to Learn Give a convincing argument that the period of sin t is 2π. That is, show that there is no smaller positive real number p such that sin $(t + p) = $ sin t for all real numbers t.

55. Refracted Light Light is *refracted* (bent) as it passes through glass. In the figure, θ_1 is the angle of incidence and θ_2 is the *angle of refraction*. The *index of refraction* is a constant μ that satisfies the equation

$$\sin \theta_1 = \mu \sin \theta_2.$$

If $\theta_1 = 83°$ and $\theta_2 = 36°$ for a certain piece of flint glass, find the index of refraction.

Glass

56. Refracted Light A certain piece of crown glass has an index of refraction of 1.52. If a light ray enters the glass at an angle $\theta_1 = 42°$, what is sin θ_2?

57. Damped Harmonic Motion A weight suspended from a spring is set into motion. Its displacement d from equilibrium is modeled by the equation

$$d = 0.4e^{-0.2t} \cos 4t,$$

where d is the displacement in inches and t is the time in seconds. Find the displacement at the given time. Use radian mode.

(a) $t = 0$

(b) $t = 3$

58. Swinging Pendulum The Columbus Museum of Science and Industry exhibits a Foucault pendulum 32 ft long that swings back and forth on a cable once in approximately 6 sec. The angle θ (in radians) between the cable and an imaginary vertical line is modeled by the equation

$$\theta = 0.25 \cos t.$$

Find the measure of angle θ when $t = 0$ and $t = 2.5$.

59. Too Close for Comfort An F-15 aircraft flying at an altitude of 8000 ft passes directly over a group of vacationers hiking at 7400 ft. If θ is the angle of elevation from the hikers to the F-15, find the distance d from the group to the jet for the given angle.

(a) $\theta = 45°$ **(b)** $\theta = 90°$ **(c)** $\theta = 140°$

60. Manufacturing Swimwear Get Wet, Inc., manufactures swimwear, a seasonal product. The monthly sales x (in thousands) for Get Wet swimsuits are modeled by the equation

$$x = 72.4 + 61.7 \sin \frac{\pi t}{6},$$

where $t = 1$ represents January, $t = 2$ February, and so on. Estimate the number of Get Wet swimsuits sold in January, April, June, October, and December. For which two of these months are sales the same? Explain why this might be so.

Explorations

In Exercises 61–64, find the value of the unique real number θ between 0 and 2π that satisfies the two given conditions.

61. $\sin \theta = \dfrac{1}{2}$ and tan $\theta < 0$.

62. $\cos \theta = \dfrac{\sqrt{3}}{2}$ and sin $\theta < 0$.

63. $\tan \theta = -1$ and sin $\theta < 0$.

64. $\sin \theta = -\dfrac{\sqrt{2}}{2}$ and tan $\theta > 0$.

Exercises 65–68 refer to the unit circle in this figure. Point P is on the terminal side of an angle t and point Q is on the terminal side of an angle $t + \pi/2$.

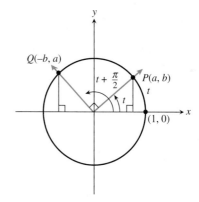

65. Using Geometry in Trigonometry Drop perpendiculars from points P and Q to the x-axis to form two right triangles. Explain how the right triangles are related.

66. Using Geometry in Trigonometry If the coordinates of point P are (a, b), explain why the coordinates of point Q are $(-b, a)$.

67. Explain why $\sin\left(t + \dfrac{\pi}{2}\right) = \cos t$.

68. Explain why $\cos\left(t + \dfrac{\pi}{2}\right) = -\sin t$.

69. Writing to Learn In the figure for Exercises 65–68, t is an angle with radian measure $0 < t < \pi/2$. Draw a similar figure for an angle with radian measure $\pi/2 < t < \pi$ and use it to explain why $\sin(t + \pi/2) = \cos t$.

70. Writing to Learn Use the accompanying figure to explain each of the following.

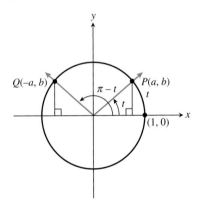

(a) $\sin(\pi - t) = \sin t$ **(b)** $\cos(\pi - t) = -\cos t$

Extending the Ideas

71. Approximation and Error Analysis Use your grapher to complete the table to show that $\sin\theta \approx \theta$ (in radians) when $|\theta|$ is small. Physicists often use the approximation $\sin\theta \approx \theta$ for small values of θ. For what values of θ is the *magnitude of the error* in approximating $\sin\theta$ by θ less than 1% of $\sin\theta$? That is, solve the relation

$$|\sin\theta - \theta| < 0.01|\sin\theta|.$$

[*Hint:* Extend the table to include a column for values of

$$\dfrac{|\sin\theta - \theta|}{|\sin\theta|}.]$$

θ	$\sin\theta$	$\sin\theta - \theta$
-0.03		
-0.02		
-0.01		
0		
0.01		
0.02		
0.03		

72. Proving a Theorem If t is any real number, prove that $1 + (\tan t)^2 = (\sec t)^2$.

Taylor Polynomials Radian measure allows the trigonometric functions to be approximated by simple polynomial functions. For example, in Exercises 73 and 74, sine and cosine are approximated by Taylor polynomials, named after the English mathematician Brook Taylor (1685–1731). Complete each table showing a Taylor polynomial in the third column. Describe the patterns in the table.

73.

θ	$\sin\theta$	$\theta - \dfrac{\theta^3}{6}$	$\sin\theta - \left(\theta - \dfrac{\theta^3}{6}\right)$
-0.3	$-0.295...$		
-0.2	$-0.198...$		
-0.1	$-0.099...$		
0	0		
0.1	$0.099...$		
0.2	$0.198...$		
0.3	$0.295...$		

74.

θ	$\cos\theta$	$1 - \dfrac{\theta^2}{2} + \dfrac{\theta^4}{24}$	$\cos\theta - \left(1 - \dfrac{\theta^2}{2} + \dfrac{\theta^4}{24}\right)$
-0.3	$0.955...$		
-0.2	$0.980...$		
-0.1	$0.995...$		
0	1		
0.1	$0.995...$		
0.2	$0.980...$		
0.3	$0.955...$		

H-7 Graphs of Sine and Cosine: Sinusoids

What you'll learn about

- The Basic Waves Revisited
- Sinusoids and Transformations
- Modeling Periodic Behavior with Sinusoids

... and why

Sine and cosine gain added significance when used to model waves and periodic behavior

The Basic Waves Revisited

You know that trigonometric functions are rooted in the geometry of triangles and circles. It is these connections with geometry that give trigonometric functions their mathematical power and make them widely applicable in many fields.

The unit circle in Lesson H-6 was the key to defining the trigonometric functions as functions of real numbers. This makes them available for the same kind of analysis as other functions. We now take a closer look at the algebraic, graphical, and numerical properties of the trigonometric functions, beginning with sine and cosine.

Recall that we can learn quite a bit about the sine function by looking at its graph. Here is a summary of sine facts:

BASIC FUNCTION The Sine Function

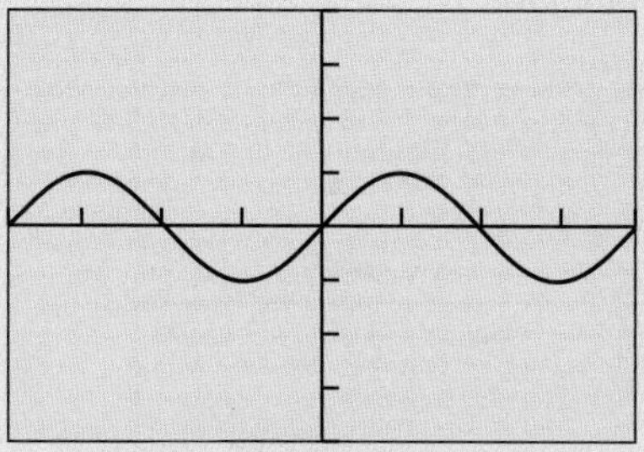

$f(x) = \sin x$
Domain: All reals
Range: $[-1, 1]$
Continuous
Alternately increasing and decreasing in periodic waves
Symmetric with respect to the origin (odd)
Bounded
Absolute maximum of 1
Absolute minimum of -1
No horizontal asymptotes
No vertical asymptotes
End behavior: $\lim\limits_{x \to -\infty} \sin x$ and $\lim\limits_{x \to \infty} \sin x$ do not exist. (The function values continually oscillate between -1 and 1 and approach no limit.)

$[-2\pi, 2\pi]$ by $[-4, 4]$

FIGURE H.59A

We can add to this list that $y = \sin x$ is *periodic*, with period 2π. We can also add understanding of where the sine function comes from: By definition, $\sin t$ is the y-coordinate of the point P on the unit circle to which the real number t gets wrapped (or, equivalently, the point P on the unit circle determined by an angle of t radians in standard position). In fact, now we can see where the wavy graph comes from. Try Exploration 1.

EXPLORATION 1 Graphing sin t as a Function of t

Set your grapher to radian mode, parametric, and "simultaneous" graphing modes.

Set Tmin = 0, Tmax = 6.3, Tstep = $\pi/24$.

Set the (x, y) window to $[-1.2, 6.3]$ by $[-2.5, 2.5]$.

Set $X_{1T} = \cos (T)$ and $Y_{1T} = \sin (T)$. This will graph the unit circle. Set $X_{2T} = T$ and $Y_{2T} = \sin (T)$. This will graph sin (T) as a function of T.

Now start the graph and watch the point go counterclockwise around the unit circle as t goes from 0 to 2π in the positive direction. You will simultaneously see the y-coordinate of the point being graphed as a function of t along the horizontal t-axis. You can clear the drawing and watch the graph as many times as you need to in order to answer the following questions.

1. Where is the point on the unit circle when the wave is at its highest?

2. Where is the point on the unit circle when the wave is at its lowest?

3. Why do both graphs cross the x-axis at the same time?

4. Double the value of Tmax and change the window to $[-2.4, 12.6]$ by $[-5, 5]$. If your grapher can change "style" to show a moving point, choose that style for the unit circle graph. Run the graph and watch how the sine curve tracks the y-coordinate of the point as it moves around the unit circle.

5. Explain from what you have seen why the period of the sine function is 2π.

6. Challenge: Can you modify the grapher settings to show dynamically how the cosine function tracks the x-coordinate as the point moves around the unit circle?

Although a static picture does not do the dynamic simulation justice, Figure H.60 shows the final screens for the two graphs in Exploration 1.

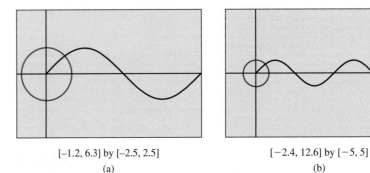

$[-1.2, 6.3]$ by $[-2.5, 2.5]$	$[-2.4, 12.6]$ by $[-5, 5]$
(a)	(b)

FIGURE H.60 The graph of $y = \sin t$ tracks the y-coordinate of the point determined by t as it moves around the unit circle.

BASIC FUNCTION The Cosine Function

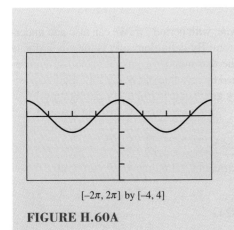

$[-2\pi, 2\pi]$ by $[-4, 4]$

FIGURE H.60A

$f(x) = \cos x$
Domain: All reals
Range: $[-1, 1]$
Continuous
Alternately increasing and decreasing in periodic waves
Symmetric with respect to the y-axis (even)
Bounded
Absolute maximum of 1
Absolute minimum of -1
No horizontal asymptotes
No vertical asymptotes
End behavior: $\lim\limits_{x \to -\infty} \cos x$ and $\lim\limits_{x \to \infty} \cos x$ do not exist. (The function values continually oscillate between -1 and 1 and approach no limit.)

As with the sine function, we can add the observation that it is periodic, with period 2π.

Sinusoids and Transformations

A comparison of the graphs of $y = \sin x$ and $y = \cos x$ suggests that either one can be obtained from the other by a horizontal translation. In fact, we will prove later in this section that $\cos x = \sin (x + \pi/2)$. Each graph is an example of a *sinusoid*. In general, any transformation of a sine function (or the graph of such a function) is a sinusoid.

DEFINITION Sinusoid

A function is a **sinusoid** if it can be written in the form

$$f(x) = a \sin (bx + c) + d$$

where a, b, c, and d are constants and neither a nor b is 0.

Since cosine functions are themselves translations of sine functions, any transformation of a cosine function is also a sinusoid by the above definition.

There is a special vocabulary used to describe some of our usual graphical transformations when we apply them to sinusoids. Horizontal stretches and shrinks affect the *period* and the *frequency*, vertical stretches and shrinks affect the *amplitude*, and horizontal translations bring about *phase shifts*. All of these terms are associated with waves, and waves are quite naturally associated with sinusoids.

DEFINITION Amplitude of a Sinusoid

The **amplitude** of the sinusoid $f(x) = a \sin (bx + c) + d$ is $|a|$. Similarly, the amplitude of $f(x) = a \cos (bx + c) + d$ is $|a|$.

Graphically, the amplitude is half the height of the wave.

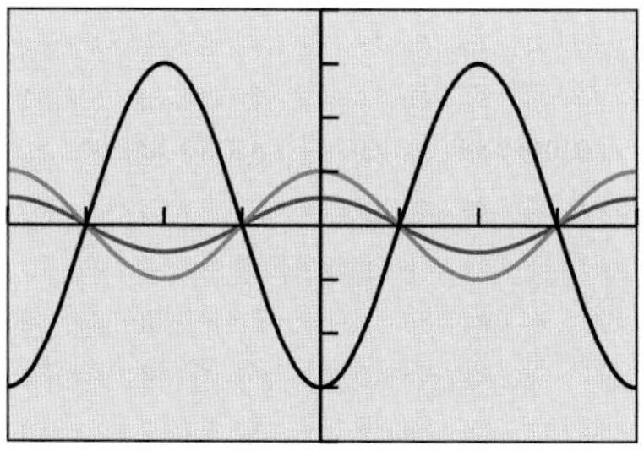

$[-2\pi, 2\pi]$ by $[-4, 4]$

FIGURE H.61 Sinusoids (in this case, cosine curves) of different amplitudes. (Example 1)

EXAMPLE 1 Vertical Stretch or Shrink and Amplitude

Find the amplitude of each function and use the language of transformations to describe how the graphs are related.

(a) $y_1 = \cos x$ **(b)** $y_2 = \dfrac{1}{2} \cos x$ **(c)** $y_3 = -3 \cos x$

SOLUTION

Solve Algebraically The amplitudes are (a) 1, (b) 1/2, and (c) $|-3| = 3$.

The graph of y_2 is a vertical shrink of the graph of y_1 by a factor of 1/2.

The graph of y_3 is a vertical stretch of the graph of y_1 by a factor of 3, and a reflection across the x-axis, performed in either order. (We do not call this a vertical stretch by a factor of -3, nor do we say that the amplitude is -3.)

Support Graphically The graphs of the three functions are shown in Figure H.61. You should be able to tell which is which quite easily by checking the amplitudes.

Now try Exercise 1.

The graph of $y = f(bx)$ when $|b| > 1$ is a horizontal shrink of the graph of $y = f(x)$ by a factor of $1/|b|$. That is exactly what happens with sinusoids, but we can add the observation that the period shrinks by the same factor. When $|b| < 1$, the effect on both the graph and the period is a horizontal stretch by a factor of $1/|b|$, plus a reflection across the y-axis if $b < 0$.

Period of a Sinusoid

The period of the sinusoid $f(x) = a \sin (bx + c) + d$ is $2\pi/|b|$. Similarly, the period of $f(x) = a \cos (bx + c) + d$ is $2\pi/|b|$.

Graphically, the period is the length of one full cycle of the wave.

EXAMPLE 2 Horizontal Stretch or Shrink and Period

Find the period of each function and use the language of transformations to describe how the graphs are related.

(a) $y_1 = \sin x$ **(b)** $y_2 = -2 \sin \left(\dfrac{x}{3}\right)$ **(c)** $y_3 = 3 \sin (-2x)$

SOLUTION

Solve Algebraically The periods are (a) 2π, (b) $2\pi/(1/3) = 6\pi$, and (c) $2\pi/|-2| = \pi$.

The graph of y_2 is a horizontal stretch of the graph of y_1 by a factor of 3, a vertical stretch by a factor of 2, and a reflection across the x-axis, performed in any order.

The graph of y_3 is a horizontal shrink of the graph of y_1 by a factor of 1/2, a vertical stretch by a factor of 3, and a reflection across the y-axis, performed in any order. (Note that we do not call this a horizontal shrink by a factor of $-1/2$, nor do we say that the period is $-\pi$.)

Support Graphically The graphs of the three functions are shown in Figure H.62. You should be able to tell which is which quite easily by checking the periods or the amplitudes. *Now try Exercise 9.*

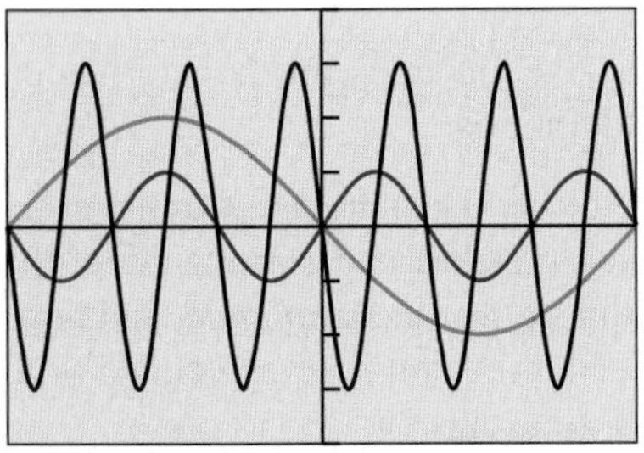

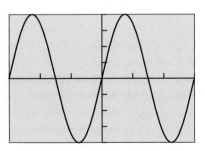

$[-3\pi, 3\pi]$ by $[-4, 4]$

FIGURE H.62 Sinusoids (in this case, sine curves) of different amplitudes and periods. (Example 2)

In some applications, the *frequency* of a sinusoid is an important consideration. The frequency is simply the reciprocal of the period.

Frequency of a Sinusoid

The **frequency** of the sinusoid $f(x) = a \sin (bx + c) + d$ is $|b|/2\pi$. Similarly, the frequency of $f(x) = a \cos (bx + c) + d$ is $|b|/2\pi$.

Graphically, the frequency is the number of complete cycles the wave completes in a unit interval.

EXAMPLE 3 Finding the Frequency of a Sinusoid

Find the frequency of the function $f(x) = 4 \sin (2x/3)$ and interpret its meaning graphically.

Sketch the graph in the window $[-3\pi, 3\pi]$ by $[-4, 4]$.

SOLUTION The frequency is $(2/3) \div 2\pi = 1/(3\pi)$. This is the reciprocal of the period, which is 3π. The graphical interpretation is that the graph completes 1 full cycle per interval of length 3π. (That, of course, is what having a period of 3π is all about.) The graph is shown in Figure H.63. *Now try Exercise 17.*

$[-3\pi, 3\pi]$ by $[-4, 4]$

FIGURE H.63 The graph of the function $f(x) = 4 \sin (2x/3)$. It has frequency $1/(3\pi)$, so it completes 1 full cycle per interval of length 3π. (Example 3)

The graph of $y = f(x + c)$ is a translation of the graph of $y = f(x)$ by c units to the left when $c > 0$. That is exactly what happens with sinusoids, but using terminology with its roots in electrical engineering, we say that the wave undergoes a **phase shift** of $-c$.

EXAMPLE 4 Getting One Sinusoid from Another by a Phase Shift

(a) Write the cosine function as a phase shift of the sine function.

(b) Write the sine function as a phase shift of the cosine function.

SOLUTION

(a) The function $y = \sin x$ has a maximum at $x = \pi/2$, while the function $y = \cos x$ has a maximum at $x = 0$. Therefore, we need to shift the sine curve $\pi/2$ units to the *left* to get the cosine curve:

$$\cos x = \sin (x + \pi/2)$$

(b) It follows from the work in (a) that we need to shift the cosine curve $\pi/2$ units to the right to get the sine curve:

$$\sin x = \cos (x - \pi/2)$$

You can support with your grapher that these statements are true. Incidentally, there are many other translations that would have worked just as well. Adding any integral multiple of 2π to the phase shift would result in the same graph.

Now try Exercise 41.

One note of caution applies when combining these transformations. A horizontal stretch or shrink affects the variable along the horizontal axis, so it *also affects the phase shift*. Consider the transformation in Example 5.

EXAMPLE 5 Combining a Phase Shift with a Period Change

Construct a sinusoid with period $\pi/5$ and amplitude 6 that goes through $(2, 0)$.

SOLUTION To find the coefficient of x, we set $2\pi/|b| = \pi/5$ and solve to find that $b = \pm 10$. We arbitrarily choose $b = 10$. (Either will satisfy the specified conditions.)

For amplitude 6, we have $|a| = 6$. Again, we arbitrarily choose the positive value. The graph of $y = 6 \sin (10x)$ has the required amplitude and period, but it does not go through the point $(2, 0)$. It does, however, go through the point $(0, 0)$, so all that is needed is a phase shift of $+2$ to finish our function. Replacing x by $x - 2$, we get

$$y = 6 \sin (10(x - 2)) = 6 \sin (10x - 20).$$

Notice that we did *not* get the function $y = 6 \sin (10x - 2)$. That function would represent a phase shift of $y = \sin (10x)$, but only by 2/10, not 2. Parentheses are important when combining phase shifts with horizontal stretches and shrinks.

Now try Exercise 59.

Graphs of Sinusoids

The graphs of $y = a \sin (b(x - h)) + k$ and $y = a \cos (b(x - h)) + k$ (where $a \neq 0$ and $b \neq 0$) have the following characteristics:

$$\text{amplitude} = |a|;$$

$$\text{period} = \frac{2\pi}{|b|};$$

$$\text{frequency} = \frac{|b|}{2\pi}.$$

When compared to the graphs of $y = a \sin bx$ and $y = a \cos bx$, respectively, they also have the following characteristics:

a phase shift of h;   a vertical translation of k.

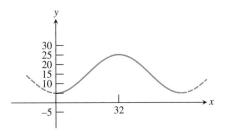

FIGURE H.64 A sinusoid with specifications. (Example 6)

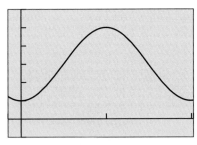

[–5, 65] by [–5, 30]

FIGURE H.65 The graph of the function $y = -10 \cos((\pi/32)x) + 15$. (Example 8)

EXAMPLE 6 Constructing a Sinusoid by Transformations

Construct a sinusoid $y = f(x)$ that rises from a minimum value of $y = 5$ at $x = 0$ to a maximum value of $y = 25$ at $x = 32$. (See Figure H.64.)

SOLUTION

Solve Algebraically The amplitude of this sinusoid is half the height of the graph: $(25 - 5)/2 = 10$. So $|a| = 10$. The period is 64 (since a full period goes from minimum to maximum and back down to the minimum). So set $2\pi/|b| = 64$. Solving, we get $|b| = \pi/32$.

We need a sinusoid that takes on its minimum value at $x = 0$. We could shift the graph of sine or cosine horizontally, but it is easier to take the cosine curve (which assumes its *maximum* value at $x = 0$) and turn it upside down. This reflection can be obtained by letting $a = -10$ rather than 10.

So far we have:

$$y = -10 \cos\left(\pm\frac{\pi}{32}x\right)$$

$$= -10 \cos\left(\frac{\pi}{32}x\right) \qquad \text{(Since cos is an even function)}$$

Finally, we note that this function ranges from a minimum of -10 to a maximum of 10. We shift the graph vertically by 15 to obtain a function that ranges from a minimum of 5 to a maximum of 25, as required. Thus

$$y = -10 \cos\left(\frac{\pi}{32}x\right) + 15.$$

Support Graphically We support our answer graphically by graphing the function (Figure H.65). *Now try Exercise 69.*

Modeling Periodic Behavior with Sinusoids

Example 6 was intended as more than just a review of the graphical transformations. Constructing a sinusoid with specific properties is often the key step in modeling physical situations that exhibit periodic behavior over time. The procedure we followed in Example 6 can be summarized as follows:

Constructing a Sinusoidal Model Using Time

1. Determine the maximum value M and minimum value m. The amplitude A of the sinusoid will be $A = \dfrac{M - m}{2}$, and the vertical shift will be $C = \dfrac{M + m}{2}$.

2. Determine the period p, the time interval of a single cycle of the periodic function. The horizontal shrink (or stretch) will be $B = \dfrac{2\pi}{p}$.

3. Choose an appropriate sinusoid based on behavior at some given time T. For example, at time T:

   $f(t) = A \cos(B(t - T)) + C$ attains a maximum value;

   $f(t) = -A \cos(B(t - T)) + C$ attains a minimum value;

   $f(t) = A \sin(B(t - T)) + C$ is halfway between a minimum and a maximum value;

   $f(t) = -A \sin(B(t - T)) + C$ is halfway between a maximum and a minimum value.

We apply the procedure in Example 7 to model the ebb and flow of a tide.

EXAMPLE 7 Calculating the Ebb and Flow of Tides

One particular July 4th in Galveston, TX, high tide occurred at 9:36 A.M. At that time the water at the end of the 61st Street Pier was 2.7 meters deep. Low tide occurred at 3:48 P.M., at which time the water was only 2.1 meters deep. Assume that the depth of the water is a sinusoidal function of time with a period of half a lunar day (about 12 hours 24 minutes).

(a) At what time on the 4th of July did the first low tide occur?

(b) What was the approximate depth of the water at 6:00 A.M. and at 3:00 P.M. that day?

(c) What was the first time on July 4th when the water was 2.4 meters deep?

SOLUTION

Model We want to model the depth D as a sinusoidal function of time t. The depth varies from a maximum of 2.7 meters to a minimum of 2.1 meters, so the amplitude $A = \dfrac{2.7 - 2.1}{2} = 0.3$, and the vertical shift will be $C = \dfrac{2.7 + 2.1}{2} = 2.4$. The period is 12 hours 24 minutes, which converts to 12.4 hours, so $B = \dfrac{2\pi}{12.4} = \dfrac{\pi}{6.2}$.

We need a sinusoid that assumes its maximum value at 9:36 A.M. (which converts to 9.6 hours after midnight, a convenient time 0). We choose the cosine model. Thus,

$$D(t) = 0.3 \cos\left(\frac{\pi}{6.2}(t - 9.6)\right) + 2.4.$$

Solve Graphically The graph over the 24-hour period of July 4th is shown in Figure H.66.

We now use the graph to answer the questions posed.

(a) The first low tide corresponds to the first local minimum on the graph. We find graphically that this occurs at $t = 3.4$. This translates to $3 + (0.4)(60) = $ 3:24 A.M.

(b) The depth at 6:00 A.M. is $D(6) \approx 2.32$ meters. The depth at 3:00 P.M. is $D(12 + 3) = D(15) \approx 2.12$ meters.

(c) The first time the water is 2.4 meters deep corresponds to the leftmost intersection of the sinusoid with the line $y = 2.4$. We use the grapher to find that $t = 0.3$. This translates to $0 + (0.3)(60) = 00{:}18$ A.M., which we write as 12:18 A.M.

Now try Exercise 75.

We will see more applications of this kind when we look at *simple harmonic motion* in Lesson H-9.

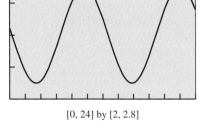

[0, 24] by [2, 2.8]

FIGURE H.66 The Galveston tide graph. (Example 7)

Exercise numbers with a gray background indicate problems that the authors have designed to be solved *without a calculator*.

In Exercises 1–6, find the amplitude of the function and use the language of transformations to describe how the graph of the function is related to the graph of $y = \sin x$.

1. $y = 2 \sin x$

2. $y = \dfrac{2}{3} \sin x$

3. $y = -4 \sin x$

4. $y = -\dfrac{7}{4} \sin x$

5. $y = 0.73 \sin x$

6. $y = -2.34 \sin x$

In Exercises 7–12, find the period of the function and use the language of transformations to describe how the graph of the function is related to the graph of $y = \cos x$.

7. $y = \cos 3x$

8. $y = \cos x/5$

9. $y = \cos(-7x)$

10. $y = \cos(-0.4x)$

11. $y = 3 \cos 2x$

12. $y = \dfrac{1}{4} \cos \dfrac{2x}{3}$

In Exercises 13–16, find the amplitude, period, and frequency of the function and use this information (not your calculator) to sketch a graph of the function in the window $[-3\pi, 3\pi]$ by $[-4, 4]$.

13. $y = 3 \sin \dfrac{x}{2}$

14. $y = 2 \cos \dfrac{x}{3}$

15. $y = -\dfrac{3}{2} \sin 2x$

16. $y = -4 \sin \dfrac{2x}{3}$

In Exercises 17–22, graph one period of the function. Use your understanding of transformations, not your graphing calculators. Be sure to show the scale on both axes.

17. $y = 2 \sin x$

18. $y = 2.5 \sin x$

19. $y = 3 \cos x$

20. $y = -2 \cos x$

21. $y = -0.5 \sin x$

22. $y = 4 \cos x$

In Exercises 23–28, graph three periods of the function. Use your understanding of transformations, not your graphing calculators. Be sure to show the scale on both axes.

23. $y = 5 \sin 2x$

24. $y = 3 \cos \dfrac{x}{2}$

25. $y = 0.5 \cos 3x$

26. $y = 20 \sin 4x$

27. $y = 4 \sin \dfrac{x}{4}$

28. $y = 8 \cos 5x$

In Exercises 29–34, specify the period and amplitude of each function. Then give the viewing window in which the graph is shown. Use your understanding of transformations, not your graphing calculators.

29. $y = 1.5 \sin 2x$

30. $y = 2 \cos 3x$

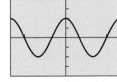

31. $y = -3 \cos 2x$

32. $y = 5 \sin \dfrac{x}{2}$

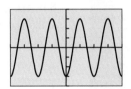
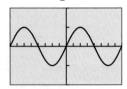

33. $y = -4 \sin \dfrac{\pi}{3} x$

34. $y = 3 \cos \pi x$

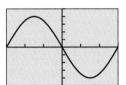
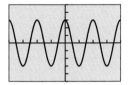

In Exercises 35–40, identify the maximum and minimum values and the zeros of the function in the interval $[-2\pi, 2\pi]$. Use your understanding of transformations, not your graphing calculators.

35. $y = 2 \sin x$

36. $y = 3 \cos \dfrac{x}{2}$

37. $y = \cos 2x$

38. $y = \dfrac{1}{2} \sin x$

39. $y = -\cos 2x$

40. $y = -2 \sin x$

41. Write the function $y = -\sin x$ as a phase shift of $y = \sin x$.

42. Write the function $y = -\cos x$ as a phase shift of $y = \sin x$.

In Exercises 43–48, describe the transformations required to obtain the graph of the given function from a basic trigonometric graph.

43. $y = 0.5 \sin 3x$

44. $y = 1.5 \cos 4x$

45. $y = -\dfrac{2}{3} \cos \dfrac{x}{3}$

46. $y = \dfrac{3}{4} \sin \dfrac{x}{5}$

47. $y = 3 \cos \dfrac{2\pi x}{3}$

48. $y = -2 \sin \dfrac{\pi x}{4}$

In Exercises 49–52, describe the transformations required to obtain the graph of y_2 from the graph of y_1.

49. $y_1 = \cos 2x$ and $y_2 = \dfrac{5}{3} \cos 2x$

50. $y_1 = 2 \cos\left(x + \dfrac{\pi}{3}\right)$ and $y_2 = \cos\left(x + \dfrac{\pi}{4}\right)$

51. $y_1 = 2 \cos \pi x$ and $y_2 = 2 \cos 2\pi x$

52. $y_1 = 3 \sin \dfrac{2\pi x}{3}$ and $y_2 = 2 \sin \dfrac{\pi x}{3}$

In Exercises 53–56, select the pair of functions that have identical graphs.

53. (a) $y = \cos x$

(b) $y = \sin\left(x + \dfrac{\pi}{2}\right)$

(c) $y = \cos\left(x + \dfrac{\pi}{2}\right)$

54. (a) $y = \sin x$ **(b)** $y = \cos\left(x - \dfrac{\pi}{2}\right)$

  (c) $y = \cos x$

55. (a) $y = \sin\left(x + \dfrac{\pi}{2}\right)$ **(b)** $y = -\cos(x - \pi)$

  (c) $y = \cos\left(x - \dfrac{\pi}{2}\right)$

56. (a) $y = \sin\left(2x + \dfrac{\pi}{4}\right)$ **(b)** $y = \cos\left(2x - \dfrac{\pi}{2}\right)$

  (c) $y = \cos\left(2x - \dfrac{\pi}{4}\right)$

In Exercises 57–60, construct a sinusoid with the given amplitude and period that goes through the given point.

57. Amplitude 3, period π, point $(0, 0)$

58. Amplitude 2, period 3π, point $(0, 0)$

59. Amplitude 1.5, period $\pi/6$, point $(1, 0)$

60. Amplitude 3.2, period $\pi/7$, point $(5, 0)$

In Exercises 61–68, state the amplitude and period of the sinusoid, and (relative to the basic function) the phase shift and vertical translation.

61. $y = -2 \sin\left(x - \dfrac{\pi}{4}\right) + 1$

62. $y = -3.5 \sin\left(2x - \dfrac{\pi}{2}\right) - 1$

63. $y = 5 \cos\left(3x - \dfrac{\pi}{6}\right) + 0.5$

64. $y = 3 \cos(x + 3) - 2$

65. $y = 2 \cos 2\pi x + 1$

66. $y = 4 \cos 3\pi x - 2$

67. $y = \dfrac{7}{3} \sin\left(x + \dfrac{5}{2}\right) - 1$

68. $y = \dfrac{2}{3} \cos\left(\dfrac{x - 3}{4}\right) + 1$

In Exercises 69 and 70, find values a, b, h, and k so that the graph of the function $y = a \sin(b(x + h)) + k$ is the curve shown.

69.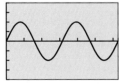

70.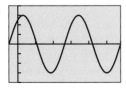

[0, 6.28] by [−4, 4]   [−0.5, 5.78] by [−4, 4]

71. Points of Intersection Graph $y = 1.3^{-x}$ and $y = 1.3^{-x} \cos x$ for x in the interval $[-1, 8]$.

  (a) How many points of intersection do there appear to be?

  (b) Find the coordinates of each point of intersection.

72. Motion of a Buoy A signal buoy in the Chesapeake Bay bobs up and down with the height h of its transmitter (in feet) above sea level modeled by $h = a \sin bt + 5$. During a small squall its height varies from 1 ft to 9 ft and there are 3.5 sec from one 9-ft height to the next. What are the values of the constants a and b?

73. Ferris Wheel A Ferris wheel 50 ft in diameter makes one revolution every 40 sec. If the center of the wheel is 30 ft above the ground, how long after reaching the low point is a rider 50 ft above the ground?

74. Tsunami Wave An earthquake occurred at 9:40 A.M. on Nov. 1, 1755, at Lisbon, Portugal, and started a *tsunami* (often called a tidal wave) in the ocean. It produced waves that traveled more than 540 ft/sec (370 mph) and reached a height of 60 ft. If the period of the waves was 30 min or 1800 sec, estimate the length L between the crests.

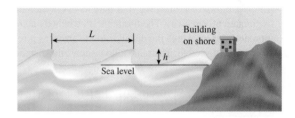

75. Ebb and Flow On a particular Labor Day, the high tide in Southern California occurs at 7:12 A.M. At that time you measure the water at the end of the Santa Monica Pier to be 11 ft deep. At 1:24 P.M. it is low tide, and you measure the water to be only 7 ft deep. Assume the depth of the water is a sinusoidal function of time with a period of 1/2 a lunar day, which is about 12 hr 24 min.

  (a) At what time on that Labor Day does the first low tide occur?

  (b) What was the approximate depth of the water at 4:00 A.M. and at 9:00 P.M.?

  (c) What is the first time on that Labor Day that the water is 9 ft deep?

76. Blood Pressure The function

$$P = 120 + 30 \sin 2\pi t$$

models the blood pressure (in millimeters of mercury) for a person who has a (high) blood pressure of 150/90; t represents seconds.

  (a) What is the period of this function?

  (b) How many heartbeats are there each minute?

  (c) Graph this function to model a 10-sec time interval.

77. Bouncing Block A block mounted on a spring is set into motion directly above a motion detector, which registers the distance to the block at intervals of 0.1 second. When the block is released, it is 7.2 cm above the motion detector. The table below shows the data collected by the motion detector during the first two seconds, with distance d measured in centimeters:

(a) Make a scatter plot of d as a function of t and estimate the maximum d visually. Use this number and the given minimum (7.2) to compute the amplitude of the block's motion.

(b) Estimate the period of the block's motion visually from the scatter plot.

(c) Model the motion of the block as a sinusoidal function $d(t)$.

(d) Graph your function with the scatter plot to support your model graphically.

t	0.1	0.2	0.3	0.4	0.5	0.6	0.7	0.8	0.9	1.0
d	9.2	13.9	18.8	21.4	20.0	15.6	10.5	7.4	8.1	12.1

t	1.1	1.2	1.3	1.4	1.5	1.6	1.7	1.8	1.9	2.0
d	17.3	20.8	20.8	17.2	12.0	8.1	7.5	10.5	15.6	19.9

78. **LP Turntable** A suction-cup-tipped arrow is secured vertically to the outer edge of a turntable designed for playing LP phonograph records (ask your parents). A motion detector is situated 60 cm away. The turntable is switched on and a motion detector measures the distance to the arrow as it revolves around the turntable. The table below shows the distance d as a function of time during the first 4 seconds.

t	0.2	0.4	0.6	0.8	1.0	1.2	1.4	1.6	1.8	2.0
d	63.5	71.6	79.8	84.7	84.7	79.8	71.6	63.5	60.0	63.5

t	2.2	2.4	2.6	2.8	3.0	3.2	3.4	3.6	3.8	4.0
d	71.6	79.8	84.7	84.7	79.8	71.6	63.5	60.0	63.5	71.6

(a) If the turntable is 25.4 cm in diameter, find the amplitude of the arrow's motion.

(b) Find the period of the arrow's motion by analyzing the data.

(c) Model the motion of the arrow as a sinusoidal function $d(t)$.

(d) Graph your function with a scatter plot to support your model graphically.

79. **Temperature Data** The normal monthly Fahrenheit temperatures in Albuquerque, NM, are shown in the table below (month 1 = Jan, month 2 = Feb, etc.):

Month	1	2	3	4	5	6	7	8	9	10	11	12
Temp	36	41	48	56	65	75	79	76	69	57	44	36

Source: National Climatic Data Center, as reported in The World Almanac and Book of Facts 2009.

Model the temperature T as a sinusoidal function of time, using 36 as the minimum value and 79 as the maximum value. Support your answer graphically by graphing your function with a scatter plot.

80. **Temperature Data** The normal monthly Fahrenheit temperatures in Helena, MT, are shown in the table below (month 1 = Jan, month 2 = Feb, etc.):

Month	1	2	3	4	5	6	7	8	9	10	11	12
Temp	20	26	35	44	53	61	68	67	56	45	31	21

Source: National Climatic Data Center, as reported in The World Almanac and Book of Facts 2009.

Model the temperature T as a sinusoidal function of time, using 20 as the minimum value and 68 as the maximum value. Support your answer graphically by graphing your function with a scatter plot.

Explorations

81. **Approximating Cosine**
  (a) Draw a scatter plot $(x, \cos x)$ for the 17 special angles x, where $-\pi \le x \le \pi$.

  (b) Find a quartic regression for the data.

  (c) Compare the approximation to the cosine function given by the quartic regression with the Taylor polynomial approximations given in Exercise 74 of Lesson H-6.

82. **Approximating Sine**
  (a) Draw a scatter plot $(x, \sin x)$ for the 17 special angles x, where $-\pi \le x \le \pi$.

  (b) Find a cubic regression for the data.

  (c) Compare the approximation to the sine function given by the cubic regression with the Taylor polynomial approximations given in Exercise 73 of Lesson H-6.

83. **Visualizing a Musical Note** A piano tuner strikes a tuning fork for the note middle C and creates a sound wave that can be modeled by

$$y = 1.5 \sin 524\pi t,$$

where t is the time in seconds.

  (a) What is the period p of this function?

  (b) What is the frequency $f = 1/p$ of this note?

  (c) Graph the function.

84. **Writing to Learn** In a certain video game a cursor bounces back and forth horizontally across the screen at a constant rate. Its distance d from the center of the screen varies with time t and hence can be described as a function of t. Explain why this horizontal distance d from the center of the screen *does not vary* according to an equation $d = a \sin bt$, where t represents seconds. You may find it helpful to include a graph in your explanation.

85. **Group Activity** Using only integer values of a and b between 1 and 9 inclusive, look at graphs of functions of the form

$$y = \sin (ax) \cos (bx) - \cos (ax) \sin (bx)$$

for various values of a and b. (A group can look at more graphs at a time than one person can.)

  (a) Some values of a and b result in the graph of $y = \sin x$. Find a general rule for such values of a and b.

  (b) Some values of a and b result in the graph of $y = \sin 2x$. Find a general rule for such values of a and b.

  (c) Can you guess which values of a and b will result in the graph of $y = \sin kx$ for an arbitrary integer k?

86. Group Activity Using only integer values of a and b between 1 and 9 inclusive, look at graphs of functions of the form

$$y = \cos(ax)\cos(bx) + \sin(ax)\sin(bx)$$

for various values of a and b. (A group can look at more graphs at a time than one person can.)

(a) Some values of a and b result in the graph of $y = \cos x$. Find a general rule for such values of a and b.

(b) Some values of a and b result in the graph of $y = \cos 2x$. Find a general rule for such values of a and b.

(c) Can you guess which values of a and b will result in the graph of $y = \cos kx$ for an arbitrary integer k?

Extending the Ideas

In Exercises 87–90, the graphs of the sine and cosine functions are waveforms like the figure below. By correctly labeling the coordinates of points A, B, and C, you will get the graph of the function given.

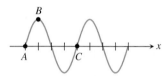

87. $y = 3\cos 2x$ and $A = \left(-\dfrac{\pi}{4}, 0\right)$. Find B and C.

88. $y = 4.5\sin\left(x - \dfrac{\pi}{4}\right)$ and $A = \left(\dfrac{\pi}{4}, 0\right)$. Find B and C.

89. $y = 2\sin\left(3x - \dfrac{\pi}{4}\right)$ and $A = \left(\dfrac{\pi}{12}, 0\right)$. Find B and C.

90. $y = 3\sin(2x - \pi)$, and A is the first x-intercept on the right of the y-axis. Find A, B, and C.

91. The Ultimate Sinusoidal Equation It is an interesting fact that any sinusoid can be written in the form

$$y = a\sin[b(x - H)] + k,$$

where both a and b are positive numbers.

(a) Explain why you can assume b is positive. [*Hint:* Replace b by $-B$ and simplify.]

(b) Use one of the horizontal translation identities to prove that the equation

$$y = a\cos[b(x - h)] + k$$

has the same graph as

$$y = a\sin[b(x - H)] + k$$

for a correctly chosen value of H. Explain how to choose H.

(c) Give a unit circle argument for the identity $\sin(\theta + \pi) = -\sin\theta$. Support your unit circle argument graphically.

(d) Use the identity from (c) to prove that

$$y = -a\sin[b(x - h)] + k, a > 0,$$

has the same graph as

$$y = a\sin[b(x - H)] + k, a > 0$$

for a correctly chosen value of H. Explain how to choose H.

(e) Combine your results from (a)–(d) to prove that any sinusoid can be represented by the equation

$$y = a\sin[b(x - H)] + k$$

where a and b are both positive.

H-8 Inverse Trigonometric Functions

What you'll learn about

- Inverse Sine Function
- Inverse Cosine and Tangent Functions
- Composing Trigonometric and Inverse Trigonometric Functions
- Applications of Inverse Trigonometric Functions

... and why

Inverse trig functions can be used to solve trigonometric equations.

Inverse Sine Function

Each function has an inverse relation, and that this inverse relation is a function only if the original function is one-to-one. The six basic trigonometric functions, being periodic, fail the horizontal line test for one-to-oneness rather spectacularly. However, some functions are important enough that we want to study their inverse behavior despite the fact that they are not one-to-one. We do this by restricting the domain of the original function to an interval on which it *is* one-to-one, then finding the inverse of the restricted function. (We did this when defining the square root function, which is the inverse of the function $y = x^2$ restricted to a nonnegative domain.)

If you restrict the domain of $y = \sin x$ to the interval $[-\pi/2, \pi/2]$, as shown in Figure H.67a, the restricted function is one-to-one. The **inverse sine function** $y = \sin^{-1} x$ is the inverse of this restricted portion of the sine function (Figure H.67b).

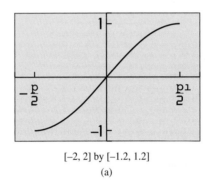
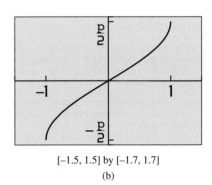

[-2, 2] by [-1.2, 1.2]   [-1.5, 1.5] by [-1.7, 1.7]

(a)   (b)

FIGURE H.67 The (a) restriction of $y = \sin x$ is one-to-one and (b) has an inverse, $y = \sin^{-1} x$.

By the usual inverse relationship, the statements

$$y = \sin^{-1} x \quad \text{and} \quad x = \sin y$$

are equivalent for y-values in the restricted domain $[-\pi/2, \pi/2]$ and x-values in $[-1, 1]$. This means that $\sin^{-1} x$ can be thought of as *the angle between $-\pi/2$ and $\pi/2$ whose sine is x*. Since angles and directed arcs on the unit circle have the same measure, the angle $\sin^{-1} x$ is also called the **arcsine of x**.

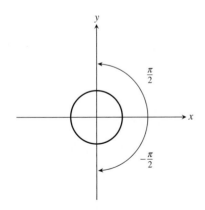

FIGURE H.68 The values of $y = \sin^{-1} x$ will always be found on the right-hand side of the unit circle, between $-\pi/2$ and $\pi/2$.

> ### Inverse Sine Function (Arcsine Function)
>
> The unique angle y in the interval $[-\pi/2, \pi/2]$ such that $\sin y = x$ is the **inverse sine** (or **arcsine**) of x, denoted $\sin^{-1} x$ or $\arcsin x$.
>
> The domain of $y = \sin^{-1} x$ is $[-1, 1]$ and the range is $[-\pi/2, \pi/2]$.

It helps to think of the range of $y = \sin^{-1} x$ as being along the right-hand side of the unit circle, which is traced out as angles range from $-\pi/2$ to $\pi/2$ (Figure H.68).

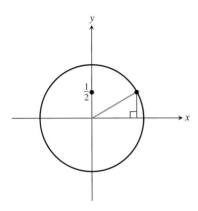

FIGURE H.69 $\sin^{-1}(1/2) = \pi/6$. (Example 1a)

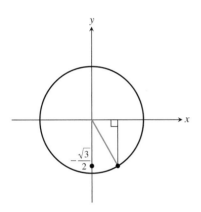

FIGURE H.70 $\sin^{-1}(-\sqrt{3}/2) = -\pi/3$. (Example 1b)

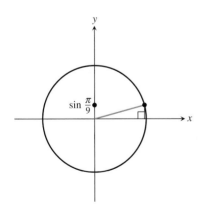

FIGURE H.71 $\sin^{-1}(\sin(\pi/9)) = \pi/9$. (Example 1d)

EXAMPLE 1 Evaluating $\sin^{-1}x$ without a Calculator

Find the exact value of each expression without a calculator.

(a) $\sin^{-1}\left(\dfrac{1}{2}\right)$ **(b)** $\sin^{-1}\left(-\dfrac{\sqrt{3}}{2}\right)$ **(c)** $\sin^{-1}\left(\dfrac{\pi}{2}\right)$

(d) $\sin^{-1}\left(\sin\left(\dfrac{\pi}{9}\right)\right)$ **(e)** $\sin^{-1}\left(\sin\left(\dfrac{5\pi}{6}\right)\right)$

SOLUTION

(a) Find the point on the right half of the unit circle whose y-coordinate is 1/2 and draw a reference triangle (Figure H.69). We recognize this as one of our special ratios, and the angle in the interval $[-\pi/2, \pi/2]$ whose sine is 1/2 is $\pi/6$. Therefore

$$\sin^{-1}\left(\frac{1}{2}\right) = \frac{\pi}{6}.$$

(b) Find the point on the right half of the unit circle whose y-coordinate is $-\sqrt{3}/2$ and draw a reference triangle (Figure H.70). We recognize this as one of our special ratios, and the angle in the interval $[-\pi/2, \pi/2]$ whose sine is $-\sqrt{3}/2$ is $-\pi/3$. Therefore

$$\sin^{-1}\left(-\frac{\sqrt{3}}{2}\right) = -\frac{\pi}{3}.$$

(c) $\sin^{-1}(\pi/2)$ does not exist, because the domain of $\sin^{-1}$ is $[-1, 1]$ and $\pi/2 > 1$.

(d) Draw an angle of $\pi/9$ in standard position and mark its y-coordinate on the y-axis (Figure H.71). The angle in the interval $[-\pi/2, \pi/2]$ whose sine is this number is $\pi/9$. Therefore

$$\sin^{-1}\left(\sin\left(\frac{\pi}{9}\right)\right) = \frac{\pi}{9}.$$

(e) Draw an angle of $5\pi/6$ in standard position (notice that this angle is *not* in the interval $[-\pi/2, \pi/2]$) and mark its y-coordinate on the y-axis. (See Figure H.72 on the next page.) The angle in the interval $[-\pi/2, \pi/2]$ whose sine is this number is $\pi - 5\pi/6 = \pi/6$. Therefore

$$\sin^{-1}\left(\sin\left(\frac{5\pi}{6}\right)\right) = \frac{\pi}{6}. \qquad \textit{Now try Exercise 1.}$$

EXAMPLE 2 Evaluating $\sin^{-1}x$ with a Calculator

Use a calculator in radian mode to evaluate these inverse sine values:

(a) $\sin^{-1}(-0.81)$ **(b)** $\sin^{-1}(\sin(3.49\pi))$

SOLUTION

(a) $\sin^{-1}(-0.81) = -0.9441521\ldots \approx -0.944$

(b) $\sin^{-1}(\sin(3.49\pi)) = -1.5393804\ldots \approx -1.539$

Although this is a calculator answer, we can use it to get an exact answer if we are alert enough to expect a multiple of π. Divide the answer by π:

$$\text{Ans}/\pi = -0.49$$

Therefore, we conclude that $\sin^{-1}(\sin(3.49\pi)) = -0.49\pi$.

You should also try to work Example 2b without a calculator. It is possible!

Now try Exercise 19.

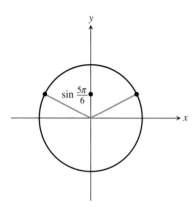

FIGURE H.72 $\sin^{-1}(\sin(5\pi/6)) = \pi/6$. (Example 1e)

What about the Inverse Composition Rule?

Does Example 1e violate the Inverse Composition Rule? That rule guarantees that $f^{-1}(f(x)) = x$ for every x in the domain of f. Keep in mind, however, that the domain of f might need to be restricted in order for f^{-1} to exist. That is certainly the case with the sine function. So Example 1e does not violate the Inverse Composition Rule, because that rule *does not apply* at $x = 5\pi/6$. It lies outside the (restricted) domain of sine.

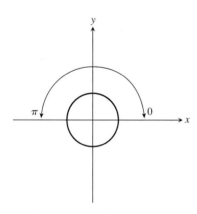

FIGURE H.74 The values of $y = \cos^{-1} x$ will always be found on the top half of the unit circle, between 0 and π.

Inverse Cosine and Tangent Functions

If you restrict the domain of $y = \cos x$ to the interval $[0, \pi]$, as shown in Figure H.73a, the restricted function is one-to-one. The **inverse cosine function** $y = \cos^{-1} x$ is the inverse of this restricted portion of the cosine function (Figure H.73b).

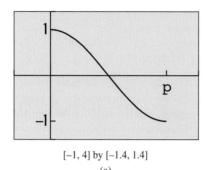

[−1, 4] by [−1.4, 1.4]

(a)

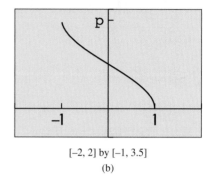

[−2, 2] by [−1, 3.5]

(b)

FIGURE H.73 The (a) restriction of $y = \cos x$ is one-to-one and (b) has an inverse, $y = \cos^{-1} x$.

By the usual inverse relationship, the statements

$$y = \cos^{-1} x \quad \text{and} \quad x = \cos y$$

are equivalent for y-values in the restricted domain $[0, \pi]$ and x-values in $[−1, 1]$. This means that $\cos^{-1} x$ can be thought of as *the angle between 0 and π whose cosine is x*. The angle $\cos^{-1} x$ is also the **arccosine of x**.

> ### Inverse Cosine Function (Arccosine Function)
>
> The unique angle y in the interval $[0, \pi]$ such that $\cos y = x$ is the **inverse cosine** (or **arccosine**) of x, denoted **$\cos^{-1} x$** or **arccos x**.
>
> The domain of $y = \cos^{-1} x$ is $[−1, 1]$ and the range is $[0, \pi]$.

It helps to think of the range of $y = \cos^{-1} x$ as being along the top half of the unit circle, which is traced out as angles range from 0 to π (Figure H.74).

If you restrict the domain of $y = \tan x$ to the interval $(-\pi/2, \pi/2)$, as shown in Figure H.75a, the restricted function is one-to-one. The **inverse tangent function** $y = \tan^{-1} x$ is the inverse of this restricted portion of the tangent function (Figure H.75b).

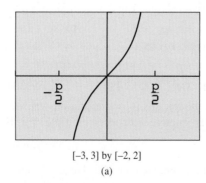

[−3, 3] by [−2, 2]

(a)

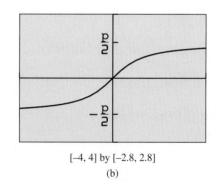

[−4, 4] by [−2.8, 2.8]

(b)

FIGURE H.75 The (a) restriction of $y = \tan x$ is one-to-one and (b) has an inverse, $y = \tan^{-1} x$.

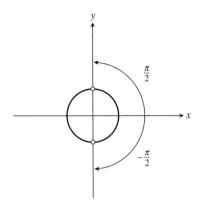

FIGURE H.76 The values of $y = \tan^{-1} x$ will always be found on the right-hand side of the unit circle, between (but not including) $-\pi/2$ and $\pi/2$.

By the usual inverse relationship, the statements

$$y = \tan^{-1} x \quad \text{and} \quad x = \tan y$$

are equivalent for y-values in the restricted domain $(-\pi/2, \pi/2)$ and x-values in $(-\infty, \infty)$. This means that $\tan^{-1} x$ can be thought of as *the angle between $-\pi/2$ and $\pi/2$ whose tangent is x*. The angle $\tan^{-1} x$ is also the **arctangent of x**.

Inverse Tangent Function (Arctangent Function)

The unique angle y in the interval $(-\pi/2, \pi/2)$ such that $\tan y = x$ is the **inverse tangent** (or **arctangent**) of x, denoted $\mathbf{tan^{-1}}\,x$ or $\mathbf{arctan}\,x$.
The domain of $y = \tan^{-1} x$ is $(-\infty, \infty)$ and the range is $(-\pi/2, \pi/2)$.

It helps to think of the range of $y = \tan^{-1} x$ as being along the right-hand side of the unit circle (minus the top and bottom points), which is traced out as angles range from $-\pi/2$ to $\pi/2$ (noninclusive) (Figure H.76).

EXAMPLE 3 Evaluating Inverse Trig Functions without a Calculator

Find the exact value of the expression without a calculator.

(a) $\cos^{-1}\left(-\dfrac{\sqrt{2}}{2}\right)$

(b) $\tan^{-1} \sqrt{3}$

(c) $\cos^{-1}\left(\cos\left(-1.1\right)\right)$

SOLUTION

(a) Find the point on the top half of the unit circle whose x-coordinate is $-\sqrt{2}/2$ and draw a reference triangle (Figure H.77). We recognize this as one of our special ratios, and the angle in the interval $[0, \pi]$ whose cosine is $-\sqrt{2}/2$ is $3\pi/4$. Therefore

$$\cos^{-1}\left(-\frac{\sqrt{2}}{2}\right) = \frac{3\pi}{4}.$$

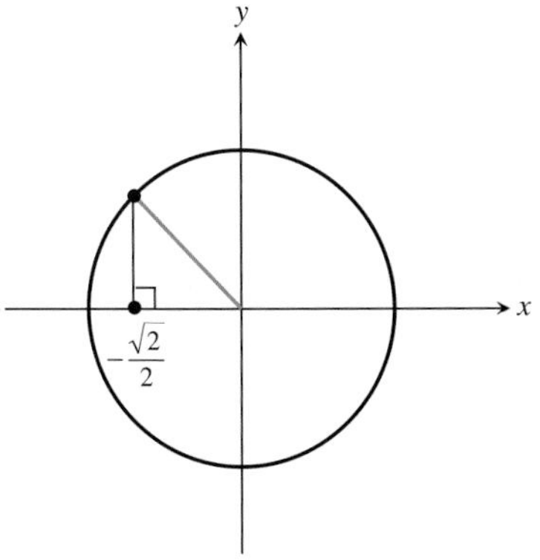

(b) Find the point on the right side of the unit circle whose y-coordinate is $\sqrt{3}$ times its x-coordinate and draw a reference triangle (Figure H.78). We recognize this as one of our special ratios, and the angle in the interval $(-\pi/2, \pi/2)$ whose tangent is $\sqrt{3}$ is $\pi/3$. Therefore

$$\tan^{-1} \sqrt{3} = \frac{\pi}{3}.$$

(c) Draw an angle of -1.1 in standard position (notice that this angle is *not* in the interval $[0, \pi]$) and mark its x-coordinate on the x-axis (Figure H.79). The angle in the interval $[0, \pi]$ whose cosine is this number is 1.1. Therefore

$$\cos^{-1}\left(\cos\left(-1.1\right)\right) = 1.1.$$

Now try Exercises 5 and 7.

FIGURE H.77 $\cos^{-1}(-\sqrt{2}/2) = 3\pi/4$.
(Example 3a)

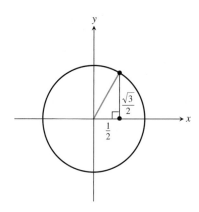

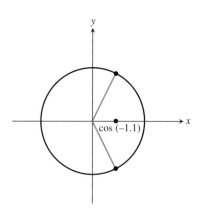

FIGURE H.78 $\tan^{-1} \sqrt{3} = \pi/3$.
(Example 3b)

FIGURE H.79 $\cos^{-1} (\cos (-1.1)) = 1.1$.
(Example 3c)

EXAMPLE 4 Describing End Behavior

Describe the end behavior of the function $y = \tan^{-1} x$.

SOLUTION We can get this information most easily by considering the graph of $y = \tan^{-1} x$, remembering how it relates to the restricted graph of $y = \tan x$. (See Figure H.80.)

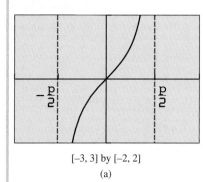

[−3, 3] by [−2, 2]
(a)

[−4, 4] by [−2.8, 2.8]
(b)

FIGURE H.80 The graphs of (a) $y = \tan x$ (restricted) and (b) $y = \tan^{-1} x$. The vertical asymptotes of $y = \tan x$ are reflected to become the horizontal asymptotes of $y = \tan^{-1} x$.
(Example 4)

When we reflect the graph of $y = \tan x$ about the line $y = x$ to get the graph of $y = \tan^{-1} x$, the vertical asymptotes $x = \pm\pi/2$ become horizontal asymptotes $y = \pm\pi/2$. We can state the end behavior accordingly:

$$\lim_{x \to -\infty} \tan^{-1} x = -\frac{\pi}{2} \quad \text{and} \quad \lim_{x \to +\infty} \tan^{-1} x = \frac{\pi}{2}.$$

Now try Exercise 21.

What about Arccot, Arcsec, and Arccsc?

Because we already have inverse functions for their reciprocals, we do not really need inverse functions for cot, sec, and csc for computational purposes. Moreover, the decision of how to choose the range of arcsec and arccsc is not as straightforward as with the other functions. See Exercises 57, 65, and 66.

Composing Trigonometric and Inverse Trigonometric Functions

We have already seen the need for caution when applying the Inverse Composition Rule to the trigonometric functions and their inverses (Examples 1e and 3c). The following equations are *always* true whenever they are defined:

$$\sin (\sin^{-1}(x)) = x \qquad \cos (\cos^{-1}(x)) = x \qquad \tan (\tan^{-1}(x)) = x$$

On the other hand, the following equations are true only for x-values in the "restricted" domains of sin, cos, and tan:

$$\sin^{-1}(\sin(x)) = x \quad \cos^{-1}(\cos(x)) = x \quad \tan^{-1}(\tan(x)) = x$$

 An even more interesting phenomenon occurs when we compose inverse trigonometric functions of one kind with trigonometric functions of another kind, as in $\sin(\tan^{-1}x)$. Surprisingly, these trigonometric compositions reduce to algebraic functions that involve no trigonometry at all! This curious situation has profound implications in calculus, where it is sometimes useful to decompose nontrigonometric functions into trigonometric components that seem to come out of nowhere. Try Exploration 1.

EXPLORATION 1   Finding Inverse Trig Functions of Trig Functions

In the right triangle shown to the right, the angle θ is measured in radians.

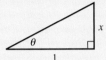

1. Find $\tan \theta$.

2. Find $\tan^{-1} x$.

3. Find the hypotenuse of the triangle as a function of x.

4. Find $\sin(\tan^{-1}(x))$ as a ratio involving no trig functions.

5. Find $\sec(\tan^{-1}(x))$ as a ratio involving no trig functions.

6. If $x < 0$, then $\tan^{-1} x$ is a negative angle in the fourth quadrant (Figure H.81). Verify that your answers to parts (4) and (5) are still valid in this case.

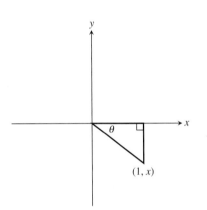

FIGURE H.81 If $x < 0$, then $\theta = \tan^{-1} x$ is an angle in the fourth quadrant. (Exploration 1)

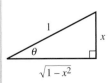

FIGURE H.82 A triangle in which $\theta = \sin^{-1} x$. (Example 5)

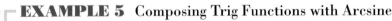 **EXAMPLE 5   Composing Trig Functions with Arcsine**

Compose each of the six basic trig functions with $\sin^{-1} x$ and reduce the composite function to an algebraic expression involving no trig functions.

SOLUTION This time we begin with the triangle shown in Figure H.82, in which $\theta = \sin^{-1} x$. (This triangle could appear in the fourth quadrant if x were negative, but the trig ratios would be the same.)

The remaining side of the triangle (which is $\cos \theta$) can be found by the Pythagorean Theorem. If we denote the unknown side by s, we have

$$s^2 + x^2 = 1$$
$$s^2 = 1 - x^2$$
$$s = \pm\sqrt{1 - x^2}$$

Note the ambiguous sign, which requires a further look. Since $\sin^{-1} x$ is always in Quadrant I or IV, the horizontal side of the triangle can only be positive.

Therefore, we can actually write s unambiguously as $\sqrt{1 - x^2}$, giving us the triangle in Figure H.83.

FIGURE H.83 If $\theta = \sin^{-1} x$, then $\cos \theta = \sqrt{1 - x^2}$. Note that $\cos \theta$ will be positive because $\sin^{-1} x$ can only be in Quadrant I or IV. (Example 5)

(continued)

We can now read all the required ratios straight from the triangle:

$$\sin\left(\sin^{-1}(x)\right) = x \qquad\qquad \csc\left(\sin^{-1}(x)\right) = \frac{1}{x}$$

$$\cos\left(\sin^{-1}(x)\right) = \sqrt{1 - x^2} \qquad\qquad \sec\left(\sin^{-1}(x)\right) = \frac{1}{\sqrt{1 - x^2}}$$

$$\tan\left(\sin^{-1}(x)\right) = \frac{x}{\sqrt{1 - x^2}} \qquad\qquad \cot\left(\sin^{-1}(x)\right) = \frac{\sqrt{1 - x^2}}{x}$$

Now try Exercise 47.

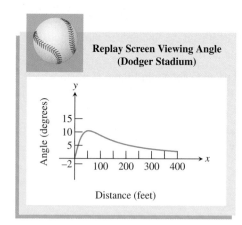

FIGURE H.84 The diagram for the stadium screen. (Example 6)

Replay Screen Viewing Angle
(Dodger Stadium)

FIGURE H.85 Viewing angle θ as a function of distance x from the wall. (Example 6)

Applications of Inverse Trigonometric Functions

When an application involves an angle as a dependent variable, as in $\theta = f(x)$, then to solve for x, it is natural to use an inverse trigonometric function and find $x = f^{-1}(\theta)$.

EXAMPLE 6 Calculating a Viewing Angle

The bottom of a 20-foot replay screen at Dodger Stadium is 45 feet above the playing field. As you move away from the wall, the angle formed by the screen at your eye changes. There is a distance from the wall at which the angle is the greatest. What is that distance?

SOLUTION

Model

The angle subtended by the screen is represented in Figure H.84 by θ, and $\theta = \theta_1 - \theta_2$. Since $\tan\theta_1 = 65/x$, it follows that $\theta_1 = \tan^{-1}(65/x)$. Similarly, $\theta_2 = \tan^{-1}(45/x)$. Thus,

$$\theta = \tan^{-1}\frac{65}{x} - \tan^{-1}\frac{45}{x}.$$

Solve Graphically

Figure H.85 shows a graph of θ that reflects degree mode. The question about distance for maximum viewing angle can be answered by finding the x-coordinate of the maximum point of this graph. Using grapher methods we see that this maximum occurs when $x \approx 54$ feet.

Therefore the maximum angle subtended by the replay screen occurs about 54 feet from the wall.

Now try Exercise 55.

Exercise numbers with a gray background indicate problems that the authors have designed to be solved *without a calculator.*

In Exercises 1–12, find the exact value.

1. $\sin^{-1}\left(\dfrac{\sqrt{3}}{2}\right)$

2. $\sin^{-1}\left(-\dfrac{1}{2}\right)$

3. $\tan^{-1} 0$

4. $\cos^{-1} 1$

5. $\cos^{-1}\left(\dfrac{1}{2}\right)$

6. $\tan^{-1} 1$

7. $\tan^{-1}(-1)$

8. $\cos^{-1}\left(-\dfrac{\sqrt{3}}{2}\right)$

9. $\sin^{-1}\left(-\dfrac{1}{\sqrt{2}}\right)$

10. $\tan^{-1}(-\sqrt{3})$

11. $\cos^{-1} 0$

12. $\sin^{-1} 1$

In Exercises 13–16, use a calculator to find the approximate value. Express your answer in degrees.

13. $\sin^{-1}(0.362)$

14. $\arcsin 0.67$

15. $\tan^{-1}(-12.5)$

16. $\cos^{-1}(-0.23)$

In Exercises 17–20, use a calculator to find the approximate value. Express your result in radians.

17. $\tan^{-1}(2.37)$

18. $\tan^{-1}(22.8)$

19. $\sin^{-1}(-0.46)$

20. $\cos^{-1}(-0.853)$

In Exercises 21 and 22, describe the end behavior of the function.

21. $y = \tan^{-1}(x^2)$

22. $y = (\tan^{-1} x)^2$

In Exercises 23–32, find the exact value without a calculator.

23. $\cos(\sin^{-1}(1/2))$

24. $\sin(\tan^{-1} 1)$

25. $\sin^{-1}(\cos(\pi/4))$

26. $\cos^{-1}(\cos(7\pi/4))$

27. $\cos(2\sin^{-1}(1/2))$

28. $\sin(\tan^{-1}(-1))$

29. $\arcsin(\cos(\pi/3))$

30. $\arccos(\tan(\pi/4))$

31. $\cos(\tan^{-1}\sqrt{3})$

32. $\tan^{-1}(\cos \pi)$

In Exercises 33–36, analyze each function for domain, range, continuity, increasing or decreasing behavior, symmetry, boundedness, extrema, asymptotes, and end behavior.

33. $f(x) = \sin^{-1} x$

34. $f(x) = \cos^{-1} x$

35. $f(x) = \tan^{-1} x$

36. $f(x) = \cot^{-1} x$ (See graph in Exercise 61.)

In Exercises 37–40, use transformations to describe how the graph of the function is related to a basic inverse trigonometric graph. State the domain and range.

37. $f(x) = \sin^{-1}(2x)$

38. $g(x) = 3\cos^{-1}(2x)$

39. $h(x) = 5\tan^{-1}(x/2)$

40. $g(x) = 3\arccos(x/2)$

In Exercises 41–46, find the solution to the equation without a calculator.

41. $\sin(\sin^{-1} x) = 1$

42. $\cos^{-1}(\cos x) = 1$

43. $2\sin x = 1$

44. $\tan x = -1$

45. $\cos(\cos^{-1} x) = 1/3$

46. $\sin^{-1}(\sin x) = \pi/10$

In Exercises 47–52, find an algebraic expression equivalent to the given expression. (*Hint:* Form a right triangle as done in Example 5.)

47. $\sin(\tan^{-1} x)$

48. $\cos(\tan^{-1} x)$

49. $\tan(\arcsin x)$

50. $\cot(\arccos x)$

51. $\cos(\arctan 2x)$

52. $\sin(\arccos 3x)$

53. Group Activity Viewing Angle You are standing in an art museum viewing a picture. The bottom of the picture is 2 ft above your eye level, and the picture is 12 ft tall. Angle θ is formed by the lines of vision to the bottom and to the top of the picture.

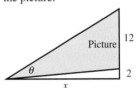

(a) Show that $\theta = \tan^{-1}\left(\dfrac{14}{x}\right) - \tan^{-1}\left(\dfrac{2}{x}\right)$.

(b) Graph θ in the $[0, 25]$ by $[0, 55]$ viewing window using degree mode. Use your grapher to show that the maximum value of θ occurs approximately 5.3 ft from the picture.

(c) How far (to the nearest foot) are you standing from the wall if $\theta = 35°$?

54. Group Activity Analysis of a Lighthouse A rotating beacon L stands 3 m across the harbor from the nearest point P along a straight shoreline. As the light rotates, it forms an angle θ as shown in the figure, and illuminates a point Q on the same shoreline as P.

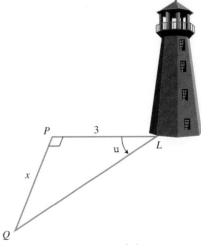

(a) Show that $\theta = \tan^{-1}\left(\dfrac{x}{3}\right)$.

(b) Graph θ in the viewing window $[-20, 20]$ by $[-90, 90]$ using degree mode. What do negative values of x represent in the problem? What does a positive angle represent? A negative angle?

(c) Find θ when $x = 15$.

55. Rising Hot-Air Balloon   The hot-air balloon festival held each year in Phoenix, Arizona, is a popular event for photographers. Jo Silver, an award-winning photographer at the event, watches a balloon rising from ground level from a point 500 ft away on level ground.

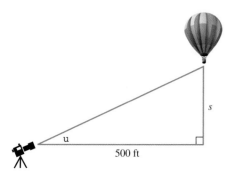

(a) Write θ as a function of the height s of the balloon.

(b) Is the change in θ greater as s changes from 10 ft to 20 ft, or as s changes from 200 ft to 210 ft? Explain.

(c) **Writing to Learn**   In the graph of this relationship shown here, do you think that the x-axis represents the height s and the y-axis angle θ, or does the x-axis represent angle θ and the y-axis height s? Explain.

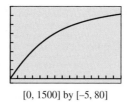

[0, 1500] by [–5, 80]

56. Find the domain and range of each of the following functions.

(a) $f(x) = \sin\left(\sin^{-1} x\right)$

(b) $g(x) = \sin^{-1}(x) + \cos^{-1}(x)$

(c) $h(x) = \sin^{-1}(\sin x)$

(d) $k(x) = \sin\left(\cos^{-1} x\right)$

(e) $q(x) = \cos^{-1}(\sin x)$

Explorations

57. Writing to Learn   Using the format demonstrated in this section for the inverse sine, cosine, and tangent functions, give a careful definition of the inverse cotangent function. [*Hint:* The range of $y = \cot^{-1} x$ is $(0, \pi)$.]

58. Writing to Learn   Use an appropriately labeled triangle to explain why $\sin^{-1} x + \cos^{-1} x = \pi/2$. For what values of x is the left-hand side of this equation defined?

59. Graph each of the following functions and interpret the graph to find the domain, range, and period of each function. Which of the three functions has points of discontinuity? Are the discontinuities removable or nonremovable?

(a) $y = \sin^{-1}(\sin x)$

(b) $y = \cos^{-1}(\cos x)$

(c) $y = \tan^{-1}(\tan x)$

Extending the Ideas

60. Practicing for Calculus   Express each of the following functions as an algebraic expression involving no trig functions.

(a) $\cos\left(\sin^{-1} 2x\right)$ (b) $\sec^2\left(\tan^{-1} x\right)$

(c) $\sin\left(\cos^{-1}\sqrt{x}\right)$ (d) $-\csc^2\left(\cot^{-1} x\right)$

(e) $\tan\left(\sec^{-1} x^2\right)$

61. Arccotangent on the Calculator   Most graphing calculators do not have a button for the inverse cotangent. The graph is shown below. Find an expression that you can put into your calculator to produce a graph of $y = \cot^{-1} x$.

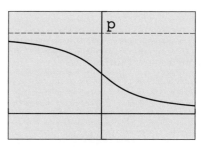

[–3, 3] by [–1, 4]

62. Advanced Decomposition   Decompose each of the following algebraic functions by writing it as a trig function of an arctrig function.

(a) $\sqrt{1 - x^2}$ (b) $\dfrac{x}{\sqrt{1 + x^2}}$ (c) $\dfrac{x}{\sqrt{1 - x^2}}$

63. Use elementary transformations and the arctangent function to construct a function with domain all real numbers that has horizontal asymptotes at $y = 24$ and $y = 42$.

64. Avoiding Ambiguities   When choosing the right triangle in Example 5, we used a hypotenuse of 1. It is sometimes necessary to use a variable quantity for the hypotenuse, in which case it is a good idea to use x^2 rather than x, just in case x is negative. (All of our definitions of the trig functions have involved triangles in which the hypotenuse is assumed to be positive.)

(a) If we use the triangle below to represent $\theta = \sin^{-1}(1/x)$, explain why side s must be positive regardless of the sign of x.

(b) Use the triangle in part (a) to find $\tan\left(\sin^{-1}(1/x)\right)$.

(c) Using an appropriate triangle, find $\sin\left(\cos^{-1}(1/x)\right)$.

65. Defining Arcsecant   The range of the secant function is $(-\infty, -1] \cup [1, \infty)$, which must become the domain of the arcsecant function. The graph of $y = \text{arcsec } x$ must therefore be the union of two unbroken curves. Two possible graphs with the correct domain are shown below.

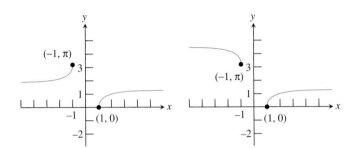

(a) The graph on the left has one horizontal asymptote. What is it?

(b) The graph on the right has two horizontal asymptotes. What are they?

(c) Which of these graphs is also the graph of $y = \cos^{-1}(1/x)$?

(d) Which of these graphs is increasing on both connected intervals?

66. Defining Arccosecant   The range of the cosecant function is $(-\infty, -1] \cup [1, \infty)$, which must become the domain of the arccosecant function. The graph of $y = \text{arccsc } x$ must therefore be the union of two unbroken curves. Two possible graphs with the correct domain are shown below.

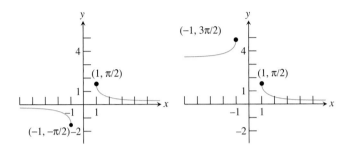

(a) The graph on the left has one horizontal asymptote. What is it?

(b) The graph on the right has two horizontal asymptotes. What are they?

(c) Which of these graphs is also the graph of $y = \sin^{-1}(1/x)$?

(d) Which of these graphs is decreasing on both connected intervals?

What you'll learn about
- More Right Triangle Problems
- Simple Harmonic Motion

... and why
These problems illustrate some of the better-known applications of trigonometry.

H-9 Solving Problems with Trigonometry

More Right Triangle Problems

An **angle of elevation** is the angle through which the eye moves up from horizontal to look at something above, and an **angle of depression** is the angle through which the eye moves down from horizontal to look at something below. For two observers at different elevations looking at each other, the angle of elevation for one equals the angle of depression for the other. The concepts are illustrated in Figure H.86 as they might apply to observers at Mount Rushmore or the Grand Canyon.

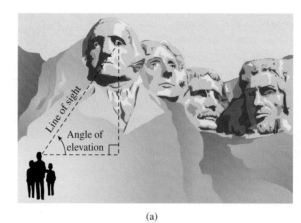
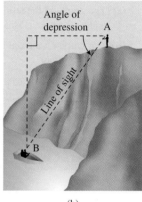

(a) (b)

FIGURE H.86 (a) Angle of elevation at Mount Rushmore. (b) Angle of depression at the Grand Canyon.

EXAMPLE 1 Using Angle of Depression

The angle of depression of a buoy from the top of the Barnegat Bay lighthouse 130 feet above the surface of the water is 6°. Find the distance x from the base of the lighthouse to the buoy.

SOLUTION Figure H.87 models the situation.

In the diagram, $\theta = 6°$ because the angle of elevation from the buoy equals the angle of depression from the lighthouse. We **solve algebraically** using the tangent function:

$$\tan \theta = \tan 6° = \frac{130}{x}$$

$$x = \frac{130}{\tan 6°} \approx 1236.9$$

Interpreting We find that the buoy is about 1237 feet from the base of the lighthouse.

Now try Exercise 3.

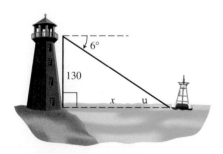

FIGURE H.87 A big lighthouse and a little buoy. (Example 1)

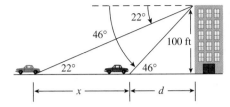

FIGURE H.88 A car approaches Altgelt Hall. (Example 2)

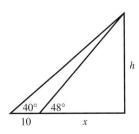

FIGURE H.89 A large, helium-filled penguin. (Example 3)

FIGURE H.90 (Example 3)

EXAMPLE 2 Making Indirect Measurements

From the top of the 100-ft-tall Altgelt Hall a man observes a car moving toward the building. If the angle of depression of the car changes from 22° to 46° during the period of observation, how far does the car travel?

SOLUTION

Solve Algebraically Figure H.88 models the situation. Notice that we have labeled the acute angles at the car's two positions as 22° and 46° (because the angle of elevation from the car equals the angle of depression from the building). Denote the distance the car moves as x. Denote its distance from the building at the second observation as d.

From the smaller right triangle we conclude:

$$\tan 46° = \frac{100}{d}$$

$$d = \frac{100}{\tan 46°}$$

From the larger right triangle we conclude:

$$\tan 22° = \frac{100}{x + d}$$

$$x + d = \frac{100}{\tan 22°}$$

$$x = \frac{100}{\tan 22°} - d$$

$$x = \frac{100}{\tan 22°} - \frac{100}{\tan 46°}$$

$$x \approx 150.9$$

Interpreting our answer, we find that the car travels about 151 feet.

Now try Exercise 7.

EXAMPLE 3 Finding Height Above Ground

A large, helium-filled penguin is moored at the beginning of a parade route awaiting the start of the parade. Two cables attached to the underside of the penguin make angles of 48° and 40° with the ground and are in the same plane as a perpendicular line from the penguin to the ground. (See Figure H.89.) If the cables are attached to the ground 10 feet from each other, how high above the ground is the penguin?

SOLUTION We can simplify the drawing to the two right triangles in Figure H.90 that share the common side h.

Model

By the definition of the tangent function,

$$\frac{h}{x} = \tan 48° \quad \text{and} \quad \frac{h}{x + 10} = \tan 40°.$$

Solve Algebraically

Solving for h,

$$h = x \tan 48° \quad \text{and} \quad h = (x + 10) \tan 40°.$$

(continued)

Set these two expressions for h equal to each other and solve the equation for x:

$$x \tan 48° = (x + 10) \tan 40°$$ Both equal h.

$$x \tan 48° = x \tan 40° + 10 \tan 40°$$

$$x \tan 48° - x \tan 40° = 10 \tan 40°$$ Isolate x terms.

$$x(\tan 48° - \tan 40°) = 10 \tan 40°$$ Factor out x.

$$x = \frac{10 \tan 40°}{\tan 48° - \tan 40°} \approx 30.90459723$$

We retain the full display for x because we are not finished yet; we need to solve for h:

$$h = x \tan 48° = (30.90459723) \tan 48° \approx 34.32$$

The penguin is approximately 34 feet above ground level.

Now try Exercise 15.

EXAMPLE 4 Using Trigonometry in Navigation

A U.S. Coast Guard patrol boat leaves Port Cleveland and averages 35 **knots** (nautical mph) traveling for 2 hours on a course of 53° and then 3 hours on a course of 143°. What is the boat's bearing and distance from Port Cleveland?

SOLUTION Figure H.91 models the situation.

Solve Algebraically In the diagram, line AB is a transversal that cuts a pair of parallel lines. Thus, $\beta = 53°$ because they are alternate interior angles. Angle α, as the supplement of a 143° angle, is 37°. Consequently, $\angle ABC = 90°$ and AC is the hypotenuse of right $\triangle ABC$.

Use distance $=$ rate $\times$ time to determine distances AB and BC.

$$AB = (35 \text{ knots})(2 \text{ hours}) = 70 \text{ nautical miles}$$
$$BC = (35 \text{ knots})(3 \text{ hours}) = 105 \text{ nautical miles}$$

Solve the right triangle for AC and θ.

$$AC = \sqrt{70^2 + 105^2}$$ Pythagorean Theorem
$$AC \approx 126.2$$
$$\theta = \tan^{-1}\left(\frac{105}{70}\right)$$
$$\theta \approx 56.3°$$

Interpreting We find that the boat's bearing from Port Cleveland is $53° + \theta$, or approximately 109.3°. They are about 126 nautical miles out.

Now try Exercise 17.

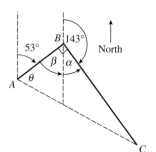

FIGURE H.91 Path of travel for a Coast Guard boat that corners well at 35 knots. (Example 4)

Simple Harmonic Motion

Because of their periodic nature, the sine and cosine functions are helpful in describing the motion of objects that oscillate, vibrate, or rotate. For example, the linkage in Figure H.92 converts the rotary motion of a motor to the back-and-forth motion needed for some machines. When the wheel rotates, the piston moves back and forth.

If the wheel rotates at a constant rate ω radians per second, the back-and-forth motion of the piston is an example of *simple harmonic motion* and can be modeled by an equation of the form

$$d = a \cos \omega t, \quad \omega > 0,$$

where a is the radius of the wheel and d is the directed distance of the piston from its center of oscillation.

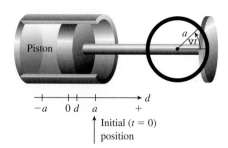

FIGURE H.92 A piston operated by a wheel rotating at a constant rate demonstrates simple harmonic motion.

For the sake of simplicity, we will define simple harmonic motion in terms of a point moving along a number line.

Frequency and Period

Notice that harmonic motion is sinusoidal, with amplitude $|a|$ and period $2\pi/\omega$. The frequency is the reciprocal of the period.

Simple Harmonic Motion

A point moving on a number line is in **simple harmonic motion** if its directed distance d from the origin is given by either

$$d = a \sin \omega t \quad \text{or} \quad d = a \cos \omega t,$$

where a and ω are real numbers and $\omega > 0$. The motion has **frequency** $\omega/2\pi$, which is the number of oscillations per unit of time.

EXPLORATION 1   Watching Harmonic Motion

You can watch harmonic motion on your graphing calculator. Set your grapher to parametric mode and set $X_{1T} = \cos(T)$ and $Y_{1T} = \sin(T)$. Set Tmin $= 0$, Tmax $= 25$, Tstep $= 0.2$, Xmin $= -1.5$, Xmax $= 1.5$, Xscl $= 1$, Ymin $= -100$, Ymax $= 100$, Yscl $= 0$.

If your calculator allows you to change style to graph a moving ball, choose that style. When you graph the function, you will see the ball moving along the x-axis between -1 and 1 in simple harmonic motion. If your grapher does not have the moving ball option, wait for the grapher to finish graphing, then press TRACE and keep your finger pressed on the right arrow key to see the tracer move in simple harmonic motion.

1. For each value of T, the parametrization gives the point $(\cos(T), \sin(T))$. What well-known curve should this parametrization produce?

2. Why does the point seem to go back and forth on the x-axis when it should be following the curve identified in part (1)? [*Hint:* Check that viewing window again!]

3. Why does the point slow down at the extremes and speed up in the middle? [*Hint:* Remember that the grapher is really following the curve identified in part (1).]

4. How can you tell that this point moves in simple harmonic motion?

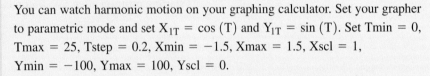

FIGURE H.93 Modeling the path of a piston by a sinusoid. (Example 5)

EXAMPLE 5   Calculating Harmonic Motion

In a mechanical linkage like the one shown in Figure H.92, a wheel with an 8-cm radius turns with an angular velocity of 8π radians/sec.

(a) What is the frequency of the piston?

(b) What is the distance from the starting position $(t = 0)$ exactly 3.45 seconds after starting?

SOLUTION Imagine the wheel to be centered at the origin and let $P(x, y)$ be a point on its perimeter (Figure H.93). As the wheel rotates and P goes around, the motion of the piston follows the path of the x-coordinate of P along the x-axis. The angle determined by P at any time t is $8\pi t$, so its x-coordinate is $8 \cos 8\pi t$. Therefore, the sinusoid $d = 8 \cos 8\pi t$ models the motion of the piston.

(continued)

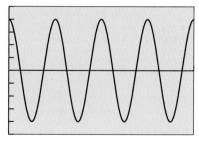

[0, 1] by [−10, 10]

FIGURE H.94 A sinusoid with frequency 4 models the motion of the piston in Example 5.

(a) The frequency of $d = 8 \cos 8\pi t$ is $8\pi/2\pi$, or 4. The piston makes four complete back-and-forth strokes per second. The graph of d as a function of t is shown in Figure H.94. The four cycles of the sinusoidal graph in the interval $[0, 1]$ model the four cycles of the motor or the four strokes of the piston. Note that the sinusoid has a period of 1/4, the reciprocal of the frequency.

(b) We must find the distance between the positions at $t = 0$ and $t = 3.45$.

The initial position at $t = 0$ is

$$d(0) = 8.$$

The position at $t = 3.45$ is

$$d(3.45) = 8 \cos (8\pi \cdot 3.45) \approx 2.47.$$

The distance between the two positions is approximately $8 - 2.47 = 5.53$.

Interpreting our answer, we conclude that the piston is approximately 5.53 cm from its starting position after 3.45 seconds. *Now try Exercise 27.*

EXAMPLE 6 Calculating Harmonic Motion

A mass oscillating up and down on the bottom of a spring (assuming perfect elasticity and no friction or air resistance) can be modeled as harmonic motion. If the weight is displaced a maximum of 5 cm, find the modeling equation if it takes 2 seconds to complete one cycle. (See Figure H.95.)

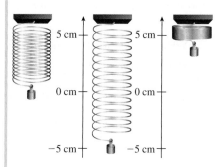

FIGURE H.95 The mass and spring in Example 6.

SOLUTION We have our choice between the two equations $d = a \sin \omega t$ or $d = a \cos \omega t$. Assuming that the spring is at the origin of the coordinate system when $t = 0$, we choose the equation $d = a \sin \omega t$.

Because the maximum displacement is 5 cm, we conclude that the amplitude $a = 5$.

Because it takes 2 seconds to complete one cycle, we conclude that the period is 2 and the frequency is 1/2. Therefore,

$$\frac{\omega}{2\pi} = \frac{1}{2},$$

$$\omega = \pi.$$

Putting it all together, our modeling equation is $d = 5 \sin \pi t$.

Now try Exercise 29.

Exercise numbers with a gray background indicate problems that the authors have designed to be solved *without a calculator*.

In Exercises 1–43, solve the problem using your knowledge of geometry and the techniques of this section. Sketch a figure if one is not provided.

1. **Finding a Cathedral Height** The angle of elevation of the top of the Ulm Cathedral from a point 300 ft away from the base of its steeple on level ground is 60°. Find the height of the cathedral.

300 ft

2. **Finding a Monument Height** From a point 100 ft from its base, the angle of elevation of the top of the Arch of Septimus Severus, in Rome, Italy, is 34°13′12″. How tall is this monument?

3. **Finding a Distance** The angle of depression from the top of the Smoketown Lighthouse 120 ft above the surface of the water to a buoy is 10°. How far is the buoy from the lighthouse?

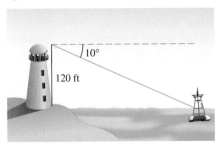

4. **Finding a Baseball Stadium Dimension** The top row of the red seats behind home plate at Cincinnati's Riverfront Stadium is 90 ft above the level of the playing field. The angle of depression to the base of the left field wall is 14°. How far is the base of the left field wall from a point on level ground directly below the top row?

5. **Finding a Guy-Wire Length** A guy wire connects the top of an antenna to a point on level ground 5 ft from the base of the antenna. The angle of elevation formed by this wire is 80°. What are the length of the wire and the height of the antenna?

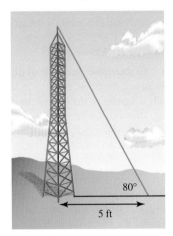

80°

5 ft

6. **Finding a Length** A wire stretches from the top of a vertical pole to a point on level ground 16 ft from the base of the pole. If the wire makes an angle of 62° with the ground, find the height of the pole and the length of the wire.

7. **Height of Eiffel Tower** The angle of elevation of the top of the TV antenna mounted on top of the Eiffel Tower in Paris is measured to be 80°1′12″ at a point 185 ft from the base of the tower. How tall is the tower plus TV antenna?

8. **Finding the Height of Tallest Chimney** The world's tallest smokestack at the International Nickel Co., Sudbury, Ontario, casts a shadow that is approximately 1580 ft long when the Sun's angle of elevation (measured from the horizon) is 38°. How tall is the smokestack?

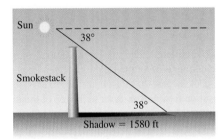

Sun
38°
Smokestack
38°
Shadow = 1580 ft

9. **Cloud Height** To measure the height of a cloud, you place a bright searchlight directly below the cloud and shine the beam straight up. From a point 100 ft away from the searchlight, you measure the angle of elevation of the cloud to be 83°12′. How high is the cloud?

10. **Ramping Up** A ramp leading to a freeway overpass is 470 ft long and rises 32 ft. What is the average angle of inclination of the ramp to the nearest tenth of a degree?

11. **Antenna Height** A guy wire attached to the top of the KSAM radio antenna is anchored at a point on the ground 10 m from the antenna's base. If the wire makes an angle of 55° with level ground, how high is the KSAM antenna?

12. **Building Height** To determine the height of the Louisiana-Pacific (LP) Tower, the tallest building in Conroe, Texas, a surveyor stands at a point on the ground, level with the base of the LP building. He measures the point to be 125 ft from the building's base and the angle of elevation to the top of the building to be 29°48′. Find the height of the building.

13. **Navigation** The *Paz Verde*, a whalewatch boat, is located at point *P*, and *L* is the nearest point on the Baja California shore. Point *Q* is located 4.25 mi down the shoreline from *L* and $\overline{PL} \perp \overline{LQ}$. Determine the distance that the *Paz Verde* is from the shore if $\angle PQL = 35°$.

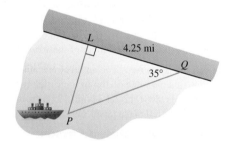

14. **Recreational Hiking** While hiking on a level path toward Colorado's front range, Otis Evans determines that the angle of elevation to the top of Long's Peak is 30°. Moving 1000 ft closer to the mountain, Otis determines the angle of elevation to be 35°. How much higher is the top of Long's Peak than Otis's elevation?

15. **Civil Engineering** The angle of elevation from an observer to the bottom edge of the Delaware River drawbridge observation deck located 200 ft from the observer is 30°. The angle of elevation from the observer to the top of the observation deck is 40°. What is the height of the observation deck?

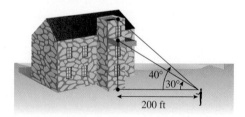

16. **Traveling Car** From the top of a 100-ft building a man observes a car moving toward him. If the angle of depression of the car changes from 15° to 33° during the period of observation, how far does the car travel?

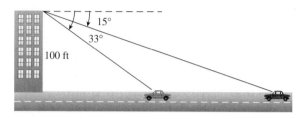

17. **Navigation** The Coast Guard cutter *Angelica* travels at 30 knots from its home port of Corpus Christi on a course of 95° for 2 hr and then changes to a course of 185° for 2 hr. Find the distance and the bearing from the Corpus Christi port to the boat.

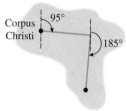

18. **Navigation** The *Cerrito Lindo* travels at a speed of 40 knots from Fort Lauderdale on a course of 65° for 2 hr and then changes to a course of 155° for 4 hr. Determine the distance and the bearing from Fort Lauderdale to the boat.

19. **Land Measure** The angle of depression is 19° from a point 7256 ft above sea level on the north rim of the Grand Canyon level to a point 6159 ft above sea level on the south rim. How wide is the canyon at that point?

20. **Ranger Fire Watch** A ranger spots a fire from a 73-ft tower in Yellowstone National Park. She measures the angle of depression to be 1°20′. How far is the fire from the tower?

21. **Civil Engineering** The bearing of the line of sight to the east end of the Royal Gorge footbridge from a point 325 ft due north of the west end of the footbridge across the Royal Gorge is 117°. What is the length *l* of the bridge?

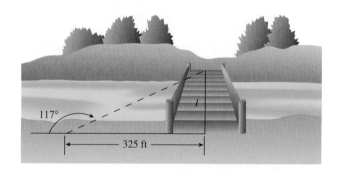

22. Space Flight The angle of elevation of a space shuttle from Cape Canaveral is 17° when the shuttle is directly over a ship 12 mi downrange. What is the altitude of the shuttle when it is directly over the ship?

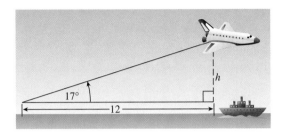

23. Architectural Design A barn roof is constructed as shown in the figure. What is the height of the vertical center span?

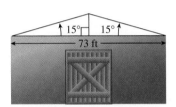

24. Recreational Flying A hot-air balloon over Park City, Utah, is 760 ft above the ground. The angle of depression from the balloon to an observer is 5.25°. Assuming the ground is relatively flat, how far is the observer from a point on the ground directly under the balloon?

25. Navigation A shoreline runs north-south, and a boat is due east of the shoreline. The bearings of the boat from two points on the shore are 110° and 100°. Assume the two points are 550 ft apart. How far is the boat from the shore?

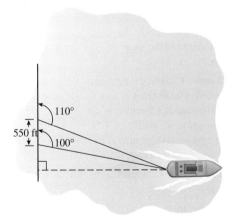

26. Navigation Milwaukee, Wisconsin, is directly west of Grand Haven, Michigan, on opposite sides of Lake Michigan. On a foggy night, a law enforcement boat leaves from Milwaukee on a course of 105° at the same time that a small smuggling craft steers a course of 195° from Grand Haven. The law enforcement boat averages 23 knots and collides with the smuggling craft. What was the smuggling boat's average speed?

27. Mechanical Design *Refer to Figure H.92.* The wheel in a piston linkage like the one shown in the figure has a radius of 6 in. It turns with an angular velocity of 16π rad/sec. The initial position is the same as that shown in Figure H.92.

  (a) What is the frequency of the piston?

  (b) What equation models the motion of the piston?

  (c) What is the distance from the initial position 2.85 sec after starting?

28. Mechanical Design Suppose the wheel in a piston linkage like the one shown in Figure H.92 has a radius of 18 cm and turns with an angular velocity of π rad/sec.

  (a) What is the frequency of the piston?

  (b) What equation models the motion of the piston?

  (c) How many cycles does the piston make in 1 min?

29. Vibrating Spring A mass on a spring oscillates back and forth and completes one cycle in 0.5 sec. Its maximum displacement is 3 cm. Write an equation that models this motion.

30. Tuning Fork A point on the tip of a tuning fork vibrates in harmonic motion described by the equation $d = 14 \sin \omega t$. Find ω for a tuning fork that has a frequency of 528 vibrations per second.

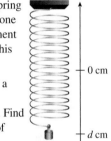

31. Ferris Wheel Motion The Ferris wheel shown in this figure makes one complete turn every 20 sec. A rider's height, h, above the ground can be modeled by the equation $h = a \sin \omega t + k$, where h and k are given in feet and t is given in seconds.

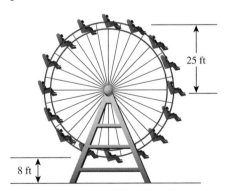

  (a) What is the value of a?

  (b) What is the value of k?

  (c) What is the value of ω?

32. Ferris Wheel Motion Jacob and Emily ride a Ferris wheel at a carnival in Billings, Montana. The wheel has a 16-m diameter and turns at 3 rpm with its lowest point 1 m above the ground. Assume that Jacob and Emily's height h above the ground is a sinusoidal function of time t (in seconds), where $t = 0$ represents the lowest point of the wheel.

(a) Write an equation for h.

(b) Draw a graph of h for $0 \leq t \leq 30$.

(c) Use h to estimate Jacob and Emily's height above the ground at $t = 4$ and $t = 10$.

33. Monthly Temperatures in Charleston The monthly normal mean temperatures for the last 30 years in Charleston, SC, are shown in Table H.26. A scatter plot suggests that the mean monthly temperatures follow a sinusoidal curve over time. Assume that the sinusoid has equation $y = a \sin (b (t - h)) + k$.

(a) Given that the period is 12 months, find b.

(b) Assuming that the high and low temperatures in the table determine the range of the sinusoid, find a and k.

(c) Find a value of h that will put the minimum at $t = 1$ and the maximum at $t = 7$.

(d) Superimpose a graph of your sinusoid on a scatter plot of the data. How good is the fit?

(e) Use your sinusoidal model to predict dates in the year when the mean temperature in Charleston will be 70°. (Assume that $t = 0$ represents January 1.)

Table H.26 Temperature Data for Charleston, SC

Month	Temperature
1	48
2	51
3	58
4	64
5	72
6	78
7	82
8	81
9	76
10	66
11	58
12	51

Source: National Climatic Data Center, as reported in the World Almanac and Book of Facts 2009.

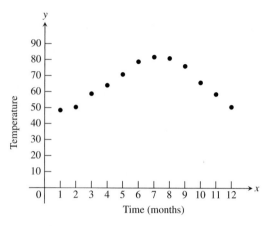

34. Writing to Learn For the Ferris wheel in Exercise 31, which equation correctly models the height of a rider who begins the ride at the bottom of the wheel when $t = 0$?

(a) $h = 25 \sin \dfrac{\pi t}{10}$

(b) $h = 25 \sin \dfrac{\pi t}{10} + 8$

(c) $h = 25 \sin \dfrac{\pi t}{10} + 33$

(d) $h = 25 \sin \left(\dfrac{\pi t}{10} + \dfrac{3\pi}{2} \right) + 33$

Explain your thought process, and use of a graphing utility in choosing the correct modeling equation.

35. Monthly Sales Owing to startup costs and seasonal variations, Gina found that the monthly profit in her bagel shop during the first year followed an up-and-down pattern that could be modeled by $P = 2t - 7 \sin (\pi t/3)$, where P was measured in hundreds of dollars and t was measured in months after January 1.

(a) In what month did the shop first begin to make money?

(b) In what month did the shop enjoy its greatest profit in that first year?

36. Weight Loss Courtney tried several different diets over a two-year period in an attempt to lose weight. She found that her weight W followed a fluctuating curve that could be modeled by the function $W = 220 - 1.5t + 9.81 \sin (\pi t/4)$, where t was measured in months after January 1 of the first year and W was measured in pounds.

(a) What was Courtney's weight at the start and at the end of two years?

(b) What was her maximum weight during the two-year period?

(c) What was her minimum weight during the two-year period?

Explorations

37. Group Activity The data for displacement versus time on a tuning fork, shown in Table H.27, were collected using a CBL and a microphone.

Table H.27 Tuning Fork Data

Time	Displacement	Time	Displacement
0.00091	−0.080	0.00362	0.217
0.00108	0.200	0.00379	0.480
0.00125	0.480	0.00398	0.681
0.00144	0.693	0.00416	0.810
0.00162	0.816	0.00435	0.827
0.00180	0.844	0.00453	0.749
0.00198	0.771	0.00471	0.581
0.00216	0.603	0.00489	0.346
0.00234	0.368	0.00507	0.077
0.00253	0.099	0.00525	−0.164
0.00271	−0.141	0.00543	−0.320
0.00289	−0.309	0.00562	−0.354
0.00307	−0.348	0.00579	−0.248
0.00325	−0.248	0.00598	−0.035
0.00344	−0.041		

(a) Graph a scatter plot of the data in the $[0, 0.0062]$ by $[-0.5, 1]$ viewing window.

(b) Select the equation that appears to be the best fit of these data.

i. $y = 0.6 \sin (2464x - 2.84) + 0.25$

ii. $y = 0.6 \sin (1210x - 2) + 0.25$

iii. $y = 0.6 \sin (2440x - 2.1) + 0.15$

(c) What is the approximate frequency of the tuning fork?

38. Writing to Learn Human sleep-awake cycles at three different ages are described by the accompanying graphs. The portions of the graphs above the horizontal lines represent times awake, and the portions below represent times asleep.

Newborn

Four years

Adult

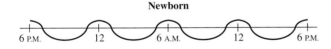

(a) What is the period of the sleep-awake cycle of a newborn? of a four-year-old? of an adult?

(b) Which of these three sleep-awake cycles is the closest to being modeled by a function $y = a \sin bx$?

Using Trigonometry in Geometry In a *regular polygon* all sides have equal length and all angles have equal measure. In Exercises 39 and 40, consider the regular seven-sided polygon whose sides are 5 cm.

39. Find the length of the *apothem*, the segment from the center of the seven-sided polygon to the midpoint of a side.

40. Find the radius of the circumscribed circle of the regular seven-sided polygon.

41. A *rhombus* is a quadrilateral with all sides equal in length. Recall that a rhombus is also a parallelogram. Find length AC and length BD in the rhombus shown here.

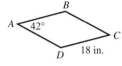

Extending the Ideas

42. A roof has two sections, one with a 50° elevation and the other with a 20° elevation, as shown in the figure.

(a) Find the height BE.

(b) Find the height CD.

(c) Find the length $AE + ED$, and double it to find the length of the roofline.

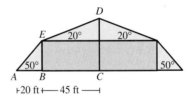

43. Steep Trucking The *percentage grade* of a road is its slope expressed as a percentage. A tractor-trailer rig passes a sign that reads, "6% grade next 7 miles." What is the average angle of inclination of the road?

44. Television Coverage Many satellites travel in *geosynchronous orbits*, which means that the satellite stays over the same point on the Earth. A satellite that broadcasts cable television is in geosynchronous orbit 100 mi above the Earth. Assume that the Earth is a sphere with radius 4000 mi, and find the arc length of coverage area for the cable television satellite on the Earth's surface.

45. Group Activity A musical note like that produced with a tuning fork or pitch meter is a pressure wave. Typically, frequency is measured in hertz (1 Hz = 1 cycle per second). Table H.28 gives frequency (in Hz) of several musical notes. The time-vs.-pressure tuning fork data in Table H.29 was collected using a CBL and a microphone.

Table H.28 Tuning Fork Data

Note	Frequency (Hz)
C	262
C♯ or D♭	277
D	294
D♯ or E♭	311
E	330
F	349
F♯ or G♭	370
G	392
G♯ or A♭	415
A	440
A♯ or B♭	466
B	494
C (next octave)	524

Table H.29 Tuning Fork Data

Time (sec)	Pressure	Time (sec)	Pressure
0.0002368	1.29021	0.0049024	−1.06632
0.0005664	1.50851	0.0051520	0.09235
0.0008256	1.51971	0.0054112	1.44694
0.0010752	1.51411	0.0056608	1.51411
0.0013344	1.47493	0.0059200	1.51971
0.0015840	0.45619	0.0061696	1.51411
0.0018432	−0.89280	0.0064288	1.43015
0.0020928	−1.51412	0.0066784	0.19871
0.0023520	−1.15588	0.0069408	−1.06072
0.0026016	−0.04758	0.0071904	−1.51412
0.0028640	1.36858	0.0074496	−0.97116
0.0031136	1.50851	0.0076992	0.23229
0.0033728	1.51971	0.0079584	1.46933
0.0036224	1.51411	0.0082080	1.51411
0.0038816	1.45813	0.0084672	1.51971
0.0041312	0.32185	0.0087168	1.50851
0.0043904	−0.97676	0.0089792	1.36298
0.0046400	−1.51971		

(a) Graph a scatter plot of the data.

(b) Determine a, b, and h so that the equation $y = a \sin (b(t - h))$ is a model for the data.

(c) Determine the frequency of the sinusoid in part (b), and use Table H.28 to identify the musical note produced by the tuning fork.

(d) Identify the musical note produced by the tuning fork used in Exercise 37.

H-10 Polar Coordinates

What you'll learn about

- Polar Coordinate System
- Coordinate Conversion
- Equation Conversion
- Finding Distance Using Polar Coordinates

... and why

Use of polar coordinates sometimes simplifies complicated rectangular equations and they are useful in calculus.

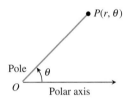

FIGURE H.96 The polar coordinate system.

Polar Coordinate System

A **polar coordinate system** is a plane with a point O, the **pole**, and a ray from O, the **polar axis**, as shown in Figure H.96. Each point P in the plane is assigned as **polar coordinates** follows: r is the **directed distance** from O to P, and θ is the **directed angle** whose initial side is on the polar axis and whose terminal side is on the line OP.

As in trigonometry, we measure θ as positive when moving counterclockwise and negative when moving clockwise. If $r > 0$, then P is on the terminal side of θ. If $r < 0$, then P is on the terminal side of $\theta + \pi$. We can use radian or degree measure for the angle θ as illustrated in Example 1.

EXAMPLE 1   Plotting Points in the Polar Coordinate System

Plot the points with the given polar coordinates.

(a) $P(2, \pi/3)$ **(b)** $Q(-1, 3\pi/4)$ **(c)** $R(3, -45°)$

SOLUTION Figure H.97 shows the three points.   *Now try Exercise 7.*

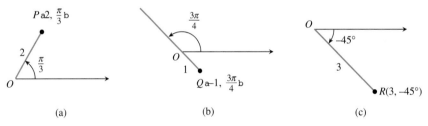

(a)   (b)   (c)

FIGURE H.97 The three points in Example 1.

Each polar coordinate pair determines a unique point. However, the polar coordinates of a point P in the plane are not unique.

EXAMPLE 2   Finding All Polar Coordinates for a Point

If the point P has polar coordinates $(3, \pi/3)$, find all polar coordinates for P.

SOLUTION Point P is shown in Figure H.98. Two additional pairs of polar coordinates for P are

$$\left(3, \frac{\pi}{3} + 2\pi\right) = \left(3, \frac{7\pi}{3}\right) \quad \text{and} \quad \left(-3, \frac{\pi}{3} + \pi\right) = \left(-3, \frac{4\pi}{3}\right)$$

We can use these two pairs of polar coordinates for P to write the rest of the possibilities:

$$\left(3, \frac{\pi}{3} + 2n\pi\right) = \left(3, \frac{(6n + 1)\pi}{3}\right) \text{ or}$$

$$\left(-3, \frac{\pi}{3} + (2n + 1)\pi\right) = \left(-3, \frac{(6n + 4)\pi}{3}\right)$$

where n is any integer.   *Now try Exercise 23.*

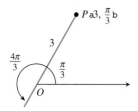

FIGURE H.98 The point P in Example 2.

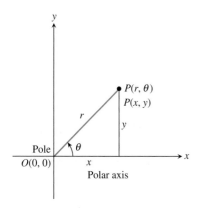

FIGURE H.99 Polar and rectangular coordinates for P.

The coordinates (r, θ), $(r, \theta + 2\pi)$, and $(-r, \theta + \pi)$ all name the same point. In general, the point with polar coordinates (r, θ) also has the following polar coordinates:

Finding all Polar Coordinates of a Point

Let P have polar coordinates (r, θ). Any other polar coordinate of P must be of the form

$$(r, \theta + 2n\pi) \text{ or } (-r, \theta + (2n + 1)\pi)$$

where n is any integer. In particular, the pole has polar coordinates $(0, \theta)$, where θ is any angle.

Coordinate Conversion

When we use both polar coordinates and Cartesian coordinates, the pole is the origin and the polar axis is the positive x-axis as shown in Figure H.99. By applying trigonometry we can find equations that relate the polar coordinates (r, θ) and the rectangular coordinates (x, y) of a point P.

Coordinate Conversion Equations

Let the point P have polar coordinates (r, θ) and rectangular coordinates (x, y). Then

$$x = r \cos \theta, \qquad r^2 = x^2 + y^2,$$
$$y = r \sin \theta, \quad \tan \theta = \frac{y}{x}.$$

These relationships allow us to convert from one coordinate system to the other.

> **EXAMPLE 3** Converting from Polar to Rectangular Coordinates
>
> Use an algebraic method to find the rectangular coordinates of the points with given polar coordinates. Approximate exact solution values with a calculator when appropriate.
>
> **(a)** $P(3, 5\pi/6)$ **(b)** $Q(2, -200°)$
>
> **SOLUTION**
>
> **(a)** For $P(3, 5\pi/6)$, $r = 3$ and $\theta = 5\pi/6$:
>
> $$x = r \cos \theta \qquad\qquad y = r \sin \theta$$
> $$x = 3 \cos \frac{5\pi}{6} \quad \text{and} \quad y = 3 \sin \frac{5\pi}{6}$$
> $$x = 3\left(-\frac{\sqrt{3}}{2}\right) \approx -2.60 \qquad y = 3\left(\frac{1}{2}\right) = 1.5$$
>
> The rectangular coordinates for P are $(-3\sqrt{3}/2, 1.5) \approx (-2.60, 1.5)$ (Figure H.100a).
>
> **(b)** For $Q(2, -200°)$, $r = 2$ and $\theta = -200°$:
>
> $$x = r \cos \theta \qquad\qquad y = r \sin \theta$$
> $$x = 2 \cos (-200°) \approx -1.88 \quad \text{and} \quad y = 2 \sin (-200°) \approx 0.68$$
>
> The rectangular coordinates for Q are approximately $(-1.88, 0.68)$ (Figure H.100b).
>
> *Now try Exercise 15.*

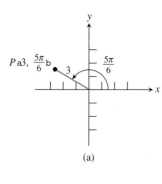

(a)

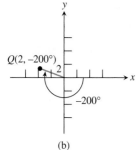

(b)

FIGURE H.100 The points P and Q in Example 3.

When converting rectangular coordinates to polar coordinates, we must remember that there are infinitely many possible polar coordinate pairs. In Example 4 we report two of the possibilities.

EXAMPLE 4   Converting from Rectangular to Polar Coordinates

Find two polar coordinate pairs for the points with given rectangular coordinates.

(a) $P(-1, 1)$ **(b)** $Q(-3, 0)$

SOLUTION

(a) For $P(-1, 1)$, $x = -1$ and $y = 1$:

$$r^2 = x^2 + y^2 \qquad\qquad \tan\theta = \frac{y}{x}$$

$$r^2 = (-1)^2 + (1)^2 \qquad \tan\theta = \frac{1}{-1} = -1$$

$$r = \pm\sqrt{2} \qquad\qquad \theta = \tan^{-1}(-1) + n\pi = -\frac{\pi}{4} + n\pi$$

We use the angles $-\pi/4$ and $-\pi/4 + \pi = 3\pi/4$. Because P is on the ray opposite the terminal side of $-\pi/4$, the value of r corresponding to this angle is negative (Figure H.101). Because P is on the terminal side of $3\pi/4$, the value of r corresponding to this angle is positive. So two polar coordinate pairs of point P are

$$\left(-\sqrt{2}, -\frac{\pi}{4}\right) \quad \text{and} \quad \left(\sqrt{2}, \frac{3\pi}{4}\right).$$

(b) For $Q(-3, 0)$, $x = -3$ and $y = 0$. Thus, $r = \pm 3$ and $\theta = n\pi$. We use the angles 0 and π. So two polar coordinate pairs for point Q are

$$(-3, 0) \quad \text{and} \quad (3, \pi).$$

Now try Exercise 27.

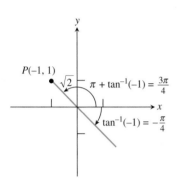

FIGURE H.101 The point P in Example 4a.

EXPLORATION 1   Using a Grapher to Convert Coordinates

Most graphers have the capability to convert polar coordinates to rectangular coordinates and vice versa. Usually they give just one possible polar coordinate pair for a given rectangular coordinate pair.

1. Use your grapher to check the conversions in Examples 3 and 4.

2. Use your grapher to convert the polar coordinate pairs $(2, \pi/3)$, $(-1, \pi/2)$, $(2, \pi)$, $(-5, 3\pi/2)$, $(3, 2\pi)$ to rectangular coordinate pairs.

3. Use your grapher to convert the rectangular coordinate pairs $(-1, -\sqrt{3})$, $(0, 2)$, $(3, 0)$, $(-1, 0)$, $(0, -4)$ to polar coordinate pairs.

Equation Conversion

We can use the coordinate conversion equations to convert polar form to rectangular form and vice versa. For example, the polar equation $r = 4 \cos \theta$ can be converted to rectangular form as follows:

$$r = 4 \cos \theta$$
$$r^2 = 4r \cos \theta$$
$$x^2 + y^2 = 4x \qquad \text{\small $r^2 = x^2 + y^2$, $r \cos \theta = x$}$$
$$x^2 - 4x + 4 + y^2 = 4 \qquad \text{\small Subtract $4x$ and add 4.}$$
$$(x - 2)^2 + y^2 = 4 \qquad \text{\small Factor.}$$

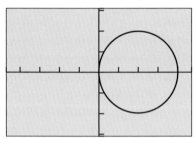

[–4.7, 4.7] by [–3.1, 3.1]

FIGURE H.102 The graph of the polar equation $r = 4 \cos \theta$ in $0 \le \theta \le 2\pi$.

Thus the graph of $r = 4 \cos \theta$ is all or part of the circle with center $(2, 0)$ and radius 2.

Figure H.102 shows the graph of $r = 4 \cos \theta$ for $0 \le \theta \le 2\pi$ obtained using the polar graphing mode of our grapher. So, the graph of $r = 4 \cos \theta$ is the entire circle.

Just as with parametric equations, the domain of a polar equation in r and θ is understood to be all values of θ for which the corresponding values of r are real numbers. You must also select a value for θ min and θ max to graph in polar mode.

You may be surprised by the polar form for a vertical line in Example 5.

EXAMPLE 5 Converting from Polar Form to Rectangular Form

Convert $r = 4 \sec \theta$ to rectangular form and identify the graph. Support your answer with a polar graphing utility.

SOLUTION

$$r = 4 \sec \theta$$
$$\frac{r}{\sec \theta} = 4 \qquad \text{\small Divide by $\sec \theta$.}$$
$$r \cos \theta = 4 \qquad \text{\small $\cos \theta = \frac{1}{\sec \theta}$.}$$
$$x = 4 \qquad \text{\small $r \cos \theta = x$}$$

The graph is the vertical line $x = 4$ (Figure H.103). *Now try Exercise 35.*

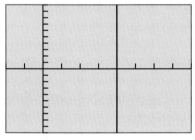

[–2, 8] by [–10, 10]

FIGURE H.103 The graph of the vertical line $r = 4 \sec \theta$ $(x = 4)$. (Example 5)

EXAMPLE 6 Converting from Rectangular Form to Polar Form

Convert $(x - 3)^2 + (y - 2)^2 = 13$ to polar form.

SOLUTION

$$(x - 3)^2 + (y - 2)^2 = 13$$
$$x^2 - 6x + 9 + y^2 - 4y + 4 = 13$$
$$x^2 + y^2 - 6x - 4y = 0$$

Substituting r^2 for $x^2 + y^2$, $r \cos \theta$ for x, and $r \sin \theta$ for y gives the following:

$$r^2 - 6r \cos \theta - 4r \sin \theta = 0$$
$$r(r - 6 \cos \theta - 4 \sin \theta) = 0$$
$$r = 0 \quad \text{or} \quad r - 6 \cos \theta - 4 \sin \theta = 0$$

The graph of $r = 0$ consists of a single point, the origin, which is also on the graph of $r - 6 \cos \theta - 4 \sin \theta = 0$. Thus, the polar form is

$$r = 6 \cos \theta + 4 \sin \theta.$$

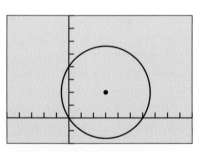

[–5, 10] by [–2, 8]

FIGURE H.104 The graph of the circle $r = 6 \cos \theta + 4 \sin \theta$. (Example 6)

The graph of $r = 6 \cos \theta + 4 \sin \theta$ for $0 \le \theta \le 2\pi$ is shown in Figure H.104 and appears to be a circle with center $(3, 2)$ and radius $\sqrt{13}$, as expected.

Now try Exercise 43.

FIGURE H.105 The distance and direction of two airplanes from a radar source. (Example 7)

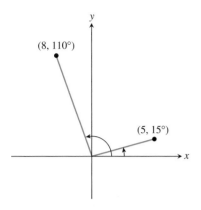

Finding Distance Using Polar Coordinates

A radar tracking system sends out high-frequency radio waves and receives their reflection from an object. The distance and direction of the object from the radar is often given in polar coordinates.

EXAMPLE 7 Using a Radar Tracking System

Radar detects two airplanes at the same altitude. Their polar coordinates are (8 mi, 110°) and (5 mi, 15°). (See Figure H.105.) How far apart are the airplanes?

SOLUTION By the Law of Cosines,

$$d^2 = 8^2 + 5^2 - 2 \cdot 8 \cdot 5 \cos (110° - 15°)$$
$$d = \sqrt{8^2 + 5^2 - 2 \cdot 8 \cdot 5 \cos 95°}$$
$$d \approx 9.80$$

The airplanes are about 9.80 mi apart.   *Now try Exercise 51.*

We can also use the Law of Cosines to derive a formula for the distance between points in the polar coordinate system. See Exercise 55.

Exercise numbers with a gray background indicate problems that the authors have designed to be solved *without a calculator*.

In Exercises 1–4, the polar coordinates of a point are given. Find its rectangular coordinates.

1.

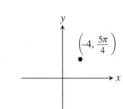

$\left(3, \frac{2\pi}{3}\right)$

2.

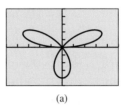

$\left(-4, \frac{5\pi}{4}\right)$

3.

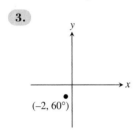

$(-2, 60°)$

4.

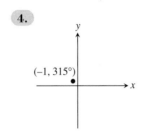

$(-1, 315°)$

In Exercises 5 and 6, **(a)** complete the table for the polar equation and **(b)** plot the corresponding points.

5. $r = 3 \sin \theta$

θ	$\pi/4$	$\pi/2$	$5\pi/6$	π	$4\pi/3$	2π
r						

6. $r = 2 \csc \theta$

θ	$\pi/4$	$\pi/2$	$5\pi/6$	π	$4\pi/3$	2π
r						

In Exercises 7–14, plot the point with the given polar coordinates.

7. $(3, 4\pi/3)$ **8.** $(2, 5\pi/6)$ **9.** $(-1, 2\pi/5)$

10. $(-3, 17\pi/10)$ **11.** $(2, 30°)$ **12.** $(3, 210°)$

13. $(-2, 120°)$ **14.** $(-3, 135°)$

In Exercises 15–22, use an algebraic method to find the rectangular coordinates of the point with given polar coordinates. Approximate the exact solution values with a calculator when appropriate.

15. $(1.5, 7\pi/3)$ **16.** $(2.5, 17\pi/4)$

17. $(-3, -29\pi/7)$ **18.** $(-2, -14\pi/5)$

19. $(-2, \pi)$ **20.** $(1, \pi/2)$

21. $(2, 270°)$ **22.** $(-3, 360°)$

In Exercises 23–26, polar coordinates of point P are given. Find all of its polar coordinates.

23. $P = (2, \pi/6)$ **24.** $P = (1, -\pi/4)$

25. $P = (1.5, -20°)$ **26.** $P = (-2.5, 50°)$

In Exercises 27–30, rectangular coordinates of a point P are given. Use an algebraic method, and approximate exact solution values with a calculator when appropriate, to find all polar coordinates of P that satisfy

    (a) $0 \le \theta \le 2\pi$ **(b)** $-\pi \le \theta \le \pi$ **(c)** $0 \le \theta \le 4\pi$.

27. $P = (1, 1)$ **28.** $P = (1, 3)$

29. $P = (-2, 5)$ **30.** $P = (-1, -2)$

In Exercises 31–34, use your grapher to match the polar equation with its graph.

31. $r = 5 \csc \theta$ **32.** $r = 4 \sin \theta$

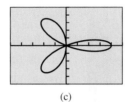

(a)

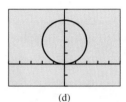

(b)

(c)

(d)

33. $r = 4 \cos 3\theta$ **34.** $r = 4 \sin 3\theta$

In Exercises 35–42, convert the polar equation to rectangular form and identify the graph. Support your answer by graphing the polar equation.

35. $r = 3 \sec \theta$ **36.** $r = -2 \csc \theta$

37. $r = -3 \sin \theta$ **38.** $r = -4 \cos \theta$

39. $r \csc \theta = 1$ **40.** $r \sec \theta = 3$

41. $r = 2 \sin \theta - 4 \cos \theta$ **42.** $r = 4 \cos \theta - 4 \sin \theta$

In Exercises 43–50, convert the rectangular equation to polar form. Sketch the graph of the rectangular equation (do *not* use a grapher), then support your hand sketch by graphing the polar equation with your grapher.

43. $x = 2$ **44.** $x = 5$

45. $2x - 3y = 5$ **46.** $3x + 4y = 2$

47. $(x - 3)^2 + y^2 = 9$ **48.** $x^2 + (y - 1)^2 = 1$

49. $(x + 3)^2 + (y + 3)^2 = 18$

50. $(x - 1)^2 + (y + 4)^2 = 17$

51. Tracking Airplanes The location, given in polar coordinates, of two planes approaching the Vicksburg airport are $(4 \text{ mi}, 12°)$ and $(2 \text{ mi}, 72°)$. Find the distance between the airplanes.

52. Tracking Ships The locations of two ships from Mays Landing Lighthouse, given in polar coordinates, are $(3 \text{ mi}, 170°)$ and $(5 \text{ mi}, 150°)$. Find the distance between the ships.

53. Using Polar Coordinates in Geometry A square with sides of length a and center at the origin has two sides parallel to the x-axis. Find polar coordinates of the vertices.

54. Using Polar Coordinates in Geometry A regular pentagon whose center is at the origin has one vertex on the positive x-axis at a distance a from the center. Find polar coordinates of the vertices.

Explorations

55. Polar Distance Formula   Let P_1 and P_2 have polar coordinates (r_1, θ_1) and (r_2, θ_2), respectively.

(a) If $\theta_1 - \theta_2$ is a multiple of π, write a formula for the distance between P_1 and P_2.

(b) Use the Law of Cosines to prove that the distance between P_1 and P_2 is given by

$$d = \sqrt{r_1^2 + r_2^2 - 2r_1r_2 \cos (\theta_1 - \theta_2)}.$$

(c) Writing to Learn   Does the formula in part (b) agree with the formula(s) you found in part (a)? Explain.

56. Watching Your θ-Step   Consider the polar curve $r = 4 \sin \theta$. Describe the graph for each of the following.

(a) $0 \le \theta \le \pi/2$ **(b)** $0 \le \theta \le 3\pi/4$

(c) $0 \le \theta \le 3\pi/2$ **(d)** $0 \le \theta \le 4\pi$

In Exercises 57–60, use the results of Exercise 55 to find the distance between the points with given polar coordinates.

57. $(2, 10°)$, $(5, 130°)$

58. $(4, 20°)$, $(6, 65°)$

59. $(-3, 25°)$, $(-5, 160°)$

60. $(6, -35°)$, $(8, -65°)$

Extending the Ideas

61. Graphing Polar Equations Parametrically   Find parametric equations for the polar curve $r = f(\theta)$.

Group Activity   In Exercises 62–65, use what you learned in Exercise 61 to write parametric equations for the given polar equation. Support your answers graphically.

62. $r = 2 \cos \theta$ **63.** $r = 5 \sin \theta$

64. $r = 2 \sec \theta$ **65.** $r = 4 \csc \theta$

H-11 Graphs of Polar Equations

Polar Curves and Parametric Curves

What you'll learn about

- Polar Curves and Parametric Curves
- Symmetry
- Analyzing Polar Graphs
- Rose Curves
- Limaçon Curves
- Other Polar Curves

... and why

Graphs that have circular or cylindrical symmetry often have simple polar equations, which is very useful in calculus.

Polar curves are actually just special cases of parametric curves. Keep in mind that polar curves are graphed in the (x, y) plane, despite the fact that they are given in terms of r and θ. That is why the polar graph of $r = 4 \cos \theta$ is a circle (see Figure H.102 in Lesson H-10) rather than a cosine curve.

In function mode, points are determined by a vertical coordinate that changes as the horizontal coordinate moves left to right. In polar mode, points are determined by a directed distance from the pole that changes as the angle sweeps around the pole. The connection is provided by the coordinate conversion equations from Lesson H-10, which show that the graph of $r = f(\theta)$ is really just the graph of the parametric equations

$$x = f(\theta) \cos \theta$$
$$y = f(\theta) \sin \theta$$

for all values of θ in some parameter interval that suffices to produce a complete graph. (In many of our examples, $0 \le \theta < 2\pi$ will do.)

Since modern graphing calculators produce these graphs so easily in polar mode, we are frankly going to assume that you do not have to sketch them by hand. Instead we will concentrate on analyzing the properties of the curves. In later courses you can discover further properties of the curves using the tools of calculus.

Symmetry

There are algebraic tests for symmetry for equations in rectangular form. Algebraic tests also exist for equations in polar form.

Figure H.106 on the next page shows a rectangular coordinate system superimposed on a polar coordinate system, with the origin and the pole coinciding and the positive x-axis and the polar axis coinciding.

The three types of symmetry figures to be considered will have:

1. The x-axis (polar axis) as a line of symmetry (Figure H.106a).

2. The y-axis (the line $\theta = \pi/2$) as a line of symmetry (Figure H.106b).

3. The origin (the pole) as a point of symmetry (Figure H.106c).

All three algebraic tests for symmetry in polar forms require replacing the pair (r, θ), which satisfies the polar equation, with another coordinate pair and determining whether it also satisfies the polar equation.

Symmetry Tests for Polar Graphs

The graph of a polar equation has the indicated symmetry if either replacement produces an equivalent polar equation.

To Test for Symmetry	Replace	By
1. about the x-axis,	(r, θ)	$(r, -\theta)$ or $(-r, \pi - \theta)$.
2. about the y-axis,	(r, θ)	$(-r, -\theta)$ or $(r, \pi - \theta)$.
3. about the origin,	(r, θ)	$(-r, \theta)$ or $(r, \theta + \pi)$.

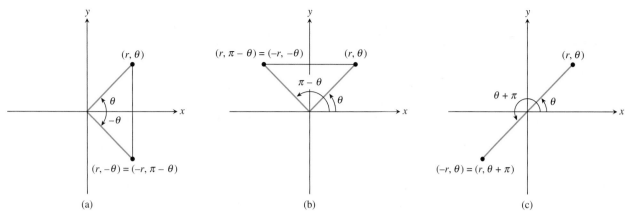

FIGURE H.106 Symmetry with respect to (a) the *x*-axis (polar axis), (b) the *y*-axis (the line $\theta = \pi/2$), and (c) the origin (the pole).

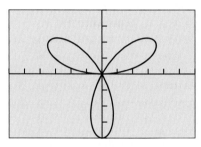

[–6,6] by [–4, 4]

FIGURE H.107 The graph of $r = 4 \sin 3\theta$ is symmetric about the *y*-axis. (Example 1)

EXAMPLE 1 Testing for Symmetry

Use the symmetry tests to prove that the graph of $r = 4 \sin 3\theta$ is symmetric about the *y*-axis.

SOLUTION Figure H.107 suggests that the graph of $r = 4 \sin 3\theta$ is symmetric about the *y*-axis and not symmetric about the *x*-axis or origin.

$$r = 4 \sin 3\theta$$
$$-r = 4 \sin 3(-\theta) \qquad \text{Replace } (r, \theta) \text{ by } (-r, -\theta).$$
$$-r = 4 \sin (-3\theta)$$
$$-r = -4 \sin 3\theta \qquad \sin \theta \text{ is an odd function of } \theta.$$
$$r = 4 \sin 3\theta \qquad \text{(Same as original)}$$

Because the equations $-r = 4 \sin 3(-\theta)$ and $r = 4 \sin 3\theta$ are equivalent, there is symmetry about the *y*-axis. *Now try Exercise 13.*

Analyzing Polar Graphs

We analyze graphs of polar equations in much the same way that we analyze graphs of rectangular equations. For example, the function *r* of Example 1 is a continuous function of θ. Also $r = 0$ when $\theta = 0$ and when θ is any integer multiple of $\pi/3$. The domain of this function is the set of all real numbers.

TRACE can be used to help determine the range of this polar function (Figure H.108). It can be shown that $-4 \le r \le 4$.

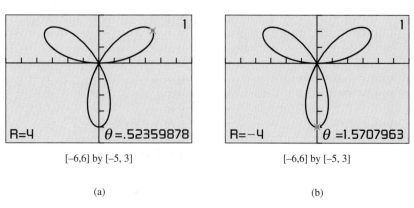

[–6,6] by [–5, 3]   [–6,6] by [–5, 3]

(a)   (b)

FIGURE H.108 The values of *r* in $r = 4 \sin 3\theta$ vary from (a) 4 to (b) -4.

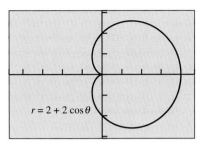

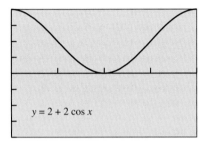

$r = 2 + 2\cos\theta$

[−4.7, 4.7] by [−3.1, 3.1]

Polar coordinates

(a)

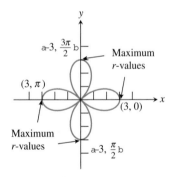

$y = 2 + 2\cos x$

[0, 2π] by [−4, 4]

Rectangular coordinates

(b)

FIGURE H.109 With $\theta = x$, the y-values in (b) are the same as the directed distance from the pole to (r, θ) in (a).

FIGURE H.110 The graph of $r = 3\cos 2\theta$. (Example 3)

Usually, we are more interested in the maximum value of $|r|$ rather than the range of r in polar equations. In this case, $|r| \le 4$ so we can conclude that the graph is bounded.

A maximum value for $|r|$ is a **maximum r-value** for a polar equation. A maximum r-value occurs at a point on the curve that is the maximum distance from the pole. In Figure H.108, a maximum r-value occurs at $(4, \pi/6)$ and $(-4, \pi/2)$. In fact, we get a maximum r-value at every (r, θ), which represents the tip of one of the three petals.

To find maximum r-values we must find maximum values of $|r|$ as opposed to the directed distance r. Example 2 shows one way to find maximum r-values graphically.

EXAMPLE 2 Finding Maximum r-Values

Find the maximum r-value of $r = 2 + 2\cos\theta$.

SOLUTION Figure H.109a shows the graph of $r = 2 + 2\cos\theta$ for $0 \le \theta \le 2\pi$. Because we are only interested in the values of r, we use the graph of the rectangular equation $y = 2 + 2\cos x$ in function graphing mode (Figure H.109b). From this graph we can see that the maximum value of r, or y, is 4. It occurs when θ is any multiple of 2π. *Now try Exercise 21.*

EXAMPLE 3 Finding Maximum r-Values

Identify the points on the graph of $r = 3\cos 2\theta$ for $0 \le \theta \le 2\pi$ that give maximum r-values.

SOLUTION Using TRACE in Figure H.110 we can show that there are four points on the graph of $r = 3\cos 2\theta$ in $0 \le \theta < 2\pi$ at maximum distance of 3 from the pole:

$$(3, 0), \quad (-3, \pi/2), \quad (3, \pi), \quad \text{and} \quad (-3, 3\pi/2).$$

Figure H.111a shows the directed distances r as the y-values of $y_1 = 3\cos 2x$, and Figure H.111b shows the distances $|r|$ as the y-values of $y_2 = |3\cos 2x|$. There are four maximum values of y_2 (i.e., $|r|$) in part (b) corresponding to the four extreme values of y_1 (i.e., r) in part (a). *Now try Exercise 23.*

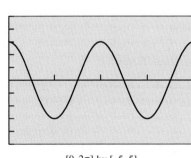

[0, 2π] by [−5, 5]

(a)

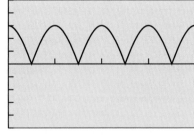

[0, 2π] by [−5, 5]

(b)

FIGURE H.111 The graph of (a) $y_1 = 3\cos 2x$ and (b) $y^2 = |3\cos 2x|$ in function graphing mode. (Example 3)

Rose Curves

The curve in Example 1 is a 3-petal rose curve, and the curve in Example 3 is a 4-petal rose curve. The graphs of the polar equations $r = a\cos n\theta$ and $r = a\sin n\theta$, where n is an integer greater than 1, are **rose curves**. If n is odd there are n petals, and if n is even there are $2n$ petals.

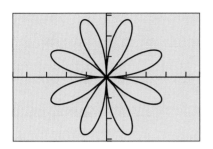

[−4.7, 4.7] by [−3.1, 3.1]

FIGURE H.112 The graph of 8-petal rose curve $r = 3 \sin 4\theta$. (Example 4)

EXAMPLE 4 Analyzing a Rose Curve

Analyze the graph of the rose curve $r = 3 \sin 4\theta$.

SOLUTION Figure H.112 shows the graph of the 8-petal rose curve $r = 3 \sin 4\theta$. The maximum r-value is 3. The graph appears to be symmetric about the x-axis, the y-axis, and the origin. For example, to prove that the graph is symmetric about the x-axis we replace (r, θ) by $(-r, \pi - \theta)$:

$$r = 3 \sin 4\theta$$
$$-r = 3 \sin 4(\pi - \theta)$$
$$-r = 3 \sin (4\pi - 4\theta)$$
$$-r = 3[\sin 4\pi \cos 4\theta - \cos 4\pi \sin 4\theta] \quad \text{Sine difference identity}$$
$$-r = 3[(0) \cos 4\theta - (1) \sin 4\theta] \quad \sin 4\pi = 0, \cos 4\pi = 1$$
$$-r = -3 \sin 4\theta$$
$$r = 3 \sin 4\theta$$

Because the new polar equation is the same as the original equation, the graph is symmetric about the x-axis. In a similar way, you can prove that the graph is symmetric about the y-axis and the origin. (See Exercise 58.)

Domain: All reals
Range: $[-3, 3]$
Continuous
Symmetric about the x-axis, the y-axis, and the origin
Bounded
Maximum r-value: 3
No asymptotes

Now try Exercise 29.

Here are the general characteristics of rose curves. You will investigate these curves in more detail in Exercises 61 and 62.

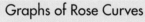

Graphs of Rose Curves

The graphs of $r = a \cos n\theta$ and $r = a \sin n\theta$, where $n > 1$ is an integer, have the following characteristics:

Domain: All reals
Range: $[-|a|, |a|]$
Continuous
Symmetry: n even, symmetric about x-, y-axis, origin
n odd, $r = a \cos n\theta$ symmetric about x-axis
n odd, $r = a \sin n\theta$ symmetric about y-axis
Bounded
Maximum r-value: $|a|$
No asymptotes
Number of petals: n, if n is odd
2n, if n is even

A ROSE IS A ROSE...

Budding botanists like to point out that the rose curve doesn't look much like a rose. However, consider the beautiful stained-glass window shown here, which is a feature of many great cathedrals and is called a "rose window."

Limaçon Curves

The **limaçon curves** are graphs of polar equations of the form

$$r = a \pm b \sin \theta \quad \text{and} \quad r = a \pm b \cos \theta,$$

where $a > 0$ and $b > 0$. *Limaçon*, pronounced "LEE-ma-sohn," is Old French for "snail." There are four different shapes of limaçons, as illustrated in Figure H.113.

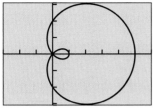

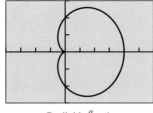

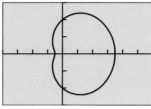

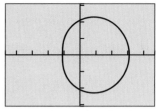

Limaçon with an inner loop: $\frac{a}{b} < 1$

Cardioid: $\frac{a}{b} = 1$

Dimpled limaçon: $1 < \frac{a}{b} < 2$

Convex limaçon: $\frac{a}{b} \geq 2$

(a)

(b)

(c)

(d)

FIGURE H.113 The four types of limaçons.

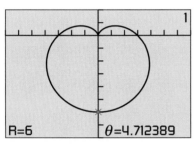

R=6 θ=4.712389

[–7, 7] by [–8, 2]

FIGURE H.114 The graph of the cardioid of Example 5.

EXAMPLE 5 Analyzing a Limaçon Curve

Analyze the graph of $r = 3 - 3 \sin \theta$.

SOLUTION We can see from Figure H.114 that the curve is a cardioid with maximum r-value 6. The graph is symmetric only about the y-axis.

Domain: All reals
Range: $[0, 6]$
Continuous
Symmetric about the y-axis
Bounded
Maximum r-value: 6
No asymptotes

Now try Exercise 33.

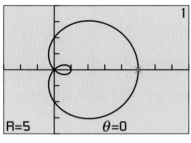

R=5 θ=0

[–3, 8] by [–4, 4]

FIGURE H.115 The graph of a limaçon with an inner loop. (Example 6)

EXAMPLE 6 Analyzing a Limaçon Curve

Analyze the graph of $r = 2 + 3 \cos \theta$.

SOLUTION We can see from Figure H.115 that the curve is a limaçon with an inner loop and maximum r-value 5. The graph is symmetric only about the x-axis.

Domain: All reals
Range: $[-1, 5]$
Continuous
Symmetric about the x-axis
Bounded
Maximum r-value: 5
No asymptotes

Now try Exercise 39.

Graphs of Limaçon Curves

The graphs of $r = a \pm b \sin \theta$ and $r = a \pm b \cos \theta$, where $a > 0$ and $b > 0$, have the following characteristics:

Domain: All reals
Range: $[a - b, a + b]$
Continuous
Symmetry: $r = a \pm b \sin \theta$, symmetric about y-axis
                 $r = a \pm b \cos \theta$, symmetric about x-axis
Bounded
Maximum r-value: $a + b$
No asymptotes

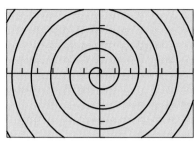

[−30, 30] by [−20, 20]

(a)

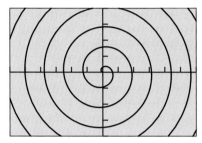

[−30, 30] by [−20, 20]

(b)

FIGURE H.116 The graph of $r = \theta$ for (a) $\theta \geq 0$ (set θmin $= 0$, θmax $= 45$, θstep $= 0.1$) and (b) $\theta \leq 0$ (set θmin $= -45$, θmax $= 0$, θstep $= 0.1$). (Example 7)

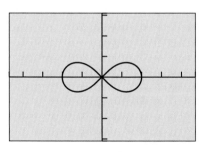

[−4.7, 4.7] by [−3.1, 3.1]

FIGURE H.117 The graph of the lemniscate $r^2 = 4 \cos 2\theta$. (Example 8)

Other Polar Curves

All the polar curves we have graphed so far have been bounded. The spiral in Example 7 is unbounded.

EXAMPLE 7 Analyzing the Spiral of Archimedes

Analyze the graph of $r = \theta$.

SOLUTION

We can see from Figure H.116 that the curve has no maximum r-value and is symmetric about the y-axis.

Domain: All reals
Range: All reals
Continuous
Symmetric about the y-axis
Unbounded
No maximum r-value
No asymptotes   *Now try Exercise 41.*

The **lemniscate curves** are graphs of polar equations of the form

$$r^2 = a^2 \sin 2\theta \quad \text{and} \quad r^2 = a^2 \cos 2\theta.$$

EXAMPLE 8 Analyzing a Lemniscate Curve

Analyze the graph of $r^2 = 4 \cos 2\theta$ for $[0, 2\pi]$.

SOLUTION It turns out that you can get the complete graph using $r = 2\sqrt{\cos 2\theta}$. You also need to choose a very small θ step to produce the graph in Figure H.117.

Domain: $[0, \pi/4] \cup [3\pi/4, 5\pi/4] \cup [7\pi/4, 2\pi]$
Range: $[-2, 2]$
Symmetric about the x-axis, the y-axis, and the origin
Continuous (on its domain)
Bounded
Maximum r-value: 2
No asymptotes   *Now try Exercise 43.*

LESSON H-11 EXERCISES

Exercise numbers with a gray background indicate problems that the authors have designed to be solved *without a calculator*.

In Exercises 1 and 2, (a) complete the table for the polar equation, and (b) plot the corresponding points.

1. $r = 3 \cos 2\theta$

θ	0	$\pi/4$	$\pi/2$	$3\pi/4$	π	$5\pi/4$	$3\pi/2$	$7\pi/4$
r								

2. $r = 2 \sin 3\theta$

θ	0	$\pi/6$	$\pi/3$	$\pi/2$	$2\pi/3$	$5\pi/6$	π
r							

In Exercises 3–6, draw a graph of the rose curve. State the smallest θ-interval $(0 \leq \theta \leq k)$ that will produce a complete graph.

3. $r = 3 \sin 3\theta$ **4.** $r = -3 \cos 2\theta$

5. $r = 3 \cos 2\theta$ **6.** $r = 3 \sin 5\theta$

Exercises 7 and 8 refer to the curves in the given figure.

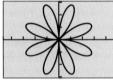

[–4.7, 4.7] by [–3.1, 3.1]

(a)

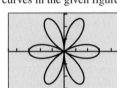

[–4.7, 4.7] by [–3.1, 3.1]

(b)

7. The graphs of which equations are shown?

$$r_1 = 3 \cos 6\theta \quad r_2 = 3 \sin 8\theta \quad r_3 = 3|\cos 3\theta|$$

8. Use trigonometric identities to explain which of these curves is the graph of $r = 6 \cos 2\theta \sin 2\theta$.

In Exercises 9–12, match the equation with its graph without using your graphing calculator.

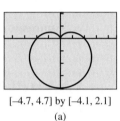

[–4.7, 4.7] by [–4.1, 2.1]

(a)

[–4.7, 4.7] by [–3.1, 3.1]

(b)

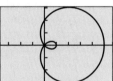

[–3.7, 5.7] by [–3.1, 3.1]

(c)

[–4.7, 4.7] by [–4.1, 2.1]

(d)

9. Does the graph of $r = 2 + 2 \sin \theta$ or $r = 2 - 2 \cos \theta$ appear in the figure? Explain.

10. Does the graph of $r = 2 + 3 \cos \theta$ or $r = 2 - 3 \cos \theta$ appear in the figure? Explain.

11. Is the graph in (a) the graph of $r = 2 - 2 \sin \theta$ or $r = 2 + 2 \cos \theta$? Explain.

12. Is the graph in (d) the graph of $r = 2 + 1.5 \cos \theta$ or $r = 2 - 1.5 \sin \theta$? Explain.

In Exercises 13–20, use the polar symmetry tests to determine if the graph is symmetric about the x-axis, the y-axis, or the origin. Support your algebraic solution with a grapher.

13. $r = 3 + 3 \sin \theta$ **14.** $r = 1 + 2 \cos \theta$

15. $r = 4 - 3 \cos \theta$ **16.** $r = 1 - 3 \sin \theta$

17. $r = 5 \cos 2\theta$ **18.** $r = 7 \sin 3\theta$

19. $r = \dfrac{3}{1 + \sin \theta}$ **20.** $r = \dfrac{2}{1 - \cos \theta}$

In Exercises 21–24, identify the points for $0 \le \theta \le 2\pi$ where maximum r-values occur on the graph of the polar equation.

21. $r = 2 + 3 \cos \theta$ **22.** $r = -3 + 2 \sin \theta$

23. $r = 3 \cos 3\theta$ **24.** $r = 4 \sin 2\theta$

In Exercises 25–44, analyze the graph of the polar curve.

25. $r = 3$ **26.** $r = -2$

27. $\theta = \pi/3$ **28.** $\theta = -\pi/4$

29. $r = 2 \sin 3\theta$ **30.** $r = -3 \cos 4\theta$

31. $r = 5 + 4 \sin \theta$ **32.** $r = 6 - 5 \cos \theta$

33. $r = 4 + 4 \cos \theta$ **34.** $r = 5 - 5 \sin \theta$

35. $r = 5 + 2 \cos \theta$ **36.** $r = 3 - \sin \theta$

37. $r = 2 + 5 \cos \theta$ **38.** $r = 3 - 4 \sin \theta$

39. $r = 1 - \cos \theta$ **40.** $r = 2 + \sin \theta$

41. $r = 2\theta$ **42.** $r = \theta/4$

43. $r^2 = \sin 2\theta, 0 \le \theta \le 2\pi$

44. $r^2 = 9 \cos 2\theta, 0 \le \theta \le 2\pi$

In Exercises 45–48, find the length of each petal of the polar curve.

45. $r = 2 + 4 \sin 2\theta$ **46.** $r = 3 - 5 \cos 2\theta$

47. $r = 1 - 4 \cos 5\theta$ **48.** $r = 3 + 4 \sin 5\theta$

In Exercises 49–52, select the two equations whose graphs are the same curve. Then, even though the graphs of the equations are identical, describe how the two paths are different as θ increases from 0 to 2π.

49. $r_1 = 1 + 3 \sin \theta$, $r_2 = -1 + 3 \sin \theta$, $r_3 = 1 - 3 \sin \theta$

50. $r_1 = 1 + 2 \cos \theta$, $r_2 = -1 - 2 \cos \theta$, $r_3 = -1 + 2 \cos \theta$

51. $r_1 = 1 + 2 \cos \theta$, $r_2 = 1 - 2 \cos \theta$, $r_3 = -1 - 2 \cos \theta$

52. $r_1 = 2 + 2 \sin \theta$, $r_2 = -2 + 2 \sin \theta$, $r_3 = 2 - 2 \sin \theta$

In Exercises 53–56, **(a)** describe the graph of the polar equation, **(b)** state any symmetry that the graph possesses, and **(c)** state its maximum r-value if it exists.

53. $r = 2 \sin^2 2\theta + \sin 2\theta$ **54.** $r = 3 \cos 2\theta - \sin 3\theta$

55. $r = 1 - 3 \cos 3\theta$ **56.** $r = 1 + 3 \sin 3\theta$

57. Group Activity Analyze the graphs of the polar equations $r = a \cos n\theta$ and $r = a \sin n\theta$ when n is an even integer.

58. Revisiting Example 4 Use the polar symmetry tests to prove that the graph of the curve $r = 3 \sin 4\theta$ is symmetric about the y-axis and the origin.

59. Writing to Learn Revisiting Example 5
Confirm the range stated for the polar function $r = 3 - 3 \sin \theta$ of Example 5 by graphing $y = 3 - 3 \sin x$ for $0 \le x \le 2\pi$. Explain why this works.

60. Writing to Learn Revisiting Example 6
Confirm the range stated for the polar function $r = 2 + 3 \cos \theta$ of Example 6 by graphing $y = 2 + 3 \cos x$ for $0 \le x \le 2\pi$. Explain why this works.

Explorations

61. Analyzing Rose Curves Consider the polar equation $r = a \cos n\theta$ for n, an odd integer.

(a) Prove that the graph is symmetric about the x-axis.

(b) Prove that the graph is not symmetric about the y-axis.

(c) Prove that the graph is not symmetric about the origin.

(d) Prove that the maximum r-value is $|a|$.

(e) Analyze the graph of this curve.

62. Analyzing Rose Curves Consider the polar equation $r = a \sin n\theta$ for n, an odd integer.

(a) Prove that the graph is symmetric about the y-axis.

(b) Prove that the graph is not symmetric about the x-axis.

(c) Prove that the graph is not symmetric about the origin.

(d) Prove that the maximum r-value is $|a|$.

(e) Analyze the graph of this curve.

63. Extended Rose Curves The graphs of $r_1 = 3 \sin ((7/2)\theta)$ and $r_2 = 3 \sin ((7/2)\theta)$ may be called rose curves.

(a) Determine the smallest θ-interval that will produce a complete graph of r_1; of r_2.

(b) How many petals does each graph have?

Extending the Ideas

In Exercises 64–66, graph each polar equation. Describe how they are related to each other.

64. (a) $r_1 = 3 \sin 3\theta$ **(b)** $r_2 = 3 \sin 3 \left(\theta + \dfrac{\pi}{12} \right)$

(c) $r_3 = 3 \sin 3 \left(\theta + \dfrac{\pi}{4} \right)$

65. (a) $r_1 = 2 \sec \theta$ **(b)** $r_2 = 2 \sec \left(\theta - \dfrac{\pi}{4} \right)$

(c) $r_3 = 2 \sec \left(\theta - \dfrac{\pi}{3} \right)$

66. (a) $r_1 = 2 - 2 \cos \theta$ **(b)** $r_2 = r_1 \left(\theta + \dfrac{\pi}{4} \right)$

(c) $r_3 = r_1 \left(\theta + \dfrac{\pi}{3} \right)$

67. Writing to Learn Describe how the graphs of $r = f(\theta)$, $r = f(\theta + \alpha)$, and $r = f(\theta - \alpha)$ are related. Explain why you think this generalization is true.

H-12 De Moivre's Theorem and *n*th Roots

What you'll learn about

- The Complex Plane
- Trigonometric Form of Complex Numbers
- Multiplication and Division of Complex Numbers
- Powers of Complex Numbers
- Roots of Complex Numbers

... and why

This material extends your equation-solving technique to include equations of the form $z^n = c$, n an integer and c a complex number.

The Complex Plane

An understanding of complex numbers is the key to understanding calculus is the graphing of functions in the Cartesian plane, which consists of two perpendicular real (not complex) lines.

We are not saying that complex numbers are impossible to graph. Just as every real number is associated with a point of the real number line, every complex number can be associated with a point of the **complex plane**. This idea evolved through the work of Caspar Wessel (1745–1818), Jean-Robert Argand (1768–1822), and Carl Friedrich Gauss (1777–1855). Real numbers are placed along the horizontal axis (the **real axis**) and imaginary numbers along the vertical axis (the **imaginary axis**), thus associating the complex number $a + bi$ with the point (a, b). In Figure H.118 we show the graph of $2 + 3i$ as an example.

EXAMPLE 1 Plotting Complex Numbers

Plot $u = 1 + 3i$, $v = 2 - i$, and $u + v$ in the complex plane. These three points and the origin determine a quadrilateral. Is it a parallelogram?

SOLUTION First notice that $u + v = (1 + 3i) + (2 + i) = 3 + 2i$. The numbers u, v, and $u + v$ are plotted in Figure H.119a. The quadrilateral is a parallelogram because the arithmetic is exactly the same as in vector addition (Figure H.119b).

Now try Exercise 1.

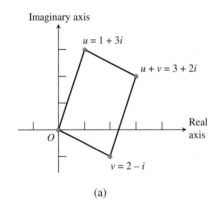
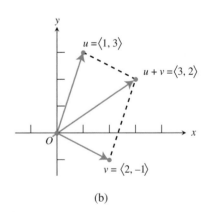

FIGURE H.119 (a) Two numbers and their sum are plotted in the complex plane. (b) The arithmetic is the same as in vector addition. (Example 1)

Example 1 shows how the complex plane representation of complex number addition is virtually the same as the Cartesian plane representation of vector addition. Another similarity between complex numbers and two-dimensional vectors is the definition of absolute value.

FIGURE H.118 Plotting points in the complex plane.

Is There a Calculus of Complex Functions?

There is a calculus of complex functions. If you study it someday, it should only be after acquiring a pretty firm algebraic and geometric understanding of the calculus of real functions.

The **absolute value** or **modulus** of a complex number $z = a + bi$ is

$$|z| = |a + bi| = \sqrt{a^2 + b^2}.$$

In the complex plane, $|a + bi|$ is the distance of $a + bi$ from the origin.

Trigonometric Form of Complex Numbers

Figure H.120 shows the graph of $z = a + bi$ in the complex plane. The distance r from the origin is the modulus of z. If we define a direction angle θ for z just as we did with vectors, we see that $a = r \cos \theta$ and $b = r \sin \theta$. Substituting these expressions for a and b gives us the **trigonometric form** (or **polar form**) of the complex number z.

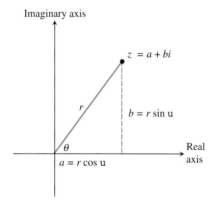

FIGURE H.120 If r is the distance of $z = a + bi$ from the origin and θ is the directional angle shown, then $z = r(\cos \theta + i \sin \theta)$, which is the trigonometric form of z.

The **trigonometric form** of the complex number $z = a + bi$ is

$$z = r(\cos \theta + i \sin \theta)$$

where $a = r \cos \theta$, $b = r \sin \theta$, $r = \sqrt{a^2 + b^2}$, and $\tan \theta = b/a$. The number r is the *absolute value* or *modulus* of z, and θ is an **argument** of z.

An angle θ for the trigonometric form of z can always be chosen so that $0 \leq \theta \leq 2\pi$, although any angle coterminal with θ could be used. Consequently, the *angle* θ and *argument* of a complex number z are not unique. It follows that the trigonometric form of a complex number z is not unique.

EXAMPLE 2 Finding Trigonometric Forms

Use an algebraic method to find the trigonometric form with $0 \leq \theta < 2\pi$ for the complex number. Approximate exact values with a calculator when appropriate.

(a) $1 - \sqrt{3}\,i$ **(b)** $-3 - 4i$

SOLUTION

(a) For $1 - \sqrt{3}i$,

$$r = |1 - \sqrt{3}\,i| = \sqrt{(1)^2 + (\sqrt{3})^2} = 2.$$

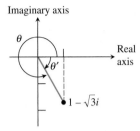

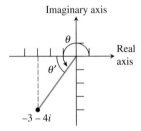

FIGURE H.121 The complex number for Example 2a.

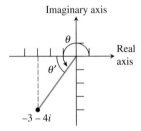

FIGURE H.122 The complex number for Example 2b.

Because the reference angle θ' for θ is $-\pi/3$ (Figure H.121),

$$\theta = 2\pi + \left(-\frac{\pi}{3}\right) = \frac{5\pi}{3}.$$

Thus,

$$1 - \sqrt{3}\,i = 2\cos\frac{5\pi}{3} + 2i\sin\frac{5\pi}{3}.$$

(b) For $-3 - 4i$,

$$\left|-3 - 4i\right| = \sqrt{(-3)^2 + (-4)^2} = 5.$$

The reference angle θ' for θ (Figure H.122) satisfies the equation

$$\tan\theta' = \frac{4}{3}, \quad \text{so}$$

$$\theta' = \tan^{-1}\frac{4}{3} = 0.927.\ldots$$

Because the terminal side of θ is in the third quadrant, we conclude that

$$\theta = \pi + \theta' \approx 4.07.$$

Therefore,

$$-3 - 4i \approx 5(\cos 4.07 + i\sin 4.07).$$

Now try Exercise 5.

Multiplication and Division of Complex Numbers

The trigonometric form for complex numbers is particularly convenient for multiplying and dividing complex numbers. The product involves the product of the moduli and the sum of the arguments. (*Moduli* is the plural of *modulus*.) The quotient involves the quotient of the moduli and the difference of the arguments.

Product and Quotient of Complex Numbers

Let $z_1 = r_1(\cos\theta_1 + i\sin\theta_1)$ and $z_2 = r_2(\cos\theta_2 + i\sin\theta_2)$. Then

1. $z_1 \cdot z_2 = r_1 r_2[\cos(\theta_1 + \theta_2) + i\sin(\theta_1 + \theta_2)]$.

2. $\dfrac{z_1}{z_2} = \dfrac{r_1}{r_2}[\cos(\theta_1 - \theta_2) + i\sin(\theta_1 - \theta_2)], \quad r_2 \neq 0.$

Proof of the Product Formula

$$z_1 \cdot z_2 = r_1(\cos\theta_1 + i\sin\theta_1) \cdot r_2(\cos\theta_2 + i\sin\theta_2)$$
$$= r_1 r_2[(\cos\theta_1\cos\theta_2 - \sin\theta_1\sin\theta_2) + i(\sin\theta_1\cos\theta_2 + \cos\theta_1\sin\theta_2)]$$
$$= r_1 r_2[\cos(\theta_1 + \theta_2) + i\sin(\theta_1 + \theta_2)]$$

You will be asked to prove the quotient formula in Exercise 63.

EXAMPLE 3 Multiplying Complex Numbers

Use an algebraic method to express the product of z_1 and z_2 in standard form. Approximate exact values with a calculator when appropriate.

$$z_1 = 25\sqrt{2}\left(\cos\frac{-\pi}{4} + i\sin\frac{-\pi}{4}\right), \quad z_2 = 14\left(\cos\frac{\pi}{3} + i\sin\frac{\pi}{3}\right)$$

SOLUTION

$$z_1 \cdot z_2 = 25\sqrt{2}\left(\cos\frac{-\pi}{4} + i\sin\frac{-\pi}{4}\right) \cdot 14\left(\cos\frac{\pi}{3} + i\sin\frac{\pi}{3}\right)$$

$$= 25 \cdot 14\sqrt{2}\left[\cos\left(\frac{-\pi}{4} + \frac{\pi}{3}\right) + i\sin\left(\frac{-\pi}{4} + \frac{\pi}{3}\right)\right]$$

$$= 350\sqrt{2}\left(\cos\frac{\pi}{12} + i\sin\frac{\pi}{12}\right)$$

$$\approx 478.11 + 128.11i \qquad\qquad \textit{Now try Exercise 19.}$$

EXAMPLE 4 Dividing Complex Numbers

Use an algebraic method to express the product z_1/z_2 in standard form. Approximate exact values with a calculator when appropriate.

$$z_1 = 2\sqrt{2}(\cos 135° + i\sin 135°), \quad z_2 = 6(\cos 300° + i\sin 300°)$$

SOLUTION

$$\frac{z_1}{z_2} = \frac{2\sqrt{2}\,(\cos 135° + i\sin 135°)}{6(\cos 300° + i\sin 300°)}$$

$$= \frac{\sqrt{2}}{3}\left[\cos\left(135° - 300°\right) + i\sin\left(135° - 300°\right)\right]$$

$$= \frac{\sqrt{2}}{3}\left[\cos\left(-165°\right) + i\sin\left(-165°\right)\right]$$

$$\approx -0.46 - 0.12i \qquad\qquad \textit{Now try Exercise 23.}$$

Powers of Complex Numbers

We can use the product formula to raise a complex number to a power. For example, let $z = r(\cos\theta + i\sin\theta)$. Then

$$z^2 = z \cdot z$$

$$= r(\cos\theta + i\sin\theta) \cdot r(\cos\theta + i\sin\theta)$$

$$= r^2[\cos(\theta + \theta) + i\sin(\theta + \theta)]$$

$$= r^2(\cos 2\theta + i\sin 2\theta)$$

Figure H.123 gives a geometric interpretation of squaring a complex number: Its argument is doubled and its distance from the origin is multiplied by a factor of r, increased if $r > 1$ or decreased if $r < 1$.

We can find z^3 by multiplying z by z^2:

$$z^3 = z \cdot z^2$$

$$= r(\cos\theta + i\sin\theta) \cdot r^2(\cos 2\theta + i\sin 2\theta)$$

$$= r^3[\cos(\theta + 2\theta) + i\sin(\theta + 2\theta)]$$

$$= r^3(\cos 3\theta + i\sin 3\theta)$$

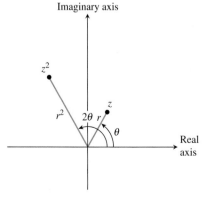

FIGURE H.123 A geometric interpretation of z^2.

Similarly,

$$z^4 = r^4(\cos 4\theta + i \sin 4\theta)$$
$$z^5 = r^5(\cos 5\theta + i \sin 5\theta)$$
$$\vdots$$

This pattern can be generalized to the following theorem, named after the mathematician Abraham De Moivre (1667–1754), who also made major contributions to the field of probability.

THEOREM 13 De Moivre's Theorem

Let $z = r(\cos \theta + i \sin \theta)$ and let n be a positive integer. Then

$$z^n = [r(\cos \theta + i \sin \theta)]^n = r^n(\cos n\theta + i \sin n\theta).$$

EXAMPLE 5 Using De Moivre's Theorem

Find $(1 + i\sqrt{3})^3$ using De Moivre's Theorem.

SOLUTION

Solve Algebraically See Figure H.124. The argument of $z = 1 + i\sqrt{3}$ is $\theta = \pi/3$, and its modulus is $|1 + i\sqrt{3}| = \sqrt{1 + 3} = 2$. Therefore,

$$z = 2\left(\cos \frac{\pi}{3} + i \sin \frac{\pi}{3}\right)$$

$$z^3 = 2^3\left[\cos \left(3 \cdot \frac{\pi}{3}\right) + i \sin \left(3 \cdot \frac{\pi}{3}\right)\right]$$

$$= 8(\cos \pi + i \sin \pi)$$

$$= 8(-1 + 0i) = -8$$

Support Numerically Figure H.125a sets the graphing calculator we use in complex number mode. Figure H.125b supports the result obtained algebraically.

Now try Exercise 31.

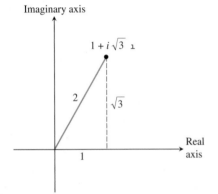

FIGURE H.124 The complex number in Example 5.

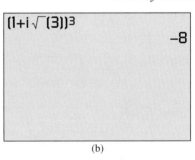

(a)   (b)

FIGURE H.125 (a) Setting a graphing calculator in complex number mode. (b) Computing $(1 + i\sqrt{3})^3$ with a graphing calculator.

EXAMPLE 6 Using De Moivre's Theorem

Find $[(-\sqrt{2}/2) + i(\sqrt{2}/2)]^8$ using De Moivre's Theorem.

SOLUTION The argument of $z = (-\sqrt{2}/2) + i(\sqrt{2}/2)$ is $\theta = 3\pi/4$, and its modulus is

$$\left|\frac{-\sqrt{2}}{2} + i\frac{\sqrt{2}}{2}\right| = \sqrt{\frac{1}{2} + \frac{1}{2}} = 1.$$

Therefore,

$$z = \cos\frac{3\pi}{4} + i\sin\frac{3\pi}{4}$$

$$z^8 = \cos\left(8\cdot\frac{3\pi}{4}\right) + i\sin\left(8\cdot\frac{3\pi}{4}\right)$$

$$= \cos 6\pi + i\sin 6\pi$$

$$= 1 + i\cdot 0 = 1 \qquad\qquad\qquad \textit{Now try Exercise 35.}$$

Roots of Complex Numbers

The complex number $1 + i\sqrt{3}$ in Example 5 is a solution of $z^3 = -8$, and the complex number $(-\sqrt{2}/2) + i(\sqrt{2}/2)$ in Example 6 is a solution of $z^8 = 1$. The complex number $1 + i\sqrt{3}$ is a third root of -8, and $(-\sqrt{2}/2) + i(\sqrt{2}/2)$ is an eighth root of 1.

---

nth Root of a Complex Number

A complex number $v = a + bi$ is an **nth root of** z if

$$v^n = z.$$

If $z = 1$, then v is an **nth root of unity**.

We use De Moivre's Theorem to develop a general formula for finding the nth roots of a nonzero complex number. Suppose that $v = s(\cos\alpha + i\sin\alpha)$ is an nth root of $z = r(\cos\theta + i\sin\theta)$. Then

$$v^n = z$$
$$[s(\cos\alpha + i\sin\alpha)]^n = r(\cos\theta + i\sin\theta)$$
$$s^n(\cos n\alpha + i\sin n\alpha) = r(\cos\theta + i\sin\theta) \qquad (1)$$

Next, we take the absolute value of both sides:

$$\left|s^n(\cos n\alpha + i\sin na)\right| = \left|r(\cos\theta + i\sin\theta)\right|$$
$$\sqrt{s^{2n}(\cos^2 n\alpha + \sin^2 n\alpha)} = \sqrt{r^2(\cos^2\theta + \sin^2\theta)}$$
$$\sqrt{s^{2n}} = \sqrt{r^2}$$
$$s^n = r \qquad\qquad s > 0, r > 0$$
$$s = \sqrt[n]{r}$$

Substituting $s^n = r$ into Equation (1), we obtain

$$\cos n\alpha + i\sin n\alpha = \cos\theta + i\sin\theta.$$

Therefore, $n\alpha$ can be any angle coterminal with θ. Consequently, for any integer k, v is an nth root of z if $s = \sqrt[n]{r}$ and

$$n\alpha = \theta + 2\pi k$$
$$\alpha = \frac{\theta + 2\pi k}{n}.$$

The expression for v takes on n different values for $k = 0, 1, \ldots, n - 1$, and the values start to repeat for $k = n, n + 1, \ldots$.

We summarize this result.

EXAMPLE 7 Finding Fourth Roots

Find the fourth roots of $z = 5(\cos (\pi/3) + i \sin (\pi/3))$.

SOLUTION The fourth roots of z are the complex numbers

$$\sqrt[4]{5}\left(\cos \frac{\pi/3 + 2\pi k}{4} + i \sin \frac{\pi/3 + 2\pi k}{4} \right)$$

for $k = 0, 1, 2, 3$.

Taking into account that $(\pi/3 + 2\pi k)/4 = \pi/12 + \pi k/2$, the list becomes

$$z_1 = \sqrt[4]{5}\left[\cos \left(\frac{\pi}{12} + \frac{0}{2} \right) + i \sin \left(\frac{\pi}{12} + \frac{0}{2} \right) \right]$$

$$= \sqrt[4]{5}\left[\cos \frac{\pi}{12} + i \sin \frac{\pi}{12} \right]$$

$$z_2 = \sqrt[4]{5}\left[\cos \left(\frac{\pi}{12} + \frac{\pi}{2} \right) + i \sin \left(\frac{\pi}{12} + \frac{\pi}{2} \right) \right]$$

$$= \sqrt[4]{5}\left[\cos \frac{7\pi}{12} + i \sin \frac{7\pi}{12} \right]$$

$$z_3 = \sqrt[4]{5}\left[\cos \left(\frac{\pi}{12} + \frac{2\pi}{2} \right) + i \sin \left(\frac{\pi}{12} + \frac{2\pi}{2} \right) \right]$$

$$= \sqrt[4]{5}\left[\cos \frac{13\pi}{12} + i \sin \frac{13\pi}{12} \right]$$

$$z_4 = \sqrt[4]{5}\left[\cos \left(\frac{\pi}{12} + \frac{3\pi}{2} \right) + i \sin \left(\frac{\pi}{12} + \frac{3\pi}{2} \right) \right]$$

$$= \sqrt[4]{5}\left[\cos \frac{19\pi}{12} + i \sin \frac{19\pi}{12} \right]$$

Now try Exercise 45.

EXAMPLE 8 Finding Cube Roots

Find the cube roots of -1 and plot them.

SOLUTION First we write the complex number $z = -1$ in trigonometric form

$$z = -1 + 0i = \cos \pi + i \sin \pi.$$

The third roots of $z = -1 = \cos \pi + i \sin \pi$ are the complex numbers

$$\cos \frac{\pi + 2\pi k}{3} + i \sin \frac{\pi + 2\pi k}{3},$$

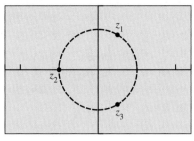

[−2.4, 2.4] by [−1.6, 1.6]

FIGURE H.126 The three cube roots z_1, z_2, and z_3 of -1 displayed on the unit circle (dashed). (Example 8)

for $k = 0, 1, 2$. The three complex numbers are

$$z_1 = \cos\frac{\pi}{3} + i\sin\frac{\pi}{3} \qquad\qquad = \frac{1}{2} + \frac{\sqrt{3}}{2}i,$$

$$z_2 = \cos\frac{\pi + 2\pi}{3} + i\sin\frac{\pi + 2\pi}{3} = -1 + 0i,$$

$$z_3 = \cos\frac{\pi + 4\pi}{3} + i\sin\frac{\pi + 4\pi}{3} = \frac{1}{2} - \frac{\sqrt{3}}{2}i.$$

Figure H.126 shows the graph of the three cube roots z_1, z_2, and z_3. They are evenly spaced (with distance of $2\pi/3$ radians) around the unit circle.

Now try Exercise 57.

EXAMPLE 9 Finding Roots of Unity

Find the eight eighth roots of unity.

SOLUTION First we write the complex number $z = 1$ in trigonometric form

$$z = 1 + 0i = \cos 0 + i\sin 0.$$

The eighth roots of $z = 1 + 0i = \cos 0 + i\sin 0$ are the complex numbers

$$\cos\frac{0 + 2\pi k}{8} + i\sin\frac{0 + 2\pi k}{8},$$

for $k = 0, 1, 2, \ldots, 7$.

$$z_1 = \cos 0 + i\sin 0 \qquad = 1 + 0i$$

$$z_2 = \cos\frac{\pi}{4} + i\sin\frac{\pi}{4} \qquad = \frac{\sqrt{2}}{2} + \frac{\sqrt{2}}{2}i$$

$$z_3 = \cos\frac{\pi}{2} + i\sin\frac{\pi}{2} \qquad = 0 + i$$

$$z_4 = \cos\frac{3\pi}{4} + i\sin\frac{3\pi}{4} = -\frac{\sqrt{2}}{2} + \frac{\sqrt{2}}{2}i$$

$$z_5 = \cos\pi + i\sin\pi \qquad = -1 + 0i$$

$$z_6 = \cos\frac{5\pi}{4} + i\sin\frac{5\pi}{4} = -\frac{\sqrt{2}}{2} - \frac{\sqrt{2}}{2}i$$

$$z_7 = \cos\frac{3\pi}{2} + i\sin\frac{3\pi}{2} = 0 - i$$

$$z_8 = \cos\frac{7\pi}{4} + i\sin\frac{7\pi}{4} = \frac{\sqrt{2}}{2} - \frac{\sqrt{2}}{2}i$$

Figure H.127 shows the eight points. They are spaced $2\pi/8 = \pi/4$ radians apart.

Now try Exercise 59.

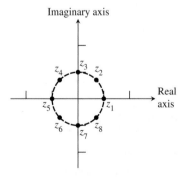

FIGURE H.127 The eight eighth roots of unity are evenly spaced on a unit circle. (Example 9)

LESSON H-12 EXERCISES

Exercise numbers with a gray background indicate problems that the authors have designed to be solved *without a calculator.*

In Exercises 1 and 2, plot all four points in the same complex plan.

1. $1 + 2i, 3 - i, -2 + 2i, i$

2. $2 - 3i, 1 + i, 3, -2 - i$

In Exercises 3–12, find the trigonometric form of the complex number where the argument satisfies $0 \le \theta < 2\pi$.

3. $3i$ **4.** $-2i$

5. $2 + 2i$ **6.** $\sqrt{3} + i$

7. $-2 + 2i\sqrt{3}$ **8.** $3 - 3i$

9. $3 + 2i$ **10.** $4 - 7i$

11.   **12.**

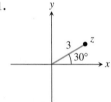

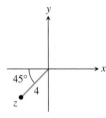

In Exercises 13–18, write the complex number in standard form $a + bi$.

13. $3(\cos 30° - i \sin 30°)$

14. $8(\cos 210° + i \sin 210°)$

15. $5[\cos (-60°) + i \sin (-60°)]$

16. $5\left(\cos \dfrac{\pi}{4} + i \sin \dfrac{\pi}{4}\right)$

17. $\sqrt{2}\left(\cos \dfrac{7\pi}{6} + i \sin \dfrac{7\pi}{6}\right)$

18. $\sqrt{7}\left(\cos \dfrac{\pi}{12} + i \sin \dfrac{\pi}{12}\right)$

In Exercises 19–22, find the product of z_1 and z_2. Leave the answer in trigonometric form.

19. $z_1 = 7(\cos 25° + i \sin 25°)$
$z_2 = 2(\cos 130° + i \sin 130°)$

20. $z_1 = \sqrt{2}(\cos 118° + i \sin 118°)$
$z_2 = 0.5[\cos (-19°) + i \sin (-19°)]$

21. $z_1 = 5\left(\cos \dfrac{\pi}{4} + i \sin \dfrac{\pi}{4}\right)$ $z_2 = 3\left(\cos \dfrac{5\pi}{3} + i \sin \dfrac{5\pi}{3}\right)$

22. $z_1 = \sqrt{3}\left(\cos \dfrac{3\pi}{4} + i \sin \dfrac{3\pi}{4}\right)$ $z_2 = \dfrac{1}{3}\left(\cos \dfrac{\pi}{6} + i \sin \dfrac{\pi}{6}\right)$

In Exercises 23–26, find the trigonometric form of the quotient.

23. $\dfrac{2(\cos 30° + i \sin 30°)}{3(\cos 60° + i \sin 60°)}$ **24.** $\dfrac{5(\cos 220° + i \sin 220°)}{2(\cos 115° + i \sin 115°)}$

25. $\dfrac{6(\cos 5\pi + i \sin 5\pi)}{3(\cos 2\pi + i \sin 2\pi)}$ **26.** $\dfrac{\cos (\pi/2) + i \sin (\pi/2)}{\cos (\pi/4) + i \sin (\pi/4)}$

In Exercises 27–30, find the product $z_1 \cdot z_2$ and quotient z_1/z_2 in two ways, **(a)** using the trigonometric form for z_1 and z_2 and **(b)** using the standard form for z_1 and z_2.

27. $z_1 = 3 - 2i$ and $z_2 = 1 + i$

28. $z_1 = 1 - i$ and $z_2 = \sqrt{3} + i$

29. $z_1 = 3 + i$ and $z_2 = 5 - 3i$

30. $z_1 = 2 - 3i$ and $z_2 = 1 - \sqrt{3}i$

In Exercises 31–38, use De Moivre's Theorem to find the indicated power of the complex number. Write your answer in standard form $a + bi$ and support with a calculator.

31. $\left(\cos \dfrac{\pi}{4} + i \sin \dfrac{\pi}{4}\right)^3$

32. $\left[3\left(\cos \dfrac{3\pi}{2} + i \sin \dfrac{3\pi}{2}\right)\right]^5$

33. $\left[2\left(\cos \dfrac{3\pi}{4} + i \sin \dfrac{3\pi}{4}\right)\right]^3$

34. $\left[6\left(\cos \dfrac{5\pi}{6} + i \sin \dfrac{5\pi}{6}\right)\right]^4$

35. $(1 + i)^5$

36. $(3 + 4i)^{20}$

37. $(1 - \sqrt{3}i)^3$ **38.** $\left(\dfrac{1}{2} + i\dfrac{\sqrt{3}}{2}\right)^3$

Use an algebraic method in Exercises 39–44 to find the cube roots of the complex number. Approximate exact solution values when appropriate.

39. $2(\cos 2\pi + i \sin 2\pi)$ **40.** $2\left(\cos \dfrac{\pi}{4} + i \sin \dfrac{\pi}{4}\right)$

41. $3\left(\cos \dfrac{4\pi}{3} + i \sin \dfrac{4\pi}{3}\right)$ **42.** $27\left(\cos \dfrac{11\pi}{6} + i \sin \dfrac{11\pi}{6}\right)$

43. $3 - 4i$ **44.** $-2 + 2i$

In Exercises 45–50, find the fifth roots of the complex number.

45. $\cos \pi + i \sin \pi$ **46.** $32\left(\cos \dfrac{\pi}{2} + i \sin \dfrac{\pi}{2}\right)$

47. $2\left(\cos \dfrac{\pi}{6} + i \sin \dfrac{\pi}{6}\right)$ **48.** $2\left(\cos \dfrac{\pi}{4} + i \sin \dfrac{\pi}{4}\right)$

49. $2i$ **50.** $1 + \sqrt{3}i$

In Exercises 51–56, find the nth roots of the complex number for the specified value of n.

51. $1 + i$, $n = 4$ **52.** $1 - i$, $n = 6$

53. $2 + 2i$, $n = 3$ **54.** $-2 + 2i$, $n = 4$

55. $-2i$, $n = 6$ **56.** 32, $n = 5$

In Exercises 57–60, express the roots of unity in standard form $a + bi$. Graph each root in the complex plane.

57. Cube roots of unity   **58.** Fourth roots of unity

59. Sixth roots of unity   **60.** Square roots of unity

61. Determine z and the three cube roots of z if one cube root of z is $1 + \sqrt{3}i$.

62. Determine z and the four fourth roots of z if one fourth root of z is $-2 - 2i$.

63. Quotient Formula   Let $z_1 = r_1(\cos \theta_1 + i \sin \theta_1)$ and $z_2 = r_2(\cos \theta_2 + i \sin \theta_2)$, $r_2 \neq 0$. Verify that $z_1/z_2 = r_1/r_2 [\cos (\theta_1 - \theta_2) + i \sin (\theta_1 - \theta_2)]$.

64. Group Activity nth Roots   Show that the nth roots of the complex number $r(\cos \theta + i \sin \theta)$ are spaced $2\pi/n$ radians apart on a circle with radius $\sqrt[n]{r}$.

Explorations

65. Complex Conjugates   The complex conjugate of $z = a + bi$ is $\bar{z} = a - bi$. Let $z = r(\cos \theta + i \sin \theta)$.

(a) Prove that $\bar{z} = r[\cos (-\theta) + i \sin (-\theta)]$.

(b) Use the trigonometric form to find $z \cdot \bar{z}$.

(c) Use the trigonometric form to find $z/\bar{z}$, if $\bar{z} \neq 0$.

(d) Prove that $-z = r[\cos (\theta + \pi) + i \sin (\theta + \pi)]$.

66. Modulus of Complex Numbers   Let $z = r(\cos \theta + i \sin \theta)$.

(a) Prove that $|z| = |r|$.

(b) Use the trigonometric form for the complex numbers z_1 and z_2 to prove that $|z_1 \cdot z_2| = |z_1| \cdot |z_2|$.

Extending the Ideas

67. Using Polar Form on a Graphing Calculator
The complex number $r(\cos \theta + i \sin \theta)$ can be entered in polar form on some graphing calculators as $re^{i\theta}$.

(a) Support the result of Example 3 by entering the complex numbers z_1 and z_2 in polar form on your graphing calculator and computing the product with your graphing calculator.

(b) Support the result of Example 4 by entering the complex numbers z_1 and z_2 in polar form on your graphing calculator and computing the quotient with your graphing calculator.

(c) Support the result of Example 5 by entering the complex number in polar form on your graphing calculator and computing the power with your graphing calculator.

68. Visualizing Roots of Unity   Set your graphing calculator in parametric mode with $0 \leq T \leq 8$, Tstep $= 1$, Xmin $= -2.4$, Xmax $= 2.4$, Ymin $= -1.6$, and Ymax $= 1.6$.

(a) Let $x = \cos ((2\pi/8)t)$ and $y = \sin ((2\pi/8)t)$. Use TRACE to visualize the eight eighth roots of unity. We say that $2\pi/8$ *generates* the eighth roots of unity. (Try both dot mode and connected mode.)

(b) Replace $2\pi/8$ in part (a) by the arguments of other eighth roots of unity. Do any others *generate* the eighth roots of unity?

(c) Repeat parts (a) and (b) for the fifth, sixth, and seventh roots of unity, using appropriate functions for x and y.

(d) What would you conjecture about an nth root of unity that generates all the nth roots of unity in the sense of part (a)?

69. Parametric Graphing   Write parametric equations that represent $(\sqrt{2} + i)^n$ for $n = t$. Draw and label an *accurate* spiral representing $(\sqrt{2} + i)^n$ for $n = 0, 1, 2, 3, 4$.

70. Parametric Graphing   Write parametric equations that represent $(-1 + i)^n$ for $n = t$. Draw and label an *accurate* spiral representing $(-1 + i)^n$ for $n = 0, 1, 2, 3, 4$.

71. Explain why the triangles formed by 0, 1, and z_1, and by 0, z_2, and z_1z_2 shown in the figure are similar triangles.

72. Compass and Straightedge Construction   Using only a compass and straightedge, construct the location of z_1z_2 given the location of 0, 1, z_1, and z_2.

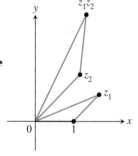

H-13 Sequences

Infinite Sequences

What you'll learn about

• Infinite Sequences

• Limits of Infinite Sequences

• Arithmetic and Geometric Sequences

• Sequences and Graphing Calculators

... and why

Infinite sequences, especially those with finite limits, are involved in some key concepts of calculus.

One of the most natural ways to study patterns in mathematics is to look at an ordered progression of numbers, called a **sequence**. Here are some examples of sequences:

1. $5, 10, 15, 20, 25$

2. $2, 4, 8, 16, 32, \ldots, 2^k, \ldots$

3. $\left\{ \dfrac{1}{k}; k = 1, 2, 3, \ldots \right\}$

4. $\{a_1, a_2, a_3, \ldots, a_k, \ldots\}$, which is sometimes abbreviated $\{a_k\}$

The first of these is a **finite sequence**, while the other three are **infinite sequences**. Notice that in (2) and (3) we were able to define a rule that gives the kth number in the sequence (called the **kth term**) as a function of k. In (4) we do not have a rule, but notice how we can use subscript notation (a_k) to identify the kth term of a "general" infinite sequence. In this sense, an infinite sequence can be thought of as a *function* that assigns a unique number (a_k) to each natural number k.

EXAMPLE 1 Defining a Sequence Explicitly

Find the first 6 terms and the 100th term of the sequence $\{a_k\}$ in which $a_k = k^2 - 1$.

SOLUTION Since we know the kth term *explicitly* as a function of k, we need only to evaluate the function to find the required terms:

$$a_1 = 1^2 - 1 = 0, \ a_2 = 3, \ a_3 = 8, \ a_4 = 15, \ a_5 = 24, \ a_6 = 35, \quad \text{and}$$
$$a_{100} = 100^2 - 1 = 9999$$

Now try Exercise 1.

Explicit formulas are the easiest to work with, but there are other ways to define sequences. For example, we can specify values for the first term (or terms) of a sequence, then define each of the following terms **recursively** by a formula relating it to previous terms. Example 2 shows how this is done.

EXAMPLE 2 Defining a Sequence Recursively

Find the first 6 terms and the 100th term for the sequence defined recursively by the conditions:

$$b_1 = 3$$
$$b_n = b_{n-1} + 2 \text{ for all } n > 1$$

SOLUTION We proceed one term at a time, starting with $b_1 = 3$ and obtaining each succeeding term by adding 2 to the term just before it:

$$b_1 = 3$$
$$b_2 = b_1 + 2 = 5$$
$$b_3 = b_2 + 2 = 7$$
$$\text{etc.}$$

Eventually it becomes apparent that we are building the sequence of odd natural numbers beginning with 3:

$$\{3, 5, 7, 9, \ldots\}$$

Agreement on Sequences

Since we will be dealing primarily with infinite sequences in this book, the word "sequence" will mean an infinite sequence unless otherwise specified.

The 100th term is 99 terms beyond the first, which means that we can get there quickly by adding 99 2's to the number 3:

$$b_{100} = 3 + 99 \times 2 = 201$$

Now try Exercise 5.

Limits of Infinite Sequences

Just as we were concerned with the end behavior of functions, we will also be concerned with the end behavior of sequences.

DEFINITION Limit of a Sequence

Let $\{a_n\}$ be a sequence of real numbers, and consider $\lim\limits_{n \to \infty} a_n$, If the limit is a finite number L, the sequence **converges** and L is the **limit of the sequence**. If the limit is infinite or nonexistent, the sequence **diverges**.

EXAMPLE 3 Finding Limits of Sequences

Determine whether the sequence converges or diverges. If it converges, give the limit.

(a) $\dfrac{1}{1}, \dfrac{1}{2}, \dfrac{1}{3}, \dfrac{1}{4}, \ldots, \dfrac{1}{n}, \ldots$

(b) $\dfrac{2}{1}, \dfrac{3}{2}, \dfrac{4}{3}, \dfrac{5}{4}, \ldots$

(c) $2, 4, 6, 8, 10, \ldots$

(d) $-1, 1, -1, 1, \ldots, (-1)^n, \ldots$

SOLUTION

(a) $\lim\limits_{x \to \infty} \dfrac{1}{n} = 0$, so the sequence converges to a limit of 0.

(b) Although the nth term is not explicitly given, we can see that $a_n = \dfrac{n+1}{n}$.

$\lim\limits_{x \to \infty} \dfrac{n+1}{n} = \lim\limits_{n \to \infty} \left(1 + \dfrac{1}{n}\right) = 1 + 0 = 1.$ The sequence converges to a limit of 1.

(c) This time we see that $a_n = 2n$. Since $\lim\limits_{n \to \infty} 2n = \infty$, the sequence diverges.

(d) This sequence oscillates forever between two values and hence has no limit. The sequence diverges. *Now try Exercise 13.*

It might help to review the rules for finding the *end behavior asymptotes* of rational functions because those same rules apply to sequences that are rational functions of n, as in Example 4.

EXAMPLE 4 Finding Limits of Sequences

Determine whether the sequence converges or diverges. If it converges, give the limit.

(a) $\left\{\dfrac{3n}{n+1}\right\}$

(b) $\left\{\dfrac{5n^2}{n^3+1}\right\}$

(c) $\left\{\dfrac{n^3+2}{n^2+n}\right\}$

SOLUTION

(a) Since the degree of the numerator is the same as the degree of the denominator, the limit is the ratio of the leading coefficients.

Thus $\lim\limits_{n\to\infty}\dfrac{3n}{n+1} = \dfrac{3}{1} = 3$. The sequence converges to a limit of 3.

(b) Since the degree of the numerator is less than the degree of the denominator, the limit is zero. Thus $\lim\limits_{n\to\infty}\dfrac{5n^2}{n^3+1} = 0$. The sequence converges to 0.

(c) Since the degree of the numerator is greater than the degree of the denominator, the limit is infinite. Thus $\lim\limits_{n\to\infty}\dfrac{n^3+2}{n^2+n}$ is infinite. The sequence diverges.

Now try Exercise 15.

Arithmetic and Geometric Sequences

There are all kinds of rules by which we can construct sequences, but two particular types of sequences dominate in mathematical applications: those in which pairs of successive terms all have a common *difference* (**arithmetic** sequences), and those in which pairs of successive terms all have a common quotient, or *ratio* (**geometric** sequences). We will take a closer look at these in this section.

DEFINITION Arithmetic Sequence

A sequence $\{a_n\}$ is an **arithmetic sequence** if it can be written in the form

$$\{a, a + d, a + 2d, \ldots, a + (n-1)d, \ldots\} \text{ for some constant } d.$$

The number d is called the **common difference**.

Each term in an arithmetic sequence can be obtained recursively from its preceding term by adding d:

$$a_n = a_{n-1} + d \text{ (for all } n \geq 2)$$

Pronunciation Tip

The word "arithmetic" is probably more familiar to you as a noun, referring to the mathematics you studied in elementary school. In this word, the second syllable ("rith") is accented. When used as an adjective, the third syllable ("met") gets the accent. (For the sake of comparison, a similar shift of accent occurs when going from the noun "analysis" to the adjective "analytic.")

EXAMPLE 5 Defining Arithmetic Sequences

For each of the following arithmetic sequences, find (a) the common difference, (b) the tenth term, (c) a recursive rule for the nth term, and (d) an explicit rule for the nth term.

(1) $-6, -2, 2, 6, 10, \ldots$

(2) $\ln 3, \ln 6, \ln 12, \ln 24, \ldots$

SOLUTION

(1) (a) The difference between successive terms is 4.

(b) $a_{10} = -6 + (10-1)(4) = 30$

(c) The sequence is defined recursively by $a_1 = -6$ and $a_n = a_{n-1} + 4$ for all $n \geq 2$.

(d) The sequence is defined explicitly by $a_n = -6 + (n-1)(4) = 4n - 10$.

(2) (a) This sequence might not look arithmetic at first, but

$\ln 6 - \ln 3 = \ln\dfrac{6}{3} = \ln 2$ (by a law of logarithms) and the difference between successive terms continues to be $\ln 2$.

(b) $a_{10} = \ln 3 + (10-1)\ln 2 = \ln 3 + 9\ln 2 = \ln(3 \cdot 2^9) = \ln 1536$

(c) The sequence is defined recursively by $a_1 = \ln 3$ and $a_n = a_{n-1} + \ln 2$ for all $n \geq 2$.

(d) The sequence is defined explicitly by $a_n = \ln 3 + (n-1)\ln 2$
$= \ln(3 \cdot 2^{n-1})$.

Now try Exercise 21.

DEFINITION Geometric Sequence

A sequence $\{a_n\}$ is a **geometric sequence** if it can be written in the form

$$\{a, a \cdot r, a \cdot r^2, \ldots, a \cdot r^{n-1}, \ldots\} \text{ for some nonzero constant } r.$$

The number r is called the **common ratio**.

Each term in a geometric sequence can be obtained recursively from its preceding term by multiplying by r:

$$a_n = a_{n-1} \cdot r \text{ (for all } n \geq 2)$$

EXAMPLE 6 Defining Geometric Sequences

For each of the following geometric sequences, find **(a)** the common ratio, **(b)** the tenth term, **(c)** a recursive rule for the nth term, and **(d)** an explicit rule for the nth term.

(1) $3, 6, 12, 24, 48, \ldots$

(2) $10^{-3}, 10^{-1}, 10^{1}, 10^{3}, 10^{5}, \ldots$

SOLUTION

(1) **(a)** The ratio between successive terms is 2.

(b) $a_{10} = 3 \cdot 2^{10-1} = 3 \cdot 2^9 = 1536$

(c) The sequence is defined recursively by $a_1 = 3$ and $a_n = 2a_{n-1}$ for $n \geq 2$.

(d) The sequence is defined explicitly by $a_n = 3 \cdot 2^{n-1}$.

(2) **(a)** Applying a law of exponents, $\dfrac{10^{-1}}{10^{-3}} = 10^{-1-(-3)} = 10^2$, and the ratio between successive terms continues to be 10^2.

(b) $a_{10} = 10^{-3} \cdot (10^2)^{10-1} = 10^{-3+18} = 10^{15}$

(c) The sequence is defined recursively by $a_1 = 10^{-3}$ and $a_n = 10^2 a_{n-1}$ for $n \geq 2$.

(d) The sequence is defined explicitly by $a_n = 10^{-3}(10^2)^{n-1} = 10^{-3+2n-2} = 10^{2n-5}$. *Now try Exercise 25.*

EXAMPLE 7 Constructing Sequences

The second and fifth terms of a sequence are 3 and 24, respectively. Find explicit and recursive formulas for the sequence if it is **(a)** arithmetic and **(b)** geometric.

SOLUTION

(a) If the sequence is arithmetic, then $a_2 = a_1 + d = 3$ and $a_5 = a_1 + 4d = 24$. Subtracting, we have

$$(a_1 + 4d) - (a_1 + d) = 24 - 3$$
$$3d = 21$$
$$d = 7$$

Then $a_1 + d = 3$ implies $a_1 = -4$.

The sequence is defined explicitly by $a_n = -4 + (n-1) \cdot 7$, or $a_n = 7n - 11$.

The sequence is defined recursively by $a_1 = -4$ and $a_n = a_{n-1} + 7$ for $n \geq 2$.

(b) If the sequence is geometric, then $a_2 = a \cdot r^1 = 3$ and $a_5 = a \cdot r^4 = 24$. Dividing, we have

$$\frac{a_1 \cdot r^4}{a_1 \cdot r^1} = \frac{24}{3}$$
$$r^3 = 8$$
$$r = 2$$

continued

Then $a_1 \cdot r^1 = 3$ implies $a_1 = 1.5$.

The sequence is defined explicitly by $a_n = 1.5(2)^{n-1}$, or $a_n = 3(2)^{n-2}$.

The sequence is defined recursively by $a_1 = 1.5$ and $a_n = 2 \cdot a_{n-1}$.

Now try Exercise 29.

Sequence Graphing

Most graphers enable you to graph in "sequence mode." Check your owner's manual to see how to use this mode.

Sequences and Graphing Calculators

As with other kinds of functions, it helps to be able to represent a sequence geometrically with a graph. There are at least two ways to obtain a sequence graph on a graphing calculator. One way to graph explicitly defined sequences is as scatter plots of points of the form (k, a_k). A second way is to use the sequence graphing mode on a graphing calculator.

EXAMPLE 8 Graphing a Sequence Defined Explicitly

Produce on a graphing calculator a graph of the sequence $\{a_k\}$ in which $a_k = k^2 - 1$.

Method 1 (Scatter Plot)

The command $\text{seq}(K, K, 1, 10) \rightarrow L_1$ puts the first 10 natural numbers in list L_1. (You could change the 10 if you wanted to graph more or fewer points.)

The command $L_1^2 - 1 \rightarrow L_2$ puts the corresponding terms of the sequence in list L_2. A scatter plot of L_1, L_2 produces the graph in Figure H.128a.

Method 2 (Sequence Mode)

With your calculator in Sequence mode, enter the sequence $a_k = k^2 - 1$ in the Y = list as $u(n) = n^2 - 1$ with $n\text{Min} = 1$, $n\text{Max} = 10$, and $u(n\text{Min}) = 0$. (You could change the 10 if you wanted to graph more or fewer points.) Figure H.128b shows the graph in the same window as Figure H.128a.

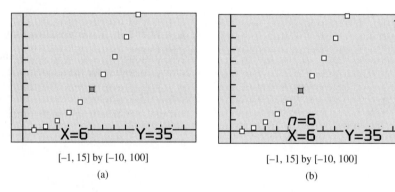

[−1, 15] by [−10, 100]   [−1, 15] by [−10, 100]
(a)   (b)

FIGURE H.128 The sequence $a_k = k^2 - 1$ graphed (a) as a scatter plot and (b) using the sequence graphing mode. Tracing along the points gives values of a_k for $k = 1, 2, 3, \ldots$. (Example 8)

Now try Exercise 33.

EXAMPLE 9 Generating a Sequence with a Calculator

Using a graphing calculator, generate the specific terms of the following sequences:

(a) (Explicit) $a_k = 3k - 5$ for $k = 1, 2, 3, \ldots$

(b) (Recursive) $a_1 = -2$ and $a_n = a_{n-1} + 3$ for $n = 2, 3, 4, \ldots$

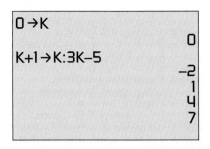

FIGURE H.130 Typing these two commands (on the left of the viewing screen) will generate the terms of the explicitly defined sequence $a_k = 3k - 5$. (Example 9a)

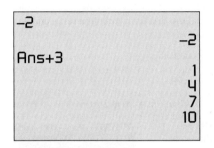

FIGURE H.131 Typing these two commands (on the left of the viewing screen) will generate the terms of the recursively defined sequence with $a_1 = -2$ and $a_n = a_{n-1} + 3$. (Example 9b)

Fibonacci Numbers

The numbers in the Fibonacci sequence have fascinated professional and amateur mathematicians alike since the thirteenth century. Not only is the sequence, like Pascal's triangle, a rich source of curious internal patterns, but the Fibonacci numbers seem to appear everywhere in nature. If you count the leaflets on a leaf, the leaves on a stem, the whorls on a pine cone, the rows on an ear of corn, the spirals in a sunflower, or the branches from a trunk of a tree, they tend to be Fibonacci numbers. (Check **phyllotaxy** in a biology book.)

SOLUTION

(a) On the home screen, type the two commands shown in Figure H.130. The calculator will then generate the terms of the sequence as you push the ENTER key repeatedly.

(b) On the home screen, type the two commands shown in Figure H.131. The first command gives the value of a_1. The calculator will generate the remaining terms of the sequence as you push the ENTER key repeatedly.

Notice that these two definitions generate the very same sequence!

Now try Exercises 1 and 5 on your calculator.

A recursive definition of a_n can be made in terms of any combination of preceding terms, just as long as those preceding terms have already been determined. A famous example is the **Fibonacci sequence**, named for Leonardo of Pisa (ca. 1170–1250), who wrote under the name Fibonacci. You can generate it with the two commands shown in Figure H.132.

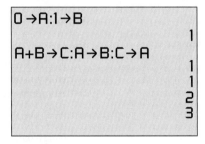

FIGURE H.132 The two commands on the left will generate the Fibonacci sequence as the ENTER key is pressed repeatedly.

The Fibonacci sequence can be defined recursively using three statements.

The Fibonacci Sequence

The Fibonacci sequence can be defined recursively by

$$a_1 = 1$$
$$a_2 = 1$$
$$a_n = a_{n-2} + a_{n-1}$$

for all positive integers $n \geq 3$.

Exercise numbers with a gray background indicate problems that the authors have designed to be solved *without a calculator*.

In Exercises 1–4, find the first 6 terms and the 100th term of the explicitly defined sequence.

1. $u_n = \dfrac{n + 1}{n}$

2. $v_n = \dfrac{4}{n + 2}$

3. $c_n = n^3 - n$

4. $d_n = n^2 - 5n$

In Exercises 5–10, find the first 4 terms and the eighth term of the recursively defined sequence.

5. $a_1 = 8$ and $a_n = a_{n-1}, - 4$, for $n \geq 2$

6. $u_1 = -3$ and $u_{k+1} = u_k + 10$, for $k \geq 1$,

7. $b_1 = 2$ and $b_{k+1} = 3b_k$, for $k \geq 1$

8. $v_1 = 0.75$ and $v_n = (-2)v_{n-1}$, for $n \geq 2$

9. $c_1 = 2$, $c_2 = -1$, and $c_{k+2} = c_k + c_{k+1}\,1$, for $k \geq 1$

10. $c_1 = -2$, $c_2 = 3$, and $c_k = c_{k-2} + c_{k-1}$, for $k \geq 3$

In Exercises 11–20, determine whether the sequence converges or diverges. If it converges, give the limit.

11. $1, 4, 9, 16, \ldots, n^2, \ldots$

12. $\dfrac{1}{2}, \dfrac{1}{4}, \dfrac{1}{8}, \dfrac{1}{16}, \ldots, \dfrac{1}{2^n}, \ldots$

13. $\dfrac{1}{1}, \dfrac{1}{4}, \dfrac{1}{9}, \dfrac{1}{16}, \ldots,$

14. $\{3n - 1\}$

15. $\left\{\dfrac{3n - 1}{2 - 3n}\right\}$

16. $\left\{\dfrac{2n - 1}{n + 1}\right\}$

17. $\{(0.5)^n\}$

18. $\{(1.5)^n\}$

19. $a_1 = 1$ and $a_{n+1} = a_n + 3$ for $n \geq 1$

20. $u_1 = 1$ and $u_{n+1} = \dfrac{u_n}{3}$ for $n \geq 1$

In Exercises 21–24, the sequences are arithmetic. Find

(a) the common difference,

(b) the tenth term,

(c) a recursive rule for the nth term, and

(d) an explicit rule for the nth term.

21. $6, 10, 14, 18, \ldots$

22. $-4, 1, 6, 11, \ldots$

23. $-5, -2, 1, 4, \ldots$

24. $-7, 4, 15, 26, \ldots$

In Exercises 25–28, the sequences are geometric. Find

(a) the common ratio,

(b) the eighth term,

(c) a recursive rule for the nth term, and

(d) an explicit rule for the nth term.

25. $2, 6, 18, 54, \ldots$

26. $3, 6, 12, 24, \ldots$

27. $1, -2, 4, -8, 16, \ldots$

28. $-2, 2, -2, 2, \ldots$

29. The fourth and seventh terms of an arithmetic sequence are -8 and 4, respectively. Find the first term and a recursive rule for the nth term.

30. The fifth and ninth terms of an arithmetic sequence are -5 and -17, respectively. Find the first term and a recursive rule for the nth term.

31. The second and eighth terms of a geometric sequence are 3 and 192, respectively. Find the first term, common ratio, and an explicit rule for the nth term.

32. The third and sixth terms of a geometric sequence are -75 and -9375, respectively. Find the first term, common ratio, and an explicit rule for the nth term.

In Exercises 33–36, graph the sequence.

33. $a_n = 2 - \dfrac{1}{n}$

34. $b_n = \sqrt{n} - 3$

35. $c_n = n^2 - 5$

36. $d_n = 3 + 2n$

37. Rain Forest Growth The bungy-bungy tree in the Amazon rain forest grows an average 2.3 cm per week. Write a sequence that represents the weekly height of a bungy-bungy over the course of 1 year if it is 7 meters tall today. Display the first four terms and the last two terms.

38. Half-Life (See Lesson H-2) Thorium-232 has a half-life of 14 billion years. Make a table showing the half-life decay of a sample of thorium-232 from 16 grams to 1 gram; list the time (in years, starting with $t = 0$) in the first column and the mass (in grams) in the second column. Which type of sequence is each column of the table?

39. Arena Seating The first row of seating in section J of the Athena Arena has 7 seats. In all, there are 25 rows of seats in section J, each row containing two more seats than the row preceding it. How many seats are in section J?

40. Patio Construction Pat designs a patio with a trapezoid-shaped deck consisting of 16 rows of congruent slate tiles. The numbers of tiles in the rows form an arithmetic sequence. The first row contains 15 tiles and the last row contains 30 tiles. How many tiles are used in the deck?

41. Group Activity Pair up with a partner to create a sequence recursively together. Each of you picks five random digits from 1 to 9 (with repetitions, if you wish). Merge your digits to make a list of ten. Now each of you constructs a ten-digit number using exactly the numbers in your list.

Let $a_1 = $ the (positive) difference between your two numbers.

Let $a_{n+1} = $ the sum of the digits of a_n for $n \geq 1$.

This sequence converges, since it is eventually constant. What is the limit? (Remember, you can check your answer in the back of the book.)

42. Group Activity Here is an interesting recursively defined word sequence. Join up with three or four classmates and, without telling it to the others, pick a word from this sentence. Then, with care, count the letters in your word. Move *ahead* that many words in the text to come to a new word. Count the letters in the new word. Move ahead again, and so on. When you come to a point when your next move would take you out of this problem, stop. Share your last word with your friends. Are they all the same?

Explorations

43. Rabbit Populations Assume that 2 months after birth, each male-female pair of rabbits begins producing one new male-female pair of rabbits each month. Further assume that the rabbit colony begins with one newborn male-female pair of rabbits and no rabbits die for 12 months. Let a_n represent the number of *pairs* of rabbits in the colony after $n - 1$ months.

(a) **Writing to Learn** Explain why $a_1 = 1$, $a_2 = 1$, and $a_3 = 2$.

(b) Find $a_4, a_5, a_6, \ldots, a_{13}$.

(c) **Writing to Learn** Explain why the sequence $\{a_n\}$, $1 \leq n \leq 13$, is a model for the size of the rabbit colony for a 1-year period.

44. Fibonacci Sequence Compute the first seven terms of the sequence whose nth term is

$$a_n = \frac{1}{\sqrt{5}}\left(\frac{1 + \sqrt{5}}{2}\right)^n - \frac{1}{\sqrt{5}}\left(\frac{1 - \sqrt{5}}{2}\right)^n.$$

How do these seven terms compare with the first seven terms of the Fibonacci sequence?

45. Connecting Geometry and Sequences In the following sequence of diagrams, regular polygons are inscribed in unit circles with at least one side of each polygon perpendicular to the positive x-axis.

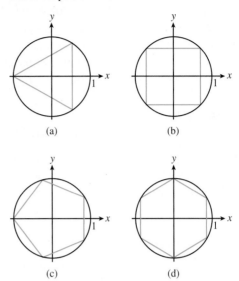

(a) Prove that the perimeter of each polygon in the sequence is given by $a_n = 2n \sin(\pi/n)$, where n is the number of sides in the polygon.

(b) Investigate the value of a_n for $n = 10, 100, 1000$, and $10,000$. What conclusion can you draw?

46. Recursive Sequence The population of Centerville was 525,000 in 1992 and is growing annually at the rate of 1.75%. Write a recursive sequence $\{P_n\}$ for the population. State the first term P_1 for your sequence.

47. Writing to Learn If $\{a_n\}$ is a geometric sequence with all positive terms, explain why $\{\log a_n\}$ must be arithmetic.

48. Writing to Learn If $\{b_n\}$ is an arithmetic sequence, explain why $\{10^{b_n}\}$ must be geometric.

Extending the Ideas

49. A Sequence of Matrices Write out the first seven terms of the "geometric sequence" with the first term the matrix $\begin{bmatrix} 1 & 1 \end{bmatrix}$ and the common ratio the matrix $\begin{bmatrix} 0 & 1 \\ 1 & 1 \end{bmatrix}$. How is this sequence of matrices related to the Fibonacci sequence?

50. Another Sequence of Matrices Write out the first seven terms of the "geometric sequence" which has for its first term the matrix $\begin{bmatrix} 1 & a \end{bmatrix}$ and for its common ratio the matrix $\begin{bmatrix} 1 & d \\ 0 & 1 \end{bmatrix}$. How is this sequence of matrices related to the arithmetic sequence?

H-14 Series

Σ Summation Notation

We want to look at the formulas for summing the terms of arithmetic and geometric sequences, but first we need a notation for writing the sum of an indefinite number of terms. The capital Greek letter sigma (Σ) provides our shorthand notation for a "summation."

Summations on a Calculator

If you think of summations as summing sequence values, it is not hard to translate sigma notation into calculator syntax. Here, in calculator syntax, are the first three summations in Exploration 1. (Don't try these on your calculator until you have first figured out the answers with pencil and paper.)

1. sum (seq (3K, K, 1, 5))
2. sum (seq (K^2, K, 5, 8))
3. sum (seq (cos (Nπ), N, 0, 12))

DEFINITION Summation Notation

In **summation notation**, the sum of the terms of the sequence $\{a_1, a_2, \ldots, a_n\}$ is denoted

$$\sum_{k=1}^{n} a_k$$

which is read "the sum of a_k from $k = 1$ to n."

The variable k is called the **index of summation**.

EXPLORATION 1   Summing with Sigma

Sigma notation is actually even more versatile than the definition above suggests. See if you can determine the number represented by each of the following expressions.

1. $\displaystyle\sum_{k=1}^{5} 3k$ 2. $\displaystyle\sum_{k=5}^{8} k^2$ 3. $\displaystyle\sum_{n=0}^{12} \cos(n\pi)$ 4. $\displaystyle\sum_{n=1}^{\infty} \sin(n\pi)$ 5. $\displaystyle\sum_{k=1}^{\infty} \frac{3}{10^k}$

(If you're having trouble with number 5, here's a hint: Write the sum as a decimal!)

Although you probably computed them correctly, there is more going on in number 4 and number 5 in the above exploration than first meets the eye. We will have more to say about these "infinite" summations toward the end of this section.

Sums of Arithmetic and Geometric Sequences

One of the most famous legends in the lore of mathematics concerns the German mathematician Karl Friedrich Gauss (1777–1855), whose mathematical talent was apparent at a very early age. One version of the story has Gauss, at age ten, being in a class that was challenged by the teacher to add up all the numbers from 1 to 100. While his classmates were still writing down the problem, Gauss walked to the front of the room to present his slate to the teacher. The teacher, certain that Gauss could only be guessing, refused to look at his answer. Gauss simply placed it face down on the teacher's desk, declared "There it is," and returned to his seat. Later, after all the slates had been collected, the teacher looked at Gauss's work, which consisted of a single number: the correct answer. No other student (the legend goes) got it right.

The important feature of this legend for mathematicians is *how* the young Gauss got the answer so quickly. We'll let you reproduce his technique in Exploration 2.

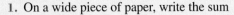

EXPLORATION 2 Gauss's Insight

Your challenge is to find the sum of the natural numbers from 1 to 100 without a calculator.

1. On a wide piece of paper, write the sum

   "$1 + 2 + 3 + \cdots + 98 + 99 + 100$."

2. Underneath this sum, write the sum

   "$100 + 99 + 98 + \cdots + 3 + 2 + 1$."

3. Add the numbers two-by-two in *vertical* columns and notice that you get the same identical sum 100 times. What is it?

4. What is the sum of the 100 identical numbers referred to in part 3?

5. Explain why half the answer in part 4 is the answer to the challenge. Can you find it without a calculator?

If this story is true, then the youthful Gauss had discovered a fact that his elders knew about arithmetic sequences. If you write a finite arithmetic sequence forward on one line and backward on the line below it, then all the pairs stacked vertically sum to the same number. Multiplying this number by the number of terms n and dividing by 2 gives us a shortcut to the sum of the n terms. We state this result as a theorem.

THEOREM 14 Sum of a Finite Arithmetic Sequence

Let $\{a_1, a_2, \ldots, a_n\}$ be a finite arithmetic sequence with common difference d. Then the sum of the terms of the sequence is

$$\sum_{k=1}^{n} a_k = a_1 + a_2 + \cdots + a_n$$

$$= n\left(\frac{a_1 + a_n}{2}\right)$$

$$= \frac{n}{2}(2a_1 + (n-1)d)$$

Proof

We can construct the sequence forward by starting with a_1 and *adding d* each time, or we can construct the sequence backward by starting at a_n and *subtracting d* each time. We thus get two expressions for the sum we are looking for:

$$\sum_{k=1}^{n} a_k = a_1 + (a_1 + d) + (a_1 + 2d) + \cdots + (a_1 + (n-1)d)$$

$$\sum_{k=1}^{n} a_k = a_n + (a_n - d) + (a_n - 2d) + \cdots + (a_n - (n-1)d)$$

Summing vertically, we get

$$2\sum_{k=1}^{n} a_k = (a_1 + a_n) + (a_1 + a_n) + \cdots + (a_1 + a_n)$$

$$2\sum_{k=1}^{n} a_k = n(a_1 + a_n)$$

$$\sum_{k=1}^{n} a_k = n\left(\frac{a_1 + a_n}{2}\right)$$

If we substitute $a_1 + (n - 1)d$ for a_n, we get the alternate formula

$$\sum_{k=1}^{n} a_k = \frac{n}{2}(2a_1 + (n - 1)d).$$

EXAMPLE 1 Summing the Terms of an Arithmetic Sequence

A corner section of a stadium has 8 seats along the front row. Each successive row has two more seats than the row preceding it. If the top row has 24 seats, how many seats are in the entire section?

SOLUTION The numbers of seats in the rows form an arithmetic sequence with

$$a_1 = 8, \quad a_n = 24, \quad \text{and} \quad d = 2.$$

Solving $a_n = a_1 + (n - 1)d$, we find that

$$24 = 8 + (n - 1)(2)$$
$$16 = (n - 1)(2)$$
$$8 = n - 1$$
$$n = 9$$

Applying the Sum of a Finite Arithmetic Sequence Theorem, the total number of seats in the section is $9(8 + 24)/2 = 144$.

We can support this answer numerically by computing the sum on a calculator:

$$\text{sum}(\text{seq}(8 + (N - 1)2, N, 1, 9) = 144$$

Now try Exercise 7.

As you might expect, there is also a convenient formula for summing the terms of a finite geometric sequence.

THEOREM 15 Sum of a Finite Geometric Sequence

Let $\{a_1, a_2, a_3, \ldots, a_n\}$ be a finite geometric sequence with common ratio $r \neq 1$.

Then the sum of the terms of the sequence is

$$\sum_{k=1}^{n} a_k = a_1 + a_2 + \cdots + a_n$$

$$= \frac{a_1(1 - r^n)}{1 - r}.$$

Proof

Because the sequence is geometric, we have

$$\sum_{k=1}^{n} a_k = a_1 + a_1 \cdot r + a_1 \cdot r^2 + \cdots + a_1 \cdot r^{n-1}.$$

Therefore,

$$r \cdot \sum_{k=1}^{n} a_k = a_1 \cdot r + a_1 \cdot r^2 + \cdots + a_1 \cdot r^{n-1} + a_1 \cdot r^n.$$

If we now *subtract* the lower summation from the one above it, we have (after eliminating a lot of zeros):

$$\left(\sum_{k=1}^{n} a_k\right) - r \cdot \left(\sum_{k=1}^{n} a_k\right) = a_1 - a_1 \cdot r^n$$

$$\left(\sum_{k=1}^{n} a_k\right)(1 - r) = a_1(1 - r^n)$$

$$\sum_{k=1}^{n} a_k = \frac{a_1(1 - r^n)}{1 - r}$$

EXAMPLE 2 **Summing the Terms of a Geometric Sequence**

Find the sum of the geometric sequence $4, -4/3, 4/9, -4/27, \ldots, 4(-1/3)^{10}$.

SOLUTION We can see that $a_1 = 4$ and $r = -1/3$. The nth term is $4(-1/3)^{10}$, which means that $n = 11$. (Remember that the exponent on the nth term is $n - 1$, not n.) Applying the Sum of a Finite Geometric Sequence Theorem, we find that

$$\sum_{n=1}^{11} 4\left(-\frac{1}{3}\right)^{n-1} = \frac{4(1 - (-1/3)^{11})}{1 - (-1/3)} \approx 3.000016935.$$

We can support this answer by having the calculator do the actual summing:

$\text{sum(seq}(4(-1/3)^{\wedge}(N - 1), N, 1, 11) = 3.000016935.$ *Now try Exercise 13.*

As one practical application of the Sum of a Finite Geometric Sequence Theorem, we can find the future value *FV* of an ordinary annuity consisting of n equal periodic payments of R dollars at an interest rate i per compounding period (payment interval) is

$$FV = R\frac{(1 + i)^n - 1}{i}.$$

We can now consider the mathematics behind this formula. The n payments remain in the account for different lengths of time and so earn different amounts of interest. The total value of the annuity after n payment periods is

$$FV = R + R(1 + i) + R(1 + i)^2 + \cdots + R(1 + i)^{n-1}.$$

The terms of this sum form a geometric sequence with first term R and common ratio $(1 + i)$. Applying the Sum of a Finite Geometric Sequence Theorem, the sum of the n terms is

$$FV = \frac{R(1 - (1 + i)^n)}{1 - (1 + i)}$$

$$= R\frac{1 - (1 + i)^n}{-i}$$

$$= R\frac{(1 + i)^n - 1}{i}$$

Infinite Series

If you change the "11" in the calculator sum in Example 2 to higher and higher numbers, you will find that the sum approaches a value of 3. This is no coincidence. In the language of limits,

$$\lim_{x \to \infty} \sum_{k=1}^{n} 4\left(-\frac{1}{3}\right)^{k-1} = \lim_{x \to \infty} \frac{4(1 - (-1/3)^n)}{1 - (-1/3)}$$

$$= \frac{4(1 - 0)}{4/3}$$

$$= 3$$

This gives us the opportunity to extend the usual meaning of the word "sum," which always applies to a *finite* number of terms being added together. By using limits, we can make sense of expressions in which an *infinite* number of terms are added together. Such expressions are called **infinite series**.

DEFINITION Infinite Series

An **infinite series** is an expression of the form

$$\sum_{n=1}^{\infty} a_n = a_1 + a_2 + \cdots + a_n + \cdots.$$

The first thing to understand about an infinite series is that it is not a true sum. There are properties of real number addition that allow us to extend the definition of $a + b$ to sums like $a + b + c + d + e + f$, but not to "infinite sums." For example, we can add any finite number of 2's together and get a real number, but if we add an *infinite* number of 2's together we do not get a real number at all. Sums do not behave that way.

What makes series so interesting is that sometimes (as in Example 2) the sequence of **partial sums**, all of which are true sums, approaches a finite limit S:

$$\lim_{n \to \infty} \sum_{k=1}^{n} a_k = \lim_{n \to \infty} (a_1 + a_2 + \cdots + a_n) = S$$

In this case we say that the series **converges** to S, and it makes sense to define S as the **sum of the infinite series**. In sigma notation,

$$\sum_{k=1}^{\infty} a_k = \lim_{n \to \infty} \sum_{k=1}^{n} a_k = S.$$

If the limit of partial sums does not exist, then the series **diverges** and has no sum.

EXAMPLE 3 Looking at Limits of Partial Sums

For each of the following series, find the first five terms in the sequence of partial sums. Which of the series appear to converge?

(a) $0.1 + 0.01 + 0.001 + 0.0001 + \cdots$

(b) $10 + 20 + 30 + 40 + \cdots$

(c) $1 - 1 + 1 - 1 + \cdots$

SOLUTION

(a) The first five partial sums are $\{0.1, 0.11, 0.111, 0.1111, 0.11111\}$. These appear to be approaching a limit of $0.\overline{1} = 1/9$, which would suggest that the series converges to a sum of 1/9.

(b) The first five partial sums are $\{10, 30, 60, 100, 150\}$. These numbers increase without bound and do not approach a limit. The series diverges and has no sum.

(c) The first five partial sums are $\{1, 0, 1, 0, 1\}$. These numbers oscillate and do not approach a limit. The series diverges and has no sum.

Now try Exercise 23.

You might have been tempted to "pair off" the terms in Example 3c to get an infinite summation of 0's (and hence a sum of 0), but you would be applying a rule (namely the *associative property of addition*) that works on *finite* sums but not, in general, on infinite series. The sequence of partial sums does not have a limit, so any manipulation of the series in Example 3c that appears to result in a sum is actually meaningless.

Convergence of Geometric Series

Determining the convergence or divergence of infinite series is an important part of a calculus course, in which series are used to represent functions. Most of the convergence tests are well beyond the scope of this course, but we are in a position to settle the issue completely for geometric series.

THEOREM 16 Sum of an Infinite Geometric Series

The geometric series $\sum_{k=1}^{\infty} a \cdot r^{k-1}$ converges if and only if $|r| < 1$. If it does converge, the sum is $a/(1 - r)$.

Proof

If $r = 1$, the series is $a + a + a + \cdots$, which is unbounded and hence diverges. If $r = -1$, the series is $a - a + a - a + \cdots$, which diverges. (See Example 3c.) If $r \neq 1$, then by the Sum of a Finite Geometric Sequence Theorem, the nth partial sum of the series is $\sum_{k=1}^{n} a \cdot r^{k-1} = a(1 - r^n)/(1 - r)$. The limit of the partial sums is $\lim_{n \to \infty}[a(1 - r^n)/(1 - r)]$, which converges if and only if $\lim_{n \to \infty} r^n$ is a finite number. But $\lim_{n \to \infty} r^n$ is 0 when $|r| < 1$ and unbounded when $|r| > 1$. Therefore, the sequence of partial sums converges if and only if $|r| < 1$, in which case the sum of the series is

$$\lim_{n \to \infty}[a(1 - r^n)/(1 - r)] = a(1 - 0)/(1 - r) = a/(1 - r).$$

EXAMPLE 4 Summing Infinite Geometric Series

Determine whether the series converges. If it converges, give the sum.

(a) $\displaystyle\sum_{k=1}^{\infty} 3(0.75)^{k-1}$ **(b)** $\displaystyle\sum_{n=0}^{\infty}\left(-\frac{4}{5}\right)^n$

(c) $\displaystyle\sum_{n=1}^{\infty}\left(\frac{\pi}{2}\right)^n$ **(d)** $1 + \dfrac{1}{2} + \dfrac{1}{4} + \dfrac{1}{8} + \cdots$

SOLUTION

(a) Since $|r| = |0.75| < 1$, the series converges. The first term is $3(0.75)^0 = 3$, so the sum is $a/(1 - r) = 3/(1 - 0.75) = 12$.

(b) Since $|r| = |-4/5| < 1$, the series converges. The first term is $(-4/5)^0 = 1$, so the sum is $a/(1 - r) = 1/(1 - (-4/5)) = 5/9$.

(c) Since $|r| = |\pi/2| > 1$, the series diverges.

(d) Since $|r| = |1/2| < 1$, the series converges. The first term is 1, and so the sum is $a/(1 - r) = 1/(1 - 1/2) = 2$.   *Now try Exercise 25.*

EXAMPLE 5 Converting a Repeating Decimal to Fraction Form

Express $0.\overline{234} = 0.234234234\ldots$ in fraction form.

SOLUTION We can write this number as a sum: $0.234 + 0.000234 + 0.000000234 + \cdots$.

This is a convergent infinite geometric series in which $a = 0.234$ and $r = 0.001$. The sum is

$$\frac{a}{1 - r} = \frac{0.234}{1 - 0.001} = \frac{0.234}{0.999} = \frac{234}{999} = \frac{26}{111}.$$

Now try Exercise 31.

Exercise numbers with a gray background indicate problems that the authors have designed to be solved *without a calculator*.

In Exercises 1–6, write each sum using summation notation, assuming the suggested pattern continues.

1. $-7 - 1 + 5 + 11 + \cdots + 53$

2. $2 + 5 + 8 + 11 + \cdots + 29$

3. $1 + 4 + 9 + \cdots + (n + 1)^2$

4. $1 + 8 + 27 + \cdots + (n + 1)^3$

5. $6 - 12 + 24 - 48 + \cdots$

6. $5 - 15 + 45 - 135 + \cdots$

In Exercises 7–12, find the sum of the arithmetic sequence.

7. $-7, -3, 1, 5, 9, 13$

8. $-8, -1, 6, 13, 20, 27$

9. $1, 2, 3, 4, \ldots, 80$

10. $2, 4, 6, 8, \ldots, 70$

11. $117, 110, 103, \ldots, 33$

12. $111, 108, 105, \ldots, 27$

In Exercises 13–16, find the sum of the geometric sequence.

13. $3, 6, 12, \ldots, 12{,}288$

14. $5, 15, 45, \ldots, 98{,}415$

15. $42, 7, \dfrac{7}{6}, \ldots, 42\left(\dfrac{1}{6}\right)^8$

16. $42, -7, \dfrac{7}{6}, \ldots, 42\left(-\dfrac{1}{6}\right)^9$

In Exercises 17–22, find the sum of the first n terms of the sequence. The sequence is either arithmetic or geometric.

17. $2, 5, 8, \ldots, ; n = 10$

18. $14, 8, 2, \ldots, ; n = 9$

19. $4, -2, 1, -\dfrac{1}{2}, \ldots; n = 12$

20. $6, -3, \dfrac{3}{2}, -\dfrac{3}{4}, \ldots; n = 11$

21. $-1, 11, -121, \ldots; n = 9$

22. $-2, 24, -288, \ldots; n = 8$

23. Find the first six partial sums of the following infinite series. If the sums have a finite limit, write "convergent." If not, write "divergent."

    (a) $0.3 + 0.03 + 0.003 + 0.0003 + \cdots$

    (b) $1 - 2 + 3 - 4 + 5 - 6 + \cdots$

24. Find the first six partial sums of the following infinite series. If the sums have a finite limit, write "convergent." If not, write "divergent."

    (a) $-2 + 2 - 2 + 2 - 2 + \cdots$

    (b) $1 - 0.7 - 0.07 - 0.007 - 0.0007 - \cdots$

In Exercises 25–30, determine whether the infinite geometric series converges. If it does, find its sum.

25. $6 + 3 + \dfrac{3}{2} + \dfrac{3}{4} + \cdots$ 26. $4 + \dfrac{4}{3} + \dfrac{4}{9} + \dfrac{4}{27} + \cdots$

27. $\dfrac{1}{64} + \dfrac{1}{32} + \dfrac{1}{16} + \dfrac{1}{8} + \cdots$

28. $\dfrac{1}{48} + \dfrac{1}{16} + \dfrac{3}{16} + \dfrac{9}{16} + \cdots$

29. $\displaystyle\sum_{j=1}^{\infty} 3\left(\dfrac{1}{4}\right)^j$ 30. $\displaystyle\sum_{n=1}^{\infty} 5\left(\dfrac{2}{3}\right)^n$

In Exercises 31–34, express the rational number as a fraction of integers.

31. $7.14141414\ldots$

32. $5.93939393\ldots$

33. $-17.268268268\ldots$

34. $-12.876876876\ldots$

35. **Savings Account** The table below shows the December balance in a fixed-rate compound savings account each year from 1996 to 2000.

Year	1996	1997	1998	1999	2000
Balance	$20,000	$22,000	$24,200	$26,620	$29,282

   (a) The balances form a geometric sequence. What is r?

   (b) Write a formula for the balance in the account n years after December 1996.

   (c) Find the sum of the December balances from 1996 to 2006, inclusive.

36. **Savings Account** The table below shows the December balance in a simple interest savings account each year from 1996 to 2000.

Year	1996	1997	1998	1999	2000
Balance	$18,000	$20,016	$22,032	$24,048	$26,064

   (a) The balances form an arithmetic sequence. What is d?

   (b) Write a formula for the balance in the account n years after December 1996.

   (c) Find the sum of the December balances from 1996 to 2006, inclusive.

37. Annuity   Mr. O'Hara deposits $120 at the end of each month into an account that pays 7% interest compounded monthly. After 10 years, the balance in the account, in dollars, is

$$120\left(1 + \frac{0.07}{12}\right)^0 + 120\left(1 + \frac{0.07}{12}\right)^1 + \cdots$$
$$+ 120\left(1 + \frac{0.07}{12}\right)^{119}.$$

(a) This is a geometric series. What is the first term? What is r?

(b) Use the formula for the sum of a finite geometric sequence to find the balance.

38. Annuity   Ms. Argentieri deposits $100 at the end of each month into an account that pays 8% interest compounded monthly. After 10 years, the balance in the account, in dollars, is

$$100\left(1 + \frac{0.08}{12}\right)^0 + 100\left(1 + \frac{0.08}{12}\right)^1 + \cdots$$
$$+ 100\left(1 + \frac{0.08}{12}\right)^{119}.$$

(a) This is a geometric series. What is the first term? What is r?

(b) Use the formula for the sum of a finite geometric sequence to find the balance.

39. Group Activity Follow the Bouncing Ball
When "superballs" sprang upon the scene in the 1960s, kids across the United States were amazed that these hard rubber balls could bounce to 90% of the height from which they were dropped. If a superball is dropped from a height of 2 m, how far does it travel until it stops bouncing? [*Hint:* The ball goes down to the first bounce, then up *and* down thereafter.]

40. Writing to Learn The Trouble with Flubber
In the 1961 movie classic *The Absent Minded Professor*, Prof. Ned Brainard discovers flubber (flying rubber). If a "super duper ball" made of flubber is dropped, it rebounds to an ever greater height with each bounce. How far does it travel if allowed to keep bouncing?

Explorations

41. Population Density   The *National Geographic Picture Atlas of Our Fifty States* (2001) groups the states into 10 regions. The two largest groupings are the Heartland (Table H.30) and the Southeast (Table H.31). Population and area data for the two regions are given in the tables. The populations are official 2000 U.S. Census figures.

(a) What is the total population of each region?

(b) What is the total area of each region?

(c) What is the population density (in persons per square mile) of each region?

(d) **Writing to Learn**   For the two regions, compute the population density of each state. What is the average of the seven state population densities for each region? Explain why these answers differ from those found in part (c).

Table H.30 The Heartland

State	Population	Area (mi^2)
Iowa	2,926,324	56,275
Kansas	2,688,418	82,277
Minnesota	4,919,479	84,402
Missouri	5,595,211	69,697
Nebraska	1,711,283	77,355
North Dakota	642,200	70,703
South Dakota	754,844	77,116

Table H.31 The Southeast

State	Population	Area (mi^2)
Alabama	4,447,100	51,705
Arkansas	2,673,400	53,187
Florida	15,982,378	58,644
Georgia	8,186,453	58,910
Louisiana	4,468,976	47,751
Mississippi	2,844,658	47,689
S. Carolina	4,012,012	31,113

42. Finding a Pattern   Write the finite series
$$-1 + 2 + 7 + 14 + 23 + \cdots + 62 \text{ in summation notation.}$$

Extending the Ideas

43. Fibonacci Sequence and Series Complete the following table, where F_n is the nth term of the Fibonacci sequence and S_n is the nth partial sum of the Fibonacci series. Make a conjecture based on the numerical evidence in the table.

$$S_n = \sum_{k=1}^{n} F_k$$

n	F_n	S_n	$F_{n+2} - 1$
1	1		
2	1		
3	2		
4			
5			
6			
7			
8			
9			

44. Triangular Numbers Revisited
Triangular numbers as numbers that count objects arranged in triangular arrays:

| 1 | 3 | 6 | 10 | 15 |

One geometric argument is that the nth triangular number was $n(n + 1)/2$. Prove that formula algebraically using the Sum of a Finite Arithmetic Sequence Theorem.

45. Square Numbers and Triangular Numbers
Prove that the sum of two consecutive triangular numbers is a square number; that is, prove

$$T_{n-1} + T_n = n^2$$

for all positive integers $n \geq 2$. Use both a geometric and an algebraic approach.

46. Harmonic Series Graph the sequence of partial sums of the *harmonic series:*

$$1 + \frac{1}{2} + \frac{1}{3} + \frac{1}{4} + \cdots + \frac{1}{n} + \cdots$$

Overlay on it the graph of $f(x) = \ln x$. The resulting picture should support the claim that

$$1 + \frac{1}{2} + \frac{1}{3} + \frac{1}{4} + \cdots + \frac{1}{n} \geq \ln n,$$

for all positive integers n. Make a table of values to further support this claim. Explain why the claim implies that the harmonic series must diverge.

Exercise numbers with a gray background indicate problems that the authors have designed to be solved *without a calculator.*

H-1 Exponential and Logistic Functions

Compute the exact value of the function for the given *x*-value without using a calculator.

1. $f(x) = -3 \cdot 4^x$ for $x = \dfrac{1}{3}$

2. $f(x) = 6 \cdot 3^x$ for $x = -\dfrac{3}{2}$

Determine a formula for the exponential function whose graph is shown in the figure.

3. **4.**

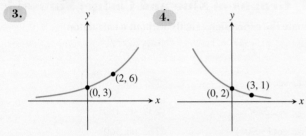

Describe how to transform the graph of f into the graph of $g(x) = 2^x$ or $h(x) = e^x$. Sketch the graph by hand and support your answer with a grapher.

5. $f(x) = 4^{-x} + 3$ **6.** $f(x) = -4^{-x}$

7. $f(x) = -8^{-x} - 3$ **8.** $f(x) = 8^{-x} + 3$

Find the *y*-intercept and the horizontal asymptotes.

9. $f(x) = \dfrac{100}{5 + 3e^{-0.05x}}$ **10.** $f(x) = \dfrac{50}{5 + 2e^{-0.04x}}$

H-2 Exponential and Logistic Modeling

State whether the function is an exponential growth function or an exponential decay function, and describe its end behavior using limits.

11. $f(x) = e^{4-x} + 2$ **12.** $f(x) = 2(5^{x-3}) + 1$

Graph the function, and analyze it for domain, range, continuity, increasing or decreasing behavior, symmetry, boundedness, extrema, asymptotes, and end behavior.

13. $f(x) = e^{3-x} + 1$ **14.** $g(x) = 3(4^{x+1}) - 2$

15. $f(x) = \dfrac{6}{1 + 3 \cdot 0.4^x}$ **16.** $g(x) = \dfrac{100}{4 + 2e^{-0.01x}}$

Find the exponential function that satisfies the given conditions.

17. Initial value = 24, increasing at a rate of 5.3% per day

18. Initial population = 67,000, increasing at a rate of 1.67% per year

Find the logistic function that satisfies the given conditions.

19. Initial value = 12, limit to growth = 30, passing through (2, 20).

20. Initial height = 6, limit to growth = 20, passing through (3, 15).

21. Compound Interest Find the amount *A* accumulated after investing a principal *P* = \$450 for 3 years at an interest rate of 4.6% compounded annually.

22. Compound Interest Find the amount *A* accumulated after investing a principal *P* = \$4800 for 17 years at an interest rate of 6.2% compounded annually.

H-3 Logarithmic Functions and Their Graphs

Evaluate the logarithmic expression without using a calculator.

23. $\log_2 32$ **24.** $\log_3 81$

25. $\log \sqrt[3]{10}$

Rewrite the equation in exponential form.

26. $\log_3 x = 5$ **27.** $\log_2 x = y$

Describe how to transform the graph of $y = \log_2 x$ into the graph of the given function. Sketch the graph by hand and support with a grapher.

28. $f(x) = \log_2(x + 4)$

29. $g(x) = \log_2(4 - x)$

30. $h(x) = -\log_2(x - 1) + 2$

31. $h(x) = -\log_2(x + 1) + 4$

32. Radioactive Decay The half-life of a certain radioactive substance is 1.5 sec. The initial amount of substance is S_0 grams.

(a) Express the amount of substance *S* remaining as a function of time *t*.

(b) How much of the substance is left after 2.5 sec? after 7.5 sec?

(c) Determine S_0 if there was 1 g left after 1 min.

H-4 Properties of Logarithmic Functions

Graph the function, and analyze it for domain, range, continuity, increasing or decreasing behavior, symmetry, boundedness, extrema, asymptotes, and end behavior.

33. $f(x) = x \ln x$ **34.** $f(x) = x^2 \ln x$

35. $f(x) = x^2 \ln |x|$ **36.** $f(x) = \dfrac{\ln x}{x}$

Solve each equation.

37. $10^x = 4$ **38.** $e^x = 0.25$

39. $1.05^x = 3$ **40.** $\ln x = 5.4$

41. $\log x = -7$ **42.** $3^{x-3} = 5$

43. $3 \log_2 x + 1 = 7$ **44.** $2 \log_3 x - 3 = 4$

45. Light Absorption The Beer-Lambert Law of Absorption applied to Lake Superior states that the light intensity I (in lumens) at a depth of x feet satisfies the equation

$$\log \frac{I}{12} = -0.0125x.$$

Find the light intensity at a depth of 25 ft.

H-5 Equation Solving and Modeling

Solve each equation.

46. $\dfrac{3^x - 3^{-x}}{2} = 5$ **47.** $\dfrac{50}{4 + e^{2x}} = 11$

48. $\log (x + 2) + \log (x - 1) = 4$

49. $\ln (3x + 4) - \ln (2x + 1) = 5$

Write the expression using only natural logarithms.

50. $\log_2 x$ **51.** $\log_{1/6} (6x^2)$

Write the expression using only common logarithms.

52. $\log_5 x$ **53.** $\log_{1/2} (4x^3)$

Match each function with its graph. All graphs were drawn in the window [–4.7, 4.7] by [–3.1, 3.1].

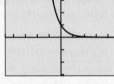
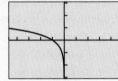

[–4.7, 4.7] by [–3.1, 3.1]
(a)

[–4.7, 4.7] by [–3.1, 3.1]
(b)

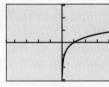
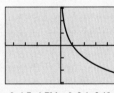

[–4.7, 4.7] by [–3.1, 3.1]
(c)

[–4.7, 4.7] by [–3.1, 3.1]
(d)

54. $f(x) = \log_5 x$ **55.** $f(x) = \log_{0.5} x$

56. $f(x) = \log_5 (-x)$ **57.** $f(x) = 5^{-x}$

58. Drug Absorption A drug is administered intravenously for pain. The function $f(t) = 90 - 52 \ln (1 + t)$, where $0 \le t \le 4$, gives the amount of the drug in the body after t hours.

(a) What was the initial ($t = 0$) number of units of drug administered?

(b) How much is present after 2 hr?

(c) Draw the graph of f.

H-6 Trigonometry Extended: The Circular Functions

The points are on the terminal side of an angle in standard position. Give the smallest positive angle measure in both degrees and radians.

59. $(\sqrt{3}, 1)$ **60.** $(-1, 1)$

Evaluate the expression exactly without a calculator.

61. $(-1, \sqrt{3})$ **62.** $(-3, -3)$

63. $(6, -12)$ **64.** $(2, 4)$

65. $\sin 30°$ **66.** $\cos 330°$

67. $\tan (-135°)$ **68.** $\sin \dfrac{5\pi}{6}$

H-7 Graphs of Sine and Cosine: Sinusoids

Evaluate the expression exactly without a calculator.

69. $\sec (-135°)$ **70.** $\csc \dfrac{2\pi}{3}$

71. $\sec \left(-\dfrac{\pi}{3}\right)$ **72.** $\tan \left(-\dfrac{2\pi}{3}\right)$

73. $\csc 270°$ **74.** $\sec 180°$

75. $\cot (-90°)$ **76.** $\tan 360°$

Use the transformations to describe how the graph of the function is related to a basic trigonometric graph, Graph two periods.

77. $y = \sin (x + \pi)$ **78.** $y = 3 + 2 \cos x$

79. $y = -\cos (x + \pi/2) + 4$

80. $y = -2 - 3 \sin (x - \pi)$

H-8 Inverse Trigonometric Functions

Use a calculator to evaluate the expression. Express your answer in both degrees and radians.

81. $\sin^{-1} (0.766)$ **82.** $\cos^{-1} (0.479)$

83. $\tan^{-1} 1$ **84.** $\sin^{-1} \left(\dfrac{\sqrt{3}}{2}\right)$

Evaluate each expression without a calculator.

85. $\tan (\tan^{-1} 1)$ **86.** $\cos^{-1} (\cos \pi/3)$

87. $\tan (\sin^{-1} 3/5)$ **88.** $\cos^{-1} (\cos(-\pi/7))$

89. Arc Length Find the length of the arc intercepted by a central angle of $2\pi/3$ rad in a circle with radius 2.

H-9 Solving Problems with Trigonometry

Solve the right triangle ABC.

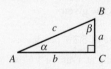

90. $\alpha = 35°, c = 15$ **91.** $b = 8, c = 10$

92. $\beta = 48°, a = 7$ **93.** $\alpha = 28°, c = 8$

94. $b = 5, c = 7$ **95.** $a = 2.5, b = 7.3$

96. Height of Building The angle of elevation of the top of a building from a point 100 m away from the building on level ground is 78°. Find the height of the building.

97. Height of Tree A tree casts a shadow 51 ft long when the angle of elevation of the Sun (measured with the horizon) is 25°. How tall is the tree?

98. Traveling Car From the top of a 150-ft building Flora observes a car moving toward her. If the angle of depression of the car changes from 18° to 42° during the observation, how far does the car travel?

99. Storing Hay A 75-ft-long conveyor is used at the Lovelady Farm to put hay bales up for winter storage. The conveyor is tilted to an angle of elevation of 22°.

(a) To what height can the hay be moved?

(b) If the conveyor is repositioned to an angle of 27°, to what height can the hay be moved?

H-10 and H-11 Polar Coordinates and Graphs of Polar Equations

Decide whether the graph of the given polar equations appears among the four graphs shown.

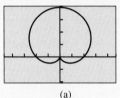

(a)

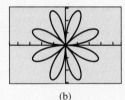

(b)

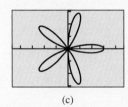

(c)

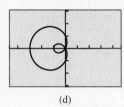

(d)

100. $r = 3 \sin 4\theta$ **101.** $r = 2 + \sin \theta$

102. $r = 2 + 2 \sin \theta$ **103.** $r = 3|\sin 3\theta|$

104. $r = 2 - 2 \sin \theta$ **105.** $r = 1 - 2 \cos \theta$

106. $r = 3 \cos 5\theta$ **107.** $r = 3 - 2 \tan \theta$

Convert the polar equation to rectangular form and identify the graph.

108. $r = -2$ **109.** $r = -2 \sin \theta$

Convert the rectangular equation to polar form. Graph the polar equation.

110. $y = -4$ **111.** $x = 5$

112. $(x - 3)^2 + (y + 1)^2 = 10$

113. $2x - 3y = 4$

H-12 De Moivre's Theorem and *n*th Roots

Find the trigonometric form with $0 \le \theta < 2\pi$ for the given complex number. Then write three other possible trigonometric forms for the number. Approximate exact values with a calculator when appropriate.

114. $3 - 3i$ **115.** $-1 + i\sqrt{2}$

116. $3 - 5i$ **117.** $-2 - 2i$

Write the complex numbers $z_1 \cdot z_2$ and z_1/z_2 in trigonometric form.

118. $z_1 = 3(\cos 30° + i \sin 30°)$ and $z_2 = 4(\cos 60° + i \sin 60°)$

119. $z_1 = 5(\cos 20° + i \sin 20°)$ and $z_2 = -2(\cos 45° + i \sin 45°)$

Use De Moivre's Theorem to find the indicated power of the complex number. Write your answer in (a) trigonometric form and (b) standard form.

120. $\left[3\left(\cos \dfrac{\pi}{4} + i \sin \dfrac{\pi}{4} \right) \right]^5$

121. $\left[2\left(\cos \dfrac{\pi}{12} + i \sin \dfrac{\pi}{12} \right) \right]^8$

122. $\left[5\left(\cos \dfrac{5\pi}{3} + i \sin \dfrac{5\pi}{3} \right) \right]^3$

123. $\left[7\left(\cos \dfrac{\pi}{24} + i \sin \dfrac{\pi}{24} \right) \right]^6$

Find and graph the *n*th roots of the complex number for the specified value of *n*.

124. $3 + 3i, \quad n = 4$ **125.** $8, \quad n = 3$

126. $1, \quad n = 5$ **127.** $-1, \quad n = 6$

H-13 Sequences

Find the first 6 terms and the 40th term of the sequence.

128. $a_n = \dfrac{n^2 - 1}{n + 1}$

129. $b_k = \dfrac{(-2)^k}{k + 1}$

Find the first 6 terms and the 12th term of the sequence.

130. $a_1 = -1$ and $a_n = a_{n-1} + 3$, for $n \ge 2$

131. $b_1 = 5$ and $b_k = 2b_{k-1}$, for $k \ge 2$

132. Arithmetic sequence, with $a_1 = -5$ and $d = 1.5$

133. Geometric sequence, with $a_1 = 3$ and $r = 1/3$

These sequences are arithmetic or geometric. Find an explicit formula for the *n*th term. State the common difference or ratio.

134. $12, 9.5, 7, 4.5, \ldots$ **135.** $-5, -1, 3, 7, \ldots$

136. The fourth and ninth terms of a geometric sequence are -192 and $196,608$, respectively.

Find the sum of the terms of the arithmetic or geometric sequence.

137. $-11, -8, -5, -2, 1, 4, 7, 10$

138. $13, 9, 5, 1, -3, -7, -11$

139. $4, -2, 1, -\dfrac{1}{2}, \dfrac{1}{4}, -\dfrac{1}{8}$

140. $-3, -1, -\dfrac{1}{3}, -\dfrac{1}{9}, -\dfrac{1}{27}$

Graph the sequence.

141. $a_n = 1 + \dfrac{(-1)^n}{n}$

142. $a_n = 2n^2 - 1$

143. Annuity What is the minimum monthly payment at month's end that must be made in an account that pays 8% interest compounded monthly if the balance at the end of 10 years is to be at least $30,000?

H-14 Series

Determine whether the geometric series converges. If it does, find the sum.

144. $\displaystyle\sum_{j=1}^{\infty} 2\left(\dfrac{3}{4}\right)^{j}$

145. $\displaystyle\sum_{k=1}^{\infty} 2\left(-\dfrac{1}{3}\right)^{k}$

146. $\displaystyle\sum_{j=1}^{\infty} 4\left(-\dfrac{4}{3}\right)^{j}$

147. $\displaystyle\sum_{k=1}^{\infty} 5\left(\dfrac{6}{5}\right)^{k}$

Write the sum in sigma notation.

148. $-8 - 3 + 2 + \cdots + 92$

149. $4 - 8 + 16 - 32 + \cdots - 2048$

150. $1^2 + 3^2 + 5^2 + \cdots$

151. $1 + \dfrac{1}{2} + \dfrac{1}{2^2} + \dfrac{1}{2^3} + \cdots$

Use summation formulas to evaluate the expression.

152. $\displaystyle\sum_{k=1}^{n} (3k + 1)$

153. $\displaystyle\sum_{k=1}^{n} 3k^2$

154. $\displaystyle\sum_{k=1}^{25} (k^2 - 3k + 4)$

155. $\displaystyle\sum_{k=1}^{175} (3k^2 - 5k + 1)$

Postulates and Theorems

Theorems

Theorem 1
Factor Theorem
The expression $x - a$ is a factor of a polynomial if and only if the value of a is a zero of the related polynomial function.

Theorem 2
Remainder Theorem
If you divide a polynomial $P(x)$ of degree $n \geq 1$ by $x - a$, then the remainder is $P(a)$.

Theorem 3
Rational Root Theorem
Let $P(x)$ be a polynomial of degree n with leading coefficient a_n and constant term a_0. Then the possible real roots of $P(x)$ are of the form $\frac{p}{q}$ where p is an integer factor of a_n and q is an integer factor of a_0.

Theorem 4
Conjugate Root Theorem
If $P(x)$ is a polynomial with rational coefficients, then the irrational roots of $P(x) = 0$ occur in conjugate pairs.

If $P(x)$ is a polynomial with real coefficients, then the complex roots of $P(x) = 0$ occur in conjugate pairs.

Theorem 5
Descartes's Rule of Signs
Let $P(x)$ be a polynomial with real coefficients written in standard form.

- The number of real roots of $P(x) = 0$ is either equal to the number of sign changes between consecutive coefficients of $P(x)$ or is less than that by an even number.
- The number of negative real roots of $P(x) = 0$ is either equal to the number of sign changes between consecutive coefficients of $P(-x)$ or is less than that by an even number.

In both cases, count multiple roots according to their multiplicity.

Theorem 6
Fundamental Theorem of Algebra
If $P(x)$ is a polynomial of degree $n \geq 1$, then $P(x) = 0$ has exactly n roots, including multiple and complex roots.

Theorem 7
Law of Sines
$$\frac{\sin A}{a} = \frac{\sin B}{b} = \frac{\sin C}{c}$$

Theorem 8
Law of Cosines
$$a^2 = b^2 + c^2 - 2bc \cos A$$
$$b^2 = a^2 + c^2 - 2ac \cos B$$
$$c^2 = a^2 + b^2 - 2ab \cos C$$

Theorem 9
Binomial Theorem
For every positive integer n,
$$(a + b)^n = P_0 a^n + P_1 a^{n-1}b + P_2 a^{n-2}b^2 + \ldots +$$
$P_{n-1}ab^{n-1} + P_n b_n$ where $P_0, P_1, \ldots, P_n$ are the numbers in the nth row of Pascal's Triangle.

Theorem 10
Perimeters and Areas of Similar Figures
If the scale factor of two similar solids figures is $\frac{a}{b}$, then

- the ratio of their perimeters is $\frac{a}{b}$, and
- the ratio of their areas is $\frac{a^2}{b^2}$.

Theorem 11
Areas and Volumes of Similar Solids
If the scale factor of two similar solids is $\frac{a}{b}$, then

- the ratio of their corresponding areas is $\frac{a^2}{b^2}$, and
- the ratio of their volumes is $\frac{a^3}{b^3}$.

Theorem 12
Exponential Functions and the Base e
Any exponential function $f(x) = a \cdot b^x$ can be rewritten as
$$f(x) = a \cdot e^{kx},$$
for an appropriately chosen real number constant k.

If $a > 0$ and $k > 0$, $f(x) = a \cdot e^{kx}$ is an exponential growth function.

If $a > 0$ and $k < 0$, $f(x) = a \cdot e^{kx}$ is an exponential decay function.

Theorem 13
De Moivre's Theorem
Let $z = r(\cos \theta + i \sin \theta)$ and let n be a positive integer. Then
$$z^n = [r(\cos \theta + i \sin \theta)]^n = r^n(\cos n\theta + i \sin n\theta).$$

Theorem 14
Sum of a Finite Arithmetic Sequence

Let $\{a_1, a_2, \ldots, a_n\}$ be a finite arithmetic sequence with common difference d. Then the sum of the terms of the sequence is

$$\sum_{k=1}^{n} a_k = a_1 + a_2 + \cdots + a_n$$

$$= n\left(\frac{a_1 + a_n}{2}\right)$$

$$= \frac{n}{2}(2a_1 + (n-1)d)$$

Theorem 15
Sum of a Finite Geometric Sequence

Let $\{a_1, a_2, a_3, \ldots, a_n\}$ be a finite geometric sequence with common ratio $r \neq 1$.

Then the sum of the terms of the sequence is

$$\sum_{k=1}^{n} a_k = a_1 + a_2 + \cdots + a_n$$

$$= \frac{a_1(1 - r^n)}{1 - r}.$$

Theorem 16
Sum of an Infinite Geometric Sequence

The geometric series $\sum_{k=1}^{\infty} a \cdot r^{k-1}$ converges if and only if $|r| < 1$. If it does converge, the sum is $a/(1 - r)$.

Visual Glossary

English   A   Spanish

Amplitude (p. 382) The amplitude of a periodic function is half the difference between the maximum and minimum values of the function.

Amplitud (p. 382) La amplitud de una función periódica es la mitad de la diferencia entre los valores máximo y mínimo de la función.

Example The maximum and minimum values of $y = 4 \sin x$ are 4 and -4, respectively. amplitude $= \frac{4 - (-4)}{2} = 4$

Angle bisector (p. 553) An angle bisector is a ray that divides an angle into two congruent angles.

Bisectriz de un ángulo (p. 553) La bisectriz de un ángulo es una semirrecta que divide al ángulo en dos ángulos congruentes.

Example

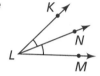

$\overrightarrow{LN}$ bisects $\angle KLM$.
$\angle KLN \cong \angle NLM$.

Arithmetic mean (p. 504) The arithmetic mean, or average, of two numbers is their sum divided by two.

Media aritmética (p. 504) La media aritmética, o promedio, de dos números es su suma dividida por dos.

Example The arithmetic mean of 12 and 15 is $\frac{12 + 15}{2} = 13.5$

Arithmetic sequence (p. 502) An arithmetic sequence is a sequence with a constant difference between consecutive terms.

Secuencia aritmética (p. 502) Una secuencia aritmética es una secuencia de números en la que la diferencia entre dos números consecutivos es constante.

Example The arithmetic sequence 1, 5, 9, 13, . . . has a common difference of 4.

Arithmetic series (p. 517) An arithmetic series is a series whose terms form an arithmetic sequence.

Serie aritmética (p. 517) Una serie aritmética es una serie cuyos términos forman una progresión aritmética.

Example $1 + 5 + 9 + 13 + 17 + 21$ is an arithmetic series with six terms.

Asymptote (p. 182) An asymptote is a line that a graph approaches as x or y increases in absolute value.

Asíntota (p. 182) Una asíntota es una recta a la cual se acerca una gráfica a medida que x o y aumentan de valor absoluto.

Example The function $y = \frac{x + 2}{x - 2}$ has $x = 2$ as a vertical asymptote and $y = 1$ as a horizontal asymptote.

Bias (p. 23) A bias is a systematic error introduced by the sampling method.

Sesgo (p. 23) El sesgo es un error sistemático introducido por medio del método de muestreo.

Bimodal (p. 4) A bimodal data set has two modes.

Bimodal (p. 4) Un conjunto bimodal de datos tiene dos modas.

Example {1, 2, 3, 3, 4, 5, 6, 6} mode = 3 and 6

Bisect (p. 553) *See* **Angle bisector; Segment bisector.**

Bisecar (p. 553) *Ver* **Angle bisector; Segment bisector.**

Box-and-whisker plot (p. 6) A box-and-whisker plot is a method of displaying data that uses quartiles to form the center box and the maximum and minimum values to form the whiskers.

Gráfica de cajas (p. 6) Una gráfica de cajas es un método para mostrar datos que utiliza cuartiles para formar una casilla central y los valores máximos y mínimos para formar los conectores.

Example

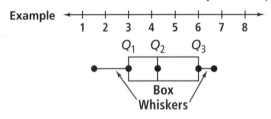

Branch (p. 183) Each piece of a discontinuous graph is called a branch.

Rama (p. 183) Cada segmento de una gráfica discontinua se llama rama.

Example

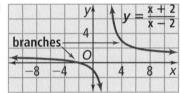

C

Central angle (p. 395) A central angle of a circle is an angle whose vertex is at the center of a circle.

Ángulo central (p. 395) El ángulo central de un círculo es un ángulo cuyo vértice está situado en el centro del círculo.

Example

intercepted arc

45°

central angle

Visual **Glossary**

English

Spanish

Change of Base Formula (p. 343) $\log_b M = \frac{\log_c M}{\log_c b}$, where M, b, and c are positive numbers, and $b \neq 1$ and $c \neq 1$.

Fórmula de cambio de base (p. 343) $\log_b M = \frac{\log_c M}{\log_c b}$, donde M, b y c son números positivos y $b \neq 1$ y $c \neq 1$.

Example $\log_3 8 = \frac{\log 8}{\log 3} \approx 1.8928$

Circumscribed circle (p. 556) A circle is circumscribed about a polygon if the vertices of the polygon are on the circle.

Círculo circunscrito (p. 556) Un círculo está circunscrito a un polígono si los vértices del polígono están en el círculo.

Example

$\odot G$ is circumscribed about $ABCD$.

Combined variation (p. 173) A combined variation is a relation in which one variable varies with respect to each of two or more variables.

Variación combinada (p. 173) Una variación combinada es una relación en la que una variable varía con respecto a cada una de dos o más variables.

Example $y = kx^2 \sqrt{z}$
$z = \frac{kx}{y}$

Common difference (p. 502) A common difference is the difference between consecutive terms of an arithmetic sequence.

Diferencia común (p. 502) La diferencia común es la diferencia entre los términos consecutivos de una progresión aritmética.

Example The arithmetic sequence 1, 5, 9, 13, . . . has a common difference of 4.

Common logarithm (p. 333) A common logarithm is a logarithm that uses base 10. You can write the common logarithm $\log_{10} y$ as $\log y$.

Logaritmo común (p.333) El logaritmo común es un logaritmo de base 10. El logaritmo común $\log_{10} y$ se expresa como $\log y$.

Example $\log 1 = 0$
$\log 10 = 1$
$\log 50 = 1.698970004 \ldots$

Common ratio (p. 509) A common ratio is the ratio of consecutive terms of a geometric sequence.

Razón común (p. 509) Una razón común es la razón de términos consecutivos en una secuencia geométrica.

Example The geometric sequence 2.5, 5, 10, 20, . . . has a common ratio of 2.

Complex fraction (p. 157) A complex fraction is a rational expression that has a fraction in its numerator or denominator, or in both its numerator and denominator.

Fracción compleja (p. 157) Una fracción compleja es una expresión racional en la que el numerador, el denominador o ambos son una fracción.

Example $\dfrac{\frac{2}{1}}{\frac{5}{}}$, $\dfrac{\frac{2}{7}}{\frac{3}{2}}$

Composite function (p. 275) A composite function is a combination of two functions such that the output from the first function becomes the input for the second function.

Función compuesta (p. 275) Una función compuesta es la combinación de dos funciones. La cantidad de salida de la primera función es la cantidad de entrada de la segunda función.

Example $f(x) = 2x + 1$, $g(x) = x^2 - 1$
$(g \circ f)(5) = g(f(5)) = g(2(5) + 1)$
$= g(11)$
$= 11^2 - 1 = 120$

Confidence interval (p. 42) Based on the mean of a sample or a sample proportion, the confidence interval indicates the interval in which the population mean or population proportion is likely to lie for a given confidence level.

Intervalo de confianza (p. 42) El intervalo de confianza se basa en la media de una muestra o en la proporción de una muestra, e indica el intervalo en el que probablemente se encuentra dicha media o proporción de la población para un nivel de confianza dado.

Example For an elementary history book, a sample of 30 trials indicates that the mean number of words in a sentence is 12.7. The margin of error at a 95% confidence level is 1.5 words per sentence. The mean number of words μ in all of the sentences in the book at a 95% confidence level is $12.7 - 1.5 \leq \mu \leq 12.7 + 1.5$.

Constant of proportionality (p. 131) If $y = ax^b$ describes y as a power function of x, then y varies directly with, or is proportional to, the bth power of x. The constant a is the constant of proportionality.

Constante de proporcionalidad (p. 131) Si $y = ax^b$ describe a y como una potencia de la función de x, entonces y varía directamente con, o es proporcional a, la $b$ma potencia de x. La constante a es la constante de proporcionalidad.

Continuous graph (p. 192) A graph is continuous if it has no jumps, breaks, or holes.

Gráfica continua (p. 192) Una gráfica es continua si no tiene saltos, interrupciones o huecos.

Continuous probability distribution (p. 34) A continuous probability distribution has as its events any of the infinitely many values in an interval of real numbers.

Distribución de probabilidad continua (p. 34) Una distribución de probabilidad continua tiene como sucesos a cualquiera del número infinito de valores en un intervalo de números reales.

Continuously compounded interest (p. 326) When interest is compounded continuously on principal P, the value A of an account is $A = Pe^{rt}$.

Interés compuesto continuo (p. 326) En un sistema donde el interés es compuesto continuamente sobre el capital P, el valor de A de una cuenta es $A = Pe^{rt}$.

Example Suppose that $P = \$1200$, $r = 0.05$, and $t = 3$.
Then $A = 1200e^{0.05 \cdot 3}$
$= 1200(2.718\ldots)^{0.15}$
≈ 1394.20

English

Spanish

Controlled experiment (p. 24) In a controlled experiment, you divide the sample into two groups. You impose a treatment on one group but not the other "control" group. Then you compare the effect on the treated group to the control group.

Experimento controlado (p. 24) En un experimento controlado, se divide la muestra en dos grupos. Uno de los grupos se manipula y el otro grupo "controlado" se mantiene en su estado original. Luego se comparan el estado del grupo manipulado y el estado del grupo controlado.

Convenience sample (p. 22) In a convenience sample you select any members of the population who are conveniently and readily available.

Muestra de conveniencia (p. 22) En una muestra de conveniencia se selecciona a cualquier miembro de la población que está convenientemente disponible.

Converge (p. 531) An infinite series $a_1 + a_2 + \ldots + a_n + \ldots$ converges if the sum $a_1 + a_2 + \ldots + a_n$ get closer and closer to a real number as n increases.

Convergir (p. 531) Una serie infinita $a_1 + a_2 + \ldots + a_n + \ldots$ es convergente si la suma $a_1 + a_2 + \ldots + a_n$ se aproxima cada vez más a un número real a medida que el valor de n incrementa.

Example $1 + \frac{1}{2} + \frac{1}{4} + \frac{1}{8} + \ldots$ converges.

Cosecant function (p. 447) The cosecant (csc) function is the reciprocal of the sine function. For all real numbers θ except those that make $\sin \theta = 0$, $\csc \theta = \frac{1}{\sin \theta}$.

Función cosecante (p. 447) La función cosecante (csc) se define como el recíproco de la función seno. Para todos los números reales θ, excepto aquéllos para los que $\sin \theta = 0$, $\csc \theta = \frac{1}{\sin \theta}$.

Example If $\sin \theta = \frac{5}{13}$, then $\csc \theta = \frac{13}{5}$.

Cosine function, Cosine of θ (pp. 390, 416) The cosine function, $y = \cos \theta$, matches the measure θ of an angle in standard position with the x-coordinate of a point on the unit circle. This point is where the terminal side of the angle intersects the unit circle. The x-coordinate is the cosine of θ.

Función coseno, Coseno de θ (pp. 390, 416) La función coseno, $y = \cos \theta$, empareja la medida θ de un ángulo en posición estándar con la coordenada x de un punto en el círculo unitario. Este es el punto en el que el lado terminal del ángulo interseca al círculo unitario. La coordenada x es el coseno de θ.

Example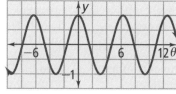

Cotangent function (p. 447) The cotangent (cot) function is the reciprocal of the tangent function. For all real numbers θ except those that make $\tan \theta = 0$, $\cot \theta = \frac{1}{\tan \theta}$.

Función cotangente (p. 447) La función cotangente (cot) es el recíproco de la función tangente. Para todos los números reales θ, excepto aquéllos para los que $\tan \theta = 0$, $\cot \theta = \frac{1}{\tan \theta}$.

Example If $\tan \theta = \frac{5}{12}$, then $\cot \theta = \frac{12}{5}$.

Visual **Glossary**

Coterminal angle (p. 389)   Two angles in standard position are coterminal if they have the same terminal side.

Ángulo coterminal (p. 389)   Dos ángulos que están en posición normal son coterminales si tienen el mismo lado terminal.

Example

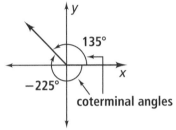

135°

−225°

coterminal angles

Angles that have measures 135°
and −225° are coterminal.

Cross section (p. 594)   A cross section is the intersection of a solid and a plane.

Sección de corte (p. 594)   Una sección de corte es la intersección de un plano y un cuerpo geométrico.

Example

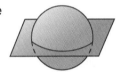

The cross section
is a circle.

Cumulative frequency (p. 31)   When you can assign numerical values to events, cumulative frequency is the number of times events with values that are less than or equal to a given value occur.

Frequencia acumulativa (p. 31)   Cuando se puede asignar valores numéricos a los eventos, la frecuencia acumulativa es el número de veces que occuren los eventos con valores que son menores que o igual a un valor dado.

Cumulative probability (p. 31)   When you can assign numerical values to events, cumulative probability is the probability that an event with a value less than or equal to a given value occurs.

Probabilidad acumulativa (p. 31)   Cuando se puede asignar valores numéricos a los eventos, la probabilidad acumulativa es la probabilidad de que un evento con un valor que es menor que o igual a un valor dado ocurra.

Cycle (p. 379)   A cycle of a periodic function is an interval of x-values over which the function provides one complete pattern of y-values.

Ciclo (p. 379)   El ciclo de una función periódica es un intervalo de valores de x de los cuales la función produce un patrón completo de valores de y.

Example

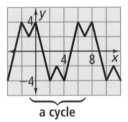

a cycle

D

Decay factor (p. 314)   In an exponential function of the form $y = ab^x$, b is the decay factor if $0 < b < 1$.

Factor de decremento (p. 314)   En una función exponencial de la forma $y = ab^x$, b es el factor de decremento si, $0 < b < 1$.

Example   In the equation $y = 0.3^x$, 0.7 is the decay factor.

English

Spanish

Degree of a monomial (p. 55) The degree of a monomial in one variable is the exponent of the variable.

Grado de un monomio (p. 55) El grado de un monomio en una variable es el exponente de la variable.

Degree of a polynomial (p. 55) The degree of a polynomial is the greatest degree among its monomial terms.

Grado de un polinomio (p. 55) El grado de un polinomio es el grado mayor entre los términos de monomios.

Example $P(x) = x^6 + 2x^3 - 3$ degree 6

Density (p. 563) The density of an object is its mass divided by its volume.

Densidad (p. 563) La densidad de un objeto es su masa dividida por su volumen.

Difference of cubes (p. 82) A difference of cubes is an expression of the form $a^3 - b^3$. It can be factored as $(a - b)(a^2 + ab + b^2)$.

Diferencia de dos cuadrados (p. 82) La diferencia de dos cuadrados es una expresión de la forma $a^3 - b^3$. Se puede factorizar como $(a - b)$ $(a^2 + ab + b^2)$.

Example $x^3 - 27 = (x - 3)(x^2 + 3x + 9)$

Discontinuous graph (p. 192) A graph is discontinuous if it has a jump, break, or hole.

Gráfica discontinua (p. 192) Una gráfica es discontinua si tiene un salto, interrupción o hueco.

Discrete probability distribution (p. 34) A discrete probability distribution has a finite number of possible events.

Distribución de probabilidad discreta (p. 34) Una distribución de probabilidad discreta tiene un número finito de sucesos posibles.

Diverge (p. 531) An infinite series diverges if it does not converge.

Divergir (p. 531) Una serie infinita es divergente si no es convergente.

Example $1 + 2 + 4 + 8 + \ldots$ diverges.

 E

Edge (p. 590) *See* **polyhedron**.

Arista (p. 590) *Ver* **polyhedron**.

End behavior (p. 57) End behavior of the graph of a function describes the directions of the graph as you move to the left and to the right, away from the origin.

Comportamiento extremo (p. 57) El comportamiento extremo de la gráfica de una función describe las direcciones de la gráfica al moverse a la izquierda y a la derecha, apartándose del origen.

Even function (p. 64) A function f is an even function if and only if $f(-x) = f(x)$ for all values of x in its domain.

Función par (p. 64) Una función f es una función par si y solo si $f(-x) = f(x)$ para todos los valores de x en su dominio.

Example $f(x) = x^2 + |x|$ is an even function
because $f(-x) = (-x)^2 + |-x|$
$= x^2 + |x| = f(x)$

Excluded value (p. 145) A value of x for which a rational expression $f(x)$ is undefined.

Valor excluido (p. 145) Valor de x para el cual una expresión racional es indefinida.

Explicit formula (p. 493) An explicit formula expresses the nth term of a sequence in terms of n.

Fórmula explícita (p. 493) Una fórmula explícita expresa el n-ésimo término de una progresión en función de n.

Example Let $a_n = 2n + 5$ for positive integers n.
If $n = 7$, then $a_7 = 2(7) + 5 = 19$.

English

Spanish

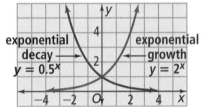

Exponential decay (p. 312) Exponential decay is modeled by a function of the form $y = ab^x$ with $0 < b < 1$.

Decaimiento exponencial (p. 312) El decaimiento exponencial se expresa con una función $y = ab^x$ donde $0 < b < 1$.

Exponential equation (p. 348) An exponential equation contains the form b^{cx}, with the exponent including a variable.

Ecuación exponencial (p. 348) Una ecuación exponencial tiene la forma b^{cx}, y su exponente incluye una variable.

$$\textbf{Example} \qquad 5^{2x} = 270$$
$$\log 5^{2x} = \log 270$$
$$2x \log 5 = \log 270$$
$$2x = \frac{\log 270}{\log 5}$$
$$2x \approx 3.4785$$
$$x \approx 1.7392$$

Exponential function (p. 311) The general form of an exponential function is $y = ab^x$, where x is a real number, $a \neq 0$, $b > 0$, and $b \neq 1$. When $b > 1$, the function models exponential growth with growth factor b. When $0 < b < 1$, the function models exponential decay with decay factor b.

Función exponencial (p. 311) La forma general de una función exponencial es $y = ab^x$, donde x es un número real, $a \neq 0$, $b > 0$ y $b \neq 1$. Cuando $b > 1$, la función representa un incremento exponencial con factor de incremento b. Cuando $0 < b < 1$, la función representa el decremento exponencial con factor de decremento b.

Example

exponential decay → $y = 0.5^x$

exponential growth ← $y = 2^x$

Exponential growth (p. 312) Exponential growth is modeled by a function of the form $y = ab^x$ with $b > 1$.

Crecimiento exponencial (p. 312) El crecimiento exponencial se expresa con una función de la forma $y = ab^x$ donde $b > 1$.

F

Face (p. 590) *See* **polyhedron.**

Cara (p. 590) *Ver* **polyhedron.**

Finite Series (p. 517) A finite series is a series with a finite number of terms.

Serie finite (p. 517) Una serie finita es una serie con un número finito de términos.

G

Geometric mean (p. 513) The geometric mean of any two positive numbers is the positive square root of the product of the two numbers.

Media geométrica (p. 513) La media geométrica de dos números positivos es la raíz cuadrada positiva del producto de los dos números.

Example The Geometric mean of 12 and 18
$$\sqrt{12 \cdot 18} \approx 14.6969.$$

English

Spanish

Geometric probability (p. 581) Geometric probability is a probability that uses a geometric model in which points represent outcomes.

Probabilidad geométrica (p. 581) La probabilidad geométrica es una probabilidad que utiliza un modelo geométrico donde se usan puntos para representar resultados.

Example

$P(H \text{ on } \overline{BC}) = \frac{BC}{AD}$

Geometric sequence (p. 509) A geometric sequence is a sequence with a constant ratio between consecutive terms.

Secuencia geométrica (p. 509) Una secuencia geométrica es una secuencia con una razón constante entre términos consecutivos.

Example The geometric sequence 2.5, 5, 10, 20, 40 . . . , has a common ratio of 2.

Geometric series (p. 529) A geometric series is the sum of the terms in a geometric sequence.

Serie geométrica (p. 529) Una serie geométrica es la suma de términos en una progresión geométrica.

Example One geometric series with five terms is $2.5 + 5 + 10 + 20 + 40$.

Growth factor (p. 314) In an exponential function of the form $y = ab^x$, b is the growth factor if $b > 1$.

Factor de incremento (p. 314) En una función exponencial de la forma $y = ab^x$, b es el factor de incremento si $b > 1$.

Example In the exponential equation $y = 2^x$, 2 is the growth factor.

Index (p. 232) With a radical sign, the index indicates the degree of the root.

Índice (p. 232) Con un signo de radical, el índice indica el grado de la raíz.

Example index 2 index 3 index 4
$$\sqrt{16} \qquad \sqrt[3]{16} \qquad \sqrt[4]{16}$$

Infinite series (p. 517) An infinite series is a series with infinitely many terms.

Serie infinita (p. 517) Una serie infinita es una serie con un número infinito de términos.

Initial side (p. 387) When an angle is in standard position, the initial side of the angle is given to be on the positive x-axis. The other ray is the terminal side of the angle.

Lado inicial (p. 387) Cuando un ángulo está en posición normal, el lado inicial del ángulo se ubica en el eje positivo de las x. El otro rayo, o semirrecta, forma el lado terminal del ángulo.

Example
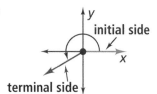

English

Spanish

Inscribed polygon (p. 558) A polygon is inscribed in a circle if the vertices of the polygon are on the circle.

Polígono inscrito (p. 558) Un polígono está inscrito en un círculo si los vertices del polígono están en el círculo.

Example

ABCD is
inscribed in ⊙*J*.

Intercepted arc (p. 395) An intercepted arc is the portion of a circle whose endpoints are on the sides of a central angle of the circle and whose remaining points lie in the interior of the angle.

Arco interceptado (p. 395) Un arco interceptado es la porción de un círculo cuyos extremos quedan sobre los lados de un ángulo central del círculo y cuyos puntos restantes quedan en el interior del ángulo.

Example

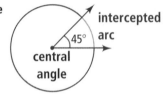

Interquartile range (p. 5) The interquartile range of a set of data is the difference between the third and first quartiles.

Intervalo intercuartil (p. 5) El rango intercuartil de un conjunto de datos es la diferencia entre el tercero y el primer cuartiles.

Example   The first and third quartiles of the
data set {2, 3, 4, 5, 5, 6, 7, 7} are
3.5 and 6.5. The interquartile
range is 6.5 − 3.5 = 3.

Inverse function (p. 283) If function *f* pairs a value *b* with *a* then its inverse, denoted f^{-1}, pairs the value *a* with *b*. If f^{-1} is also a function, then *f* and f^{-1} are inverse functions.

Funcion inversa (p. 283) Si la función *f* empareja un valor *b* con *a*, entonces su inversa, cuya notación es f^{-1}, empareja el valor *a* con *b*. Si f^{-1} también es una función, entonces *f* y f^{-1} son funciones inversas.

Example   If $f(x) = x + 3$, then $f^{-1}(x) = x - 3$.

Inverse relation (p. 283) If a relation pairs element *a* of its domain with element *b* of its range, the inverse relation "undoes" the relation and pairs *b* with *a*. If (*a*, *b*) is an ordered pair of a relation, then (*b*, *a*) is an ordered pair of its inverse.

Relación inversa (p. 283) Si una relación empareja el elemento *a* de su dominio con el elemento *b* de su rango, la relación inversa "deshace" la relación y empareja *b* con *a*. Si (*a*, *b*) es un par ordenado de una relación, entonces (*b*, *a*) es un par ordenado de su inversa.

English

Spanish

Inverse variation (p. 169) An inverse variation is a relation represented by an equation of the form $xy = k$, $y = \frac{x}{k}$, or $x = \frac{y}{k}$, where $k \neq 0$.

Variación inversa (p. 169) Una variación inversa es una relación representada por la ecuación $xy = k$, $y = \frac{x}{k}$, ó $x = \frac{y}{k}$. donde $k \neq 0$.

Example

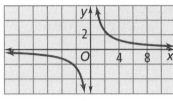

$xy = 5$, or $y = \frac{5}{x}$

J

Joint variation (p. 173) A joint variation is a relation in which one variable varies directly with respect to each of two or more variables.

Variación conjunta (p. 173) Una variación conjunta es una relación en la cual el valor de una variable varía directamente con respecto a cada una de dos o más variables.

Example $z = 8xy$
$T = kPV$

L

Like radicals (p. 246) Like radicals are radical expressions that have the same index and the same radicand.

Radicales semejantes (p. 246) Los radicales semejantes son expresiones radicales que tienen el mismo índice y el mismo radicando.

Example $4\sqrt[3]{7}$ and $\sqrt[3]{7}$ are like radicals.

Limits (p. 520) Limits in summation notation are the least and greatest integer values of the index n.

Límites (p. 520) Los límites en notación de sumatoria son el menor y el mayor valor del índice n en números enteros.

Example

$$\text{limits} \nearrow \begin{array}{c} 3 \\ \Sigma \\ n = 1 \end{array} (3n + 5)$$

Locus (p. 610) A locus is a set of points, all of which meet a stated condition.

Lugar geométrico (p. 610) Un lugar geométrico es un conjunto de puntos que cumplen una condición dada.

Example

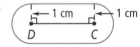

The points in blue are the locus of points in a plane 1 cm from $\overline{DC}$.

English

Spanish

Logarithm (p. 331) The logarithm base b of a positive number x is defined as follows: $\log_b x = y$, if and only if $x = b^y$.

Logaritmo (p. 331) La base del logaritmo b de un número positivo x se define como $\log_b x = y$, si y sólo si $x = b^y$.

Example $\log_2 8 = 3$
$$\log_{10} 100 = \log 100 = 2$$
$$\log_5 5^7 = 7$$

Logarithmic equation (p. 352) A logarithmic equation is an equation that includes a logarithm involving a variable.

Ecuación logarítmica (p. 352) Una ecuación logarítmica es una ecuación que incluye un logaritmo con una variable.

Example $\log_3 x = 4$

Logarithmic function (p. 334) A logarithmic function is the inverse of an exponential function.

Función logarítmica (p. 334) Una función logarítmica es la inversa de una función exponencial.

Example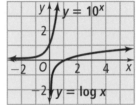

Logarithmic scale (p. 333) A logarithmic scale is a scale that uses the logarithm of a quantity instead of the quantity itself.

Escala logarítmica (p. 333) Una escala logarítmica es una escala que usa el logaritmo de una cantidaden vez de la cantidad misma.

M

Margin of error (p. 42) The distance from the sample mean or sample proportion that is used to create a confidence interval for the population mean or the population proportion. For a 95% confidence level, $ME = 1.96 \cdot \frac{s}{\sqrt{n}}$, where ME is the margin of error, s is the standard deviation of the sample data, and n is the number of values in the sample.

Margen de error (p. 42) La distancia desde la media de una muestra o desde la proporción de una muestra que se usa para crear el intervalo de confianza para la media o proporción de una población. Para un nivel de confianza de 95%, $ME = 1.96 \cdot \frac{s}{\sqrt{n}}$, siendo ME el margen de error, s la desviación estándar de los datos de la muestra, y n el número de valores en la muestra.

Example The standard deviation of a sample is 5.0 and the number of trials is 30. The margin of error at a 95% confidence level is
$$ME = 1.96 \cdot \frac{50}{\sqrt{30}} \approx 1.79.$$

Mean (p. 3) The sum of the data values divided by the number of data values is the mean. *See also* **Arithmetic mean.**

Media (p. 3) La suma de los valores de datos dividida por el número de valores de datos sumados es la media. *Ver también* **Arithmetic mean.**

Example $\{1, 2, 3, 3, 6, 6\}$
$$\text{mean} = \frac{1 + 2 + 3 + 3 + 6 + 6}{6}$$
$$= \frac{21}{6} = 3.5$$

English

Spanish

Measures of central tendency (p. 3)   The mean, the median, and the mode are each central values that help describe a set of data. They are called measures of central tendency.

Medidas de tendencia central (p. 3)   La media, la mediana y la moda son los valores centrales que facilitan la descripción de un conjunto de datos. A estos valores se les llama medidas de tendencia central.

Example {1, 2, 3, 3, 4, 5, 6, 6}
mean = 3.75
median = 3.5
modes = 3 and 6

Measure of variation (p. 15)   Measures of variation, such as the range, the interquartile range, and the standard deviation, describe how the data in a data set are spread out.

Medida de dispersión (p. 15)   Las medidas de dispersión, tal como el rango, el intervalo intercuartil y la desviación típica, describen cómo se dispersan los datos en un conjunto de datos.

Median (p. 3)   The median is the middle value in a data set. If the data set contains an even number of values, the median is the mean of the two middle values.

Mediana (p. 3)   La mediana es el valor situado en el medio en un conjunto de datos. Si el conjunto de datos contiene un número par de valores, la mediana es la media de los dos valores del medio.

Example {1, 2, 3, 3, 4, 5, 6, 6}
$$\text{median} = \frac{3+4}{2} = \frac{7}{2} = 3.5$$

Midline (p. 382)   The horizontal line through the average of the maximum and minimum values.

Línea media (p. 382)   La recta horizontal que pasa a través de la meda de los valores máximos y mínimos.

Example

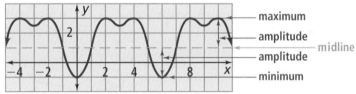

Mode (p. 3)   The mode is the most frequently occurring value (or values) in a set of data.

Moda (p. 3)   La moda es el valor o valores que ocurren con mayor frecuencia en un conjunto de datos.

Example {1, 2, 3, 3, 4, 5, 6, 6}
The modes are 3 and 6.

Monomial (p. 55)   A monomial is either a real number, a variable, or a product of real numbers and variables with whole number exponents.

Monomio (p. 55)   Un monomio es un número real, una variable o un producto de números reales y variables cuyos exponentes son números enteros.

Example 1, x, 2z, 4ab^2

English

Spanish

Multiple zero (p. 75)   If a linear factor is repeated in the complete factored form of a polynomial, the zero related to that factor is a multiple zero.

Cero múltiplo (p. 75)   Si un factor lineal se repite en la forma factorizada completa de un polinomio, el cero relacionado con ese factor es un cero múltiplo.

Example   The zeros of the function $P(x) = 2x(x - 3)^2(x + 1)$ are 0, 3, and -1. Since $(x - 3)$ occurs twice as a factor, 3 is a multiple zero.

Multiplicity (p. 75)   The multiplicity of a zero of a polynomial function is the number of times the related linear factor is repeated in the factored form of the polynomial.

Multiplicidad (p. 75)   La multiplicidad de un cero de una función polinomial es el número de veces que el factor lineal relacionado se repite en la forma factorizada del polinomio.

Example   The zeros of the function $P(x) = 2x(x - 3)^2(x + 1)$ are 0, 3, and -1. Since $(x - 3)$ occurs twice as a factor, the zero 3 has multiplicity 2.

N

Natural base exponential function (p. 325)   A natural base exponential function is an exponential function with base e.

Función exponencial con base natural (p. 325)   Una función exponencial con base natural es una función exponencial con base e.

Natural logarithmic function (p. 359)   A natural logarithmic function is a logarithmic function with base e. The natural logarithmic function, $y = \ln x$, is $y = \log_e x$. It is the inverse of $y = e^x$.

Función logarítmica natural (p. 359)   Una función logarítmica natural es una función logarítmica con base e. La función logarítmica natural, $y = \ln x$, es $y = \log_e x$. Ésta es la función inversa de $y = e^x$.

Example

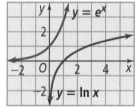

$\ln e^3 = 3$
$\ln 10 \approx 2.3026$
$\ln 36 \approx 3.5835$

Non-removable discontinuity (p. 192)   A non-removable discontinuity is a point of discontinuity that is not removable. It represents a break in the graph of f where you cannot redefine f to make the graph continuous.

Discontinuidad irremovible (p. 192)   Una discontinuidad irremovible es un punto de discontinuidad que no se puede remover. Representa una interrupción en la gráfica f donde no se puede redefinir f para volverla una gráfica continua.

English

Normal distribution (p. 34)   A normal distribution shows data that vary randomly from the mean in the pattern of a bell-shaped curve.

Spanish

Distribución normal (p. 34)   Una distribución normal muestra, con una curva en forma de campana, datos que varían alcatoriamento respecto de la media.

Example   **Distribution of Test Scores**

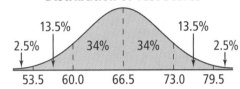

In a class of 200 students, the scores on a test were normally distributed. The mean score was 66.5 and the standard deviation was 6.5. The number of students who scored greater than 73 was about 13.5% + 2.5% of those who took the test.
16% of 200 = 32
About 32 students scored 73 or higher on the test.

---

nth root (p. 231)   For any real numbers a and b, and any positive integer n, if $a^n = b$, then a is an nth root of b.

raíz n-ésima (p. 231)   Para todos los números reales a y b, y todo número entero positivo n, si $a^n = b$, entonces a es la n-ésima raíz de b.

Example $\sqrt[5]{32} = 2$ because $2^5 = 32$.
$\sqrt[4]{81} = 3$ because $3^4 = 81$.

O

Observational study (p. 24)   In an observational study, you measure or observe members of a sample in such a way that they are not affected by the study.

Estudio de observación (p. 24)   En un estudio de observación, se miden u observan a los miembros de una muestra de tal manera que no les afecte el estudio.

Odd function (p. 64)   A function f is an odd function if and only if $f(-x) = -f(x)$ for all values of x in its domain.

Función impar (p. 64)   Una función f es una función impar si y solo si $f(-x) = -f(x)$ para todos los valores de x en su dominio.

Example   The function $f(x) = x^3 + 2x$ is odd because $f(-x) = (-x)^3 + 2(-x)$
$= -x^3 - 2x = -f(x)$

Outlier (p. 5)   An outlier is a value substantially different from the rest of the data in a set.

Valor extremo (p. 5)   Un valor extremo es un valor considerablemente diferente al resto de los datos de un conjunto.

Example   The outlier in the data set {56, 64, 73, 59, 98, 65, 59} is 98.

English

P

Pascal's Triangle (p. 538) Pascal's Triangle is a triangular array of numbers in which the first and last number is 1. Each of the other numbers in the row is the sum of the two numbers above it.

Spanish

Triángulo de Pascal (p. 538) El Triángulo de Pascal es una distribución triangular de números en la cual el primer número y el último número son 1. Cada uno de los otros números en la fila es la suma de los dos números de encima.

Example **Pascal's Triangle**

```
              1
            1   1
          1   2   1
        1   3   3   1
      1   4   6   4   1
    1   5  10  10   5   1
```

Percentiles (p. 7) A percentile is a number from 0 to 100 that you can associate with a value x from a data set. It shows the percent of the data that are less than or equal to x.

Percentiles (p. 7) Un percentil es un número de 0 a 100 que se puede asociar con un valor x de un conjunto de datos. Éste muestra el porcentaje de los datos que son menores o iguales a x.

Period (p. 379) The period of a periodic function is the horizontal length of one cycle.

Período (p. 379) El período de una función periódica es el intervalo horizontal de un ciclo.

Example

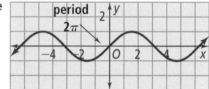

The periodic function $y = \sin x$ has period 2π.

Periodic function (p. 379) A periodic function repeats a pattern of y-values at regular intervals.

Función periódica (p. 379) Una función periódica repite un patrón de valores y a intervalos regulares.

Example

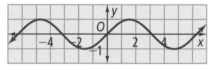

$y = \sin x$

Phase shift (p. 434) A horizontal translation of a periodic function is a phase shift.

Cambio de fase (p. 434) Una traslación horizontal de una función periódica es un cambio de fase.

Example

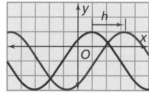

$g(x)$: horizontal translation of $f(x)$
$$g(x) = f(x - h)$$

English

Spanish

Point of discontinuity (p. 192)   A point of discontinuity is the x-coordinate of a point where the graph of $f(x)$ is not continuous.

Punto de discontinuidad (p. 192)   Un punto de discontinuidad es la coordenada x de un punto donde la gráfica de $f(x)$ no es continua.

Example $f(x) = \frac{2}{x-2}$ has a point of discontinuity at $x = 2$.

Polyhedron (p. 590)   A polyhedron is a three-dimensional figure whose surfaces, or *faces*, are polygons. The *vertices* of the polygons are the vertices of the polyhedron. The intersections of the faces are the *edges* of the polyhedron.

Poliedro (p. 590)   Un poliedro es una figura tridimensional cuyas superficies, o *caras*, son polígonos. Los *vértices* de los polígonos son los vértices del poliedro. Las intersecciones de las caras son las *aristas* del poliedro.

Example
Vertices — Faces — Edges

Polynomial (p. 55)   A polynomial is a monomial or the sum of monomials.

Polinomio (p. 55)   Un polinomio es un monomio o la suma de dos o más monomios.

Example $3x^3 + 4x^2 - 2x + 58x \qquad x^2 + 4x + 2$

Polynomial function (p. 55)   A polynomial in the variable x defines a polynomial function of x.

Función polinomial (p. 55)   Un polinomio en la variable x define una función polinomial de x.

Example $P(x) = a_n x^n + a_{n-1}x^{n-1} + \ldots + a_1 x + a_0$ is a polynomial function, where n is a nonnegative integer and the coefficients $a_n, \ldots, a_0$ are real numbers.

Population (p. 22)   A population is the members of a set.

Población (p. 22)   Una población está compuesta por los miembros de un conjunto.

Population density (p. 563)   Population density is the number of individuals of a population divided by the total area or volume that they occupy.

Densidad de población (p. 563)   La densidad de población es el número de individuos de una población dividida por el área total o el volumen total que ocupan.

Power function (p. 131)   A power function is a function of the form $y = a \cdot x^b$, where a and b are nonzero real numbers.

Función de potencia (p. 131)   Una función de potencia es una función de la forma $y = a \cdot x^b$, donde a y b son números reales diferentes de cero.

Principal root (p. 231)   When a number has two real roots, the positive root is called the principal root. A radical sign indicates the principal root. The principal root of a negative number a is $i\sqrt{|a|}$.

Raíz principal (p. 231)   Cuando un número tiene dos raíces reales, la raíz positiva es la raíz principal. El signo del radical indica la raíz principal. La raíz principal de un número negativo a es $i\sqrt{|a|}$.

Example   The number 25 has two square roots, 5 and -5. The principal square root, 5, is indicated by $\sqrt{25}$ or $25^{\frac{1}{2}}$.

Visual Glossary

Probability distribution (p. 29)   A probability distribution is a function that tells the probability of each outcome in a sample space.

Distribución de probabilidades (p. 29)   Una distribución de probabilidades es una función que señala la probabilidad de que cada resultado ocurra en un espacio muestral.

Example

Roll	Fr.	Prob.
1	5	0.125
2	9	0.225
3	7	0.175
4	8	0.2
5	8	0.2
6	3	0.075

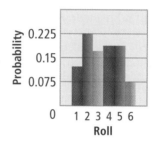

The table and graph both show the experimental probability distribution for the outcomes of 40 rolls of a standard number cube.

Q

Quartile (p. 5)   Quartiles are values that separate a finite data set into four equal parts. The second quartile (Q_2) is the median of the data. The first and third quartiles (Q_1 and Q_3) are the medians of the lower half and upper half of the data, respectively.

Cuartil (p. 5)   Los cuartiles son valores que separan un conjunto finito de datos en cuatro partes iguales. El segundo cuartil (Q_2) es la mediana de los datos. Los cuartiles primero y tercero (Q_1 y Q_3) son las medianas de la mitad superior e inferior de los datos, respectivamente.

Example   {2, 3, 4, 5, 5, 6, 7, 7}
$Q_1 = 3.5$
Q_2 (median) = 5
$Q_3 = 6.5$

R

Radian (p. 395) $\frac{a°}{180°} = \frac{r\ \text{radians}}{\pi\ \text{radians}}$

Radián (p. 395) $\frac{a°}{180°} = \frac{r\ \text{radians}}{\pi\ \text{radians}}$

Example $60° \rightarrow \frac{60}{180} = \frac{x}{\pi}$
$$x = \frac{60\pi}{180}$$
$$= \frac{\pi}{3}$$
Thus, $60° = \frac{\pi}{3}$ radians.

Radical equation (p. 265)   A radical equation is an equation that has a variable in a radicand or has a variable with a rational exponent.

Ecuación radical (p. 265)   La ecuación radical es una ecuación que contiene una variable en el radicando o una variable con un exponente racional.

Example $(\sqrt{x})^3 + 1 = 65$
$$x^{\frac{3}{2}} + 1 = 65$$

English

Spanish

Radical function (p. 295)   A radical function is a function that can be written in the form $f(x) = a\sqrt[n]{x - h} + k$, where $a \neq 0$. For even values of n, the domain of a radical function is the real numbers $x \geq h$. *See also* **Square root function.**

Función radical (p. 295)   Una función radical es una función quepuede expresarse como $f(x) = a\sqrt[n]{x - h} + k$, donde $a \neq 0$. Para n par, el dominio de la función radical son los números reales tales que $x \geq h$. *Ver también* **Square root function.**

Example $f(x) = \sqrt{x - 2}$

Radicand (p. 232)   The number under a radical sign is the radicand.

Radicando (p. 232)   La expresión que aparece debajo del signo radical es el radicando.

Example   The radicand in $3\sqrt[4]{7}$ is 7.

Random sample (p. 22)   In a random sample, all members of the population are equally likely to be chosen as every other member.

Muestra aleatoria (p. 22)   En una muestra aleatoria, la probabilidad de ser seleccionado es igual para todos los miembros.

Example   Let the set of all females between the ages of 19 and 34 be the population. A random selection of 900 females between those ages would be a sample of the population.

Range of a set of data (p. 5)   The range of a set of data is the difference between the greatest and least values.

Rango de un conjunto de datos (p. 5)   El rango de un conjunto de datos es la diferencia entre el valor máximo y el valor mínimo de los datos.

Example   The range of the set {3.2, 4.1, 2.2, 3.4, 3.8, 4.0, 4.2, 2.8} is $4.2 - 2.2 = 2$.

Rational equation (p. 207)   A rational equation is an equation that contains a rational expression.

Ecuación racional (p. 207)   Una ecuación racional es una ecuación que contiene una expresión racional.

Rational exponent (p. 257)   If the nth root of a is a real number and m is an integer, then $a^{\frac{1}{n}} = \sqrt[n]{a}$ and $a^{\frac{m}{n}} = \sqrt[n]{a^m} = (\sqrt[n]{a})^m$. If m is negative, $a \neq 0$.

Exponente racional (p. 257)   Si la raíz n-ésima de a es un número real y m es un número entero, entonces $a^{\frac{1}{n}} = \sqrt[n]{a}$ y $a^{\frac{m}{n}} = \sqrt[n]{a^m} = (\sqrt[n]{a})^m$. Si m es negativo, $a \neq 0$.

Example $4^{\frac{1}{3}} = \sqrt[3]{4}$

$5^{\frac{3}{2}} = \sqrt{5^3} = (\sqrt{5})^3$

Rational expression (p. 145)   A rational expression is the quotient of two polynomials.

Expresión racional (p. 145)   Una expresión racional es el cociente de dos polinomios.

Rational function (p. 191) A rational function $f(x)$ can be written as $f(x) = \frac{P(x)}{Q(x)}$, where $P(x)$ and $Q(x)$ are polynomial functions. The domain of a rational function is all real numbers except those for which $Q(x) = 0$.

Función racional (p. 191) Una función racional $f(x)$ se puede expresar como $f(x) = \frac{P(x)}{Q(x)}$, donde $P(x)$ y $Q(x)$ son funciones de polinomios. El dominio de una función racional son todos los números reales excepto aquéllos para los cuales $Q(x) = 0$.

Example

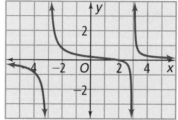

The function $y = \frac{x-2}{x^2-9}$ is a rational function with three branches separated by asymptotes $x = -3$ and $x = 3$.

Rationalize the denominator (p. 241) To rationalize the denominator of an expression, rewrite it so there are no radicals in any denominator and no denominators in any radical.

Racionalizar el denominador (p. 241) Para racionalizar el denominador de una expresión, ésta se escribe de modo que no haya radicales en ningún denominador y no haya denominadores en ningún radical.

Example $\frac{1}{\sqrt{2}} = \frac{1}{\sqrt{2}} \times \frac{\sqrt{2}}{\sqrt{2}} = \frac{\sqrt{2}}{2}$

Reciprocal function (p. 182) A reciprocal function belongs to the family whose parent function is $f(x) = \frac{1}{x}$ where $x \neq 0$. You can write a reciprocal function in the form $f(x) = \left(\frac{a}{x} - h\right) + k$, where $a \neq 0$ and $x \neq h$.

Función recíproca (p. 182) Una función recíproca pertenece a la familia cuya función madre es $f(x) = \frac{1}{x}$ donde $x \neq 0$. Se puede escribir una función recíproca como $f(x) = \left(\frac{a}{x} - h\right) + k$, donde $a \neq 0$ y $x \neq h$.

Example $f(x) = \frac{1}{2x+5}$
$p(v) = \frac{3}{v} + 5$

Recursive formula (p. 494) A recursive formula defines the terms in a sequence by relating each term to the ones before it.

Fórmula recursiva (p. 494) Una fórmula recursiva define los términos de una secuencia al relacionar cada término con los términos que lo anteceden.

Example Let $a_n = 2.5a_{n-1} + 3a_{n-2}$.
If $a_5 = 3$ and $a_4 = 7.5$, then
$a_6 = 2.5(3) + 3(7.5) = 30$.

English

Spanish

Relative maximum (minimum) (p. 76)   A relative maximum (minimum) is the value of the function at an up-to-down (down-to-up) turning point.

Máximo (mínimo) relativo (p. 76)   El máximo (mínimo) relativo es el valor de la función en un punto de giro de arriba hacia abajo (de abajo hacia arriba).

Example

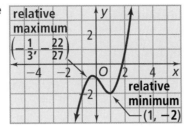

Removable discontinuity (p. 192)   A removable discontinuity is a point of discontinuity, a, of function f that you can remove by redefining f at $x = a$. Doing so fills in a hole in the graph of f with the point $(a, f(a))$.

Discontinuidad removible (p. 192)   Una discontinuidad removible es un punto de discontinuidad a en una función f que se puede remover al redefinir f en $x = a$. Al hacer esto, se llena un hueco en la gráfica f con el punto $(a, f(a))$.

S

Sample (p. 22)   A sample from a population is some of the population.

Muestra (p. 22)   Una muestra de una población es una parte de la población.

Example   Let the set of all males between the ages of 19 and 34 be the population. A random selection of 900 males between those ages would be a sample of the population.

Sample proportion (p. 43)   The ratio $\hat{p}$ compares x to n where x is the number of times an event occurs and n is the sample size. $\hat{p} = \frac{x}{n}$.

Proporción de una muest7ra (p. 43)   La razón $\hat{p}$ compara x a n, siendo x el número de veces que sucede un evento y n el tamaño de la muestra. $\hat{p} = \frac{x}{n}$.

Example   In a taste test, 120 persons sampled two types of cola; 40 people preferred cola A. The sample proportion is $\frac{40}{120}$, or $\frac{1}{3}$.

Secant function (p. 447)   The secant (sec) function is the reciprocal of the cosine function. For all real numbers θ except those that make $\cos \theta = 0$, $\sec \theta = \frac{1}{\cos \theta}$.

Función secante (p. 447)   La función secante (sec) es el recíproco de la función coseno. Para todos los números reales θ, excepto aquéllos para los que $\cos \theta = 0$, $\sec \theta = \frac{1}{\cos \theta}$.

Example   If $\cos \theta = \frac{5}{13}$, then $\sec \theta = \frac{13}{5}$.

Segment bisector (p. 553)   A segment bisector is a line, segment, ray, or plane that intersects a segment at its midpoint.

Bisectriz de un segmento (p. 553)   La bisectriz de un segmento es una recta, segmento, semirrecta o plano que corta un segmento en su punto medio.

Example

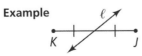

ℓ bisects $\overline{KJ}$.

English

Spanish

Self-selected sample (p. 22) In a self-selected sample you select only members of the population who volunteered for the sample.

Muestra de voluntarios (p. 22) En una muestra de voluntarios se seleccionan sólo a los miembros de la población que se ofrecen voluntariamente para ser parte de la muestra.

Sequence (p. 493) A sequence is an ordered list of numbers.

Progresión (p. 493) Una progresión es una sucesión de números.

Example 1, 4, 7, 10, . . .

Series (p. 517) A series is the sum of the terms of a sequence.

Serie (p. 517) Una serie es la suma de los términos de una secuencia.

Example The series $3 + 6 + 9 + 12 + 15$ corresponds to the sequence 3, 6, 9, 12, 15. The sum of the series is 45.

Similar solids (p. 601) Similar solids have the same shape and have all their corresponding dimensions proportional.

Cuerpos geométricos semejantes (p. 601) Los cuerpos geométricos semejantes tienen la misma forma y todas sus dimensiones correspondientes son proporcionales.

Example

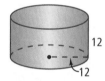

10
10

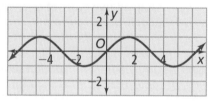

12
12

Simplest form of a radical expression (p. 239) A radical expression with index n is in simplest form if there are no radicals in any denominator, no denominators in any radical, and any radicand has no nth power factors.

Mínima expresión de una expresión radical (p. 239) Una expresión radical con índice n está en su mínima expresión si no tiene radicales en ningún denominador ni denominadores en ningún radical y los radicandos no tienen factores de potencia.

Sine curve (p. 405) A sine curve is the graph of a sine function.

Sinusoide (p. 405) Sinusoide es la gráfica de la función seno.

Example

English

Sine function, Sine of θ (pp. 390, 403) The sine function, $y = \sin\theta$, matches the measure θ of an angle in standard position with the y-coordinate of a point on the unit circle. This point is where the terminal side of the angle intersects the unit circle. The y-coordinate is the sine of θ.

Spanish

Función seno, Seno de θ (pp. 390, 403) La función seno, $y = \sin\theta$, empareja la medida θ de un ángulo en posición estándar con la coordenada y de un punto en el círculo unitario. Este es el punto en el que el lado terminal del ángulo interseca al círculo unitario. La coordenada y es el seno de θ.

Example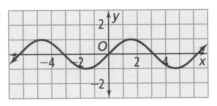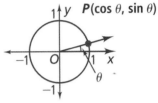

Square root function (p. 295) A square root function is a function that can be written in the form $f(x) = a\sqrt{x - h} + k$, where $a \neq 0$. The domain of a square root function is all real numbers $x \geq h$.

Función de raíz cuadrada (p. 295) Una función de raíz cuadrada es una función que puede ser expresada como $f(x) = a\sqrt{x - h} + k$, donde $a \neq 0$. El dominio de una función de raíz cuadrada son todos los números reales tales que $x \geq h$.

Example $f(x) = 2\sqrt{x - 3} + 4$

Standard deviation (p. 15) Standard deviation is a measure of how much the values in a data set vary, or deviate, from the mean, $\bar{x}$. To find the standard deviation, follow five steps:
- Find the mean of the data set.
- Find the difference between each data value and the mean.
- Square each difference.
- Find the mean of the squares.
- Take the square root of the mean of the squares. This is the standard deviation.

Desviación típica (p. 15) La desviación típica denota cuánto los valores de un conjunto de datos varían, o se desvían, de la media, $\bar{x}$. Para hallar la desviación típica, se siguen cinco pasos:
- Se halla la media del conjunto de datos.
- Se calcula la diferencia entre cada valor de datos y la media.
- Se eleva al cuadrado cada diferencia.
- Se halla la media de los cuadrados.
- Se calcula la raíz cuadrada de la media de los cuadrados. Ésa es la desviación típica.

Example $\{0, 2, 3, 4, 6, 7, 8, 9, 10, 11\}$
$\bar{x} = 6$
standard deviation $= \sqrt{12} \approx 3.46$

Standard form of a polynomial function (p. 56) The standard form of a polynomial function arranges the terms by degree in descending numerical order. A polynomial function, $P(x)$, in standard form is $P(x) = a_nx^n + a_{n-1}x^{n-1} + \ldots + a_1x + a_0$, where n is a nonnegative integer and $a_n, \ldots, a_0$ are real numbers.

Forma normal de una función polinomial (p. 56) La forma normal de una función polinomial organiza los términos por grado en orden numérico descendiente. Una función polinomial, $P(x)$, en forma normal es $P(x) = a_nx^n + a_{n-1}x^{n-1} + \ldots + a_1x + a_0$, donde n es un número entero no negativo y $a_n, \ldots, a_0$ son números reales.

Example $2x^3 - 5x^2 - 2x + 5$

Visual Glossary

Standard position (p. 387)   An angle in the coordinate plane is in standard position when the vertex is at the origin and one ray is on the positive *x*-axis.

Posición estándar (p. 387)   Un ángulo en el plano de coordenadas se encuentra en posición estándar si el vértice se encuentra en el origen y una semirrecta se encuentra en el eje *x* positivo.

Example

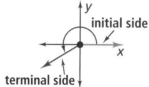

Sum of cubes (p. 82)   The sum of cubes is an expression of the form $a^3 + b^3$. It can be factored as $(a + b)(a^2 - ab + b^2)$.

Suma de dos cubos (p. 82)   La suma de dos cubos es una expresión de la forma $a^3 + b^3$. Se puede factorizar como $(a + b)(a^2 - ab + b^2)$.

Example $x^3 + 27 = (x + 3)(x^2 - 3x + 9)$

Survey (p. 24)   In a survey, you ask every member of a sample the same set of questions.

Encuesta (p. 24)   En una encuesta, se le hace a cada miembro de una muestra la misma serie de preguntas.

Synthetic division (p. 92)   Synthetic division is a process for dividing a polynomial by a linear expression $x - a$. You list the standard-form coefficients (including zeros) of the polynomial, omitting all variables and exponents. You use a for the "divisor" and add instead of subtract throughout the process.

División sintética (p. 92)   La división sintética es un proceso para dividir un polinomio por una expresión lineal $x - a$. En este proceso, escribes los coeficientes de forma normal (incluyendo los ceros) del polinomio, omitiendo todas las variables y todos los exponentes. Usas a como "divisor" y sumas, en vez de restar, a lo largo del proceso.

Example
$$
\begin{array}{r|rrrrr}
-3 & 2 & 5 & 0 & -2 & -8 \\
   &   & -6 & 3 & -9 & 33 \\
\hline
   & 2 & -1 & 3 & -11 & 25
\end{array}
$$

$2x^4 + 5x^3 - 2x - 8$ divided by $x + 3$ gives $2x^3 - x^2 + 3x - 11$ as quotient and 25 as remainder.

Systematic sample (p. 22)   In a systematic sample you order the population in some way, and then select from it at regular intervals.

Muestra sistemática (p. 22)   En una muestra sistemática se ordena la población de cierta manera y luego se selecciona una muestra de esa población a intervalos regulares.

English

Tangent function, Tangent of θ (pp. 425, 427) The tangent function, $y = \tan \theta$, matches the measure θ, of an angle in standard position with the y/x ratio of the (x, y) coordinates of a point on the unit circle. This point is where the terminal side of the angle intersects the unit circle. y/x is the tangent of θ.

Spanish

Función tangente, Tangente de θ (pp. 425, 427) La función tangente, $y = \tan \theta$, empareja la medida θ, de un ángulo en posición estándar con la razón y/x de las coordenadas (x, y) de un punto en el círculo unitario. Este es el punto en el que el lado terminal del ángulo interseca al círculo unitario. y/x es la tangente de θ.

Example

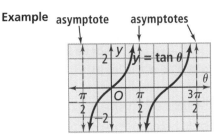 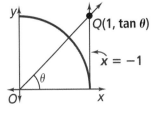

Term of a sequence (p. 493) Each number in a sequence is a term.

Término de una progresión (p. 493) Cada número de una progresión es un término.

Example 1, 4, 7, 10, . . .
The second term is 4.

Terminal side (p. 387) *See* **Initial side.**

Lado terminal (p. 387) *Ver* **Initial side.**

Trigonometric identity (p. 457) A trigonometric identity in one variable is a trigonometric equation that is true for all values of the variable for which both sides of the equation are defined.

Identidad trigonométrica (p. 457) Una identidad trigonométrica en una variable es una ecuación trigonométrica que es verdadera para todos los valores de la variable para los cuales se definen los dos lados de la ecuación.

Example $\tan \theta = \frac{\sin \theta}{\cos \theta}$

Turning point (p. 57) A turning point of the graph of a function is a point where the graph changes direction from upwards to downwards or from downwards to upwards.

Punto de giro (p. 57) Un punto de giro de la gráfica de una función es un punto donde la gráfica cambia de dirección de arriba hacia abajo o vice versa.

U

Uniform Distribution (p. 29) A uniform distribution is a probability distribution that is equal for each event in the sample space.

Distribución uniforme (p. 29) Una distribución uniforme es una distribución de probabilidad que es igual para cada suceso en el espacio muestral.

Unit circle (p. 390) The unit circle has a radius of 1 unit and its center is at the origin of the coordinate plane.

Círculo unitario (p. 390) El círculo unitario tiene un radio de 1 unidad y el centro está situado en el origen del plano de coordenadas.

Example

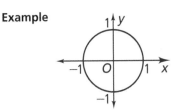

English

V

Variance (p. 15) Variance is the square of the standard deviation. $\sigma^2 = \frac{\Sigma(x-\bar{x})^2}{n}$

Vertex (p. 590) *See* **polyhedron.** The plural form of *vertex* is *vertices*.

Z

z-score (p. 46) The *z*-score of a value is the number of standard deviations that the value is from the mean.

Spanish

Varianza (p. 15) La varianza es el cuadrado de la desviación estándar. $\sigma^2 = \frac{\Sigma(x-\bar{x})^2}{n}$

Vértice (p. 590) *Ver* **polyhedron.**

Puntaje z (p. 46) El puntaje *z* de un valor es el número de desviaciones normales que tiene ese valor de la media.

Example {0, 2, 3, 4, 6, 7, 8, 9, 10, 11}
$\bar{x} = 6$
standard deviation $= \sqrt{12} \approx 3.46$
For 8, *z*-score $= \frac{8-6}{\sqrt{12}} \approx 0.58$

Appendix **Glossary**

A

Absolute maximum A value $f(c)$ is an absolute maximum value of f if $f(c) \geq f(x)$ for all x in the domain of f, p. A12.

Absolute minimum A value $f(c)$ is an absolute minimum value of f if $f(c) \leq f(x)$ for all x in the domain of f, p. A12.

Absolute value of a complex number The absolute value of the complex number $z = a + bi$ is given by $\sqrt{a^2 + b^2}$; also, the length of the segment from the origin to z in the complex plane, p. H113.

Amplitude See *Sinusoid*.

Angle Union of two rays with a common endpoint (the vertex). The beginning ray (the initial side) can be rotated about its endpoint to obtain the final position (the terminal side), p. H53.

Angle of depression The acute angle formed by the line of sight (downward) and the horizontal, p. H86.

Angle of elevation The acute angle formed by the line of sight (upward) and the horizontal, p. H86.

Arccosecant function See *Inverse cosecant function*.

Arccosine function See *Inverse cosine function*.

Arccotangent function See *Inverse cotangent function*.

Arcsecant function See *Inverse secant function*.

Arcsine function See *Inverse sine function*.

Arctangent function See *Inverse tangent function*.

Argument of a complex number The argument of $a + bi$ is the direction angle of the vector $\langle a, b \rangle$, p. H113.

Arithmetic sequence A sequence $\{a_n\}$ in which $a_n = a_{n-1} + d$ for every integer $n \geq 2$. The number d is the common difference, p. H124.

B

Base See *Exponential function, Logarithmic function*.

Basic logistic function The function $f(x) = \dfrac{1}{1 + e^{-x}}$, p. H9.

Bounded A function f is bounded if there are numbers b and B such that $b \leq f(x) \leq B$ for all x in the domain of f, p. A11.

Bounded above A function f is bounded above if there is a number B such that $f(x) \leq B$ for all x in the domain of f, p. A11.

Bounded below A function f is bounded below if there is a number b such that $b \leq f(x)$ for all x in the domain of f, p. A11.

C

Cardioid A limaçon whose polar equation is $r = a \pm a \sin \theta$, or $r = a \pm a \cos \theta$, where $a > 0$, p. H108.

Circular functions Trigonometric functions when applied to real numbers are circular functions, p. H59.

Common difference See *Arithmetic sequence*.

Common logarithm A logarithm with base 10, p. H24.

Common ratio See *Geometric sequence*.

Complex plane A coordinate plane used to represent the complex numbers. The x-axis of the complex plane is called the real axis and the y-axis is the imaginary axis, p. H112.

Constant function (on an interval) $f(x_1) = f(x_2)$ for any x_1 and x_2 (in the interval), pp. A9, A15.

Continuous function A function that is continuous on its entire domain, p. A24.

Continuous at $x = a$ $\lim\limits_{x \to a} f(x) = f(a)$, p. A7.

Convergence of a sequence A sequence $\{a_n\}$ converges to a if $\lim\limits_{n \to \infty} a_n = a$, p. H123.

Convergence of a series A series $\sum\limits_{k=1}^{\infty} a_k$ converges to a sum S if $\lim\limits_{n \to \infty} \sum\limits_{k=1}^{n} a_k = S$, p. H134.

Cosine The function $y = \cos x$, p. H66.

Coterminal angles Two angles having the same initial side and the same terminal side, p. H53.

Cube root nth root, where $n = 3$ (see *Principal nth root*), p. H118.

D

De Moivre's theorem

$(r(\cos \theta + i \sin \theta))^n = r^n(\cos n\theta + i \sin n\theta)$, p. H116.

Decreasing on an interval A function f is decreasing on an interval I if, for any two points in I, a positive change in x results in a negative change in $f(x)$, pp. A9, A15.

Appendix Glossary

Deductive reasoning The process of utilizing general information to prove a specific hypothesis, p. A2.

Dependent variable Variable representing the range value of a function (usually y), p. A2.

Divergence A sequence or series diverges if it does not converge, p. H134.

Domain of a function The set of all input values for a function, p. A2.

E

Even function A function whose graph is symmetric about the y-axis ($f(-x) = f(x)$ for all x in the domain of f), p. A12.

Expanded form of a series A series written explicitly as a sum of terms (not in summation notation), p. H134.

Explicitly defined sequence A sequence in which the kth term is given as a function of k, p. H122.

Exponential decay function Decay modeled by $f(x) = a \cdot b^x$, $a > 0$ with $0 < b < 1$, p. H4.

Exponential form An equation written with exponents instead of logarithms, p. H23.

Exponential function A function of the form $f(x) = a \cdot b^x$, where $a \neq 0$, $b > 0$, $b \neq 1$, p. H2.

Exponential growth function Growth modeled by $f(x) = a \cdot b^x$, $a > 0$, $b > 1$, p. H4.

F

Fibonacci numbers The terms of the Fibonacci sequence, p. H127.

Fibonacci sequence The sequence 1, 1, 2, 3, 5, 8, 13, . . . , p. H127.

Finite sequence A function whose domain is the first n positive integers for some fixed integer n, p. H122.

Finite series Sum of a finite number of terms, p. H130.

Frequency Reciprocal of the period of a sinusoid, p. H68.

Function A relation that associates each value in the domain with exactly one value in the range, p. A2.

G

Geometric sequence A sequence $\{a_n\}$ in which $a_n = a_{n-1} \cdot r$ for every positive integer $n \geq 2$. The nonzero number r is called the common ratio, p. H125.

Geometric series A series whose terms form a geometric sequence, p. H135.

Graph of a function f The set of all points in the coordinate plane corresponding to the pairs $(x, f(x))$ for x in the domain of f, p. A3.

Graph of a polar equation The set of all points in the polar coordinate system corresponding to the ordered pairs (r, θ) that are solutions of the polar equation, p. H104.

H

Half-life The amount of time required for half of a radioactive substance to decay, p. H15.

Horizontal asymptote The line $y = b$ is a horizontal asymptote of the graph of a function f if $\lim\limits_{x \to -\infty} f(x) = b$ or $\lim\limits_{x \to \infty} f(x) = b$, p. A15.

I

Identity function The function $f(x) = x$, p. A21.

Imaginary axis See *Complex plane*.

Implied domain The domain of a function's algebraic expression, p. A4.

Increasing on an interval A function f is increasing on an interval I if, for any two points in I, a positive change in x results in a positive change in $f(x)$, p. A9.

Independent variable Variable representing the domain value of a function (usually x), p. A2.

Index of summation See *Summation notation*.

Infinite discontinuity at $x = a$ $\lim\limits_{x \to a^+} f(x) = \pm\infty$ or $\lim\limits_{x \to a^-} f(x) = \pm\infty$, p. A7.

Infinite sequence A function whose domain is the set of all natural numbers, p. H122.

Inverse cosecant function The function $y = \csc^{-1} x$.

Inverse cosine function The function $y = \cos^{-1} x$, p. H78.

Inverse cotangent function The function $y = \cot^{-1} x$.

Inverse secant function The function $y = \sec^{-1} x$.

Inverse sine function The function $y = \sin^{-1} x$, p. H76.

Inverse tangent function The function $y = \tan^{-1} x$, p. H79.

J

Jump discontinuity at $x = a$ $\lim\limits_{x \to a^-} f(x)$ and $\lim\limits_{x \to a^+} f(x)$ exist but are not equal, p. A7.

K

kth term of a sequence The kth expression in the sequence, p. H122.

Lemniscate A graph of a polar equation of the form $r^2 = a^2 \sin 2\theta$ or $r^2 = a^2 \cos 2\theta$, p. H109.

Limaçon A graph of a polar equation $r = a \pm b \sin \theta$ or $r = a \pm b \cos \theta$ with $a > 0$, $b > 0$, p. H107.

Limit to growth See *Logistic growth function.*

Local extremum A local maximum or a local minimum, p. A12.

Local maximum A value $f(c)$ is a local maximum of f if there is an open interval I containing c such that $f(x) \leq f(c)$ for all values of x in I, p. A12.

Local minimum A value $f(c)$ is a local minimum of f if there is an open interval I containing c such that $f(x) \geq f(c)$ for all values of x in I, p. A12.

Logarithm An expression of the form $\log_b x$ (see *Logarithmic function*), p. H23.

Logarithmic form An equation written with logarithms instead of exponents, p. H23.

Logarithmic function with base b The inverse of the exponential function $y = b_x$, denoted by $y = \log_b x$, pp. H23, H36.

Logarithmic re-expression of data Transformation of a data set involving the natural logarithm: exponential regression, natural logarithmic regression, power regression, p. H47.

Logistic growth function A model of population growth:

$$f(x) = \frac{c}{1 + a \cdot b^x} \text{ or } f(x) = \frac{c}{1 + ae^{-kx}}, \text{ where } a,$$

b, c, and k are positive with $b < 1$. c is the limit to growth, p. H8.

Lower bound of f Any number b for which $b \leq f(x)$ for all x in the domain of f, p. A11.

Mapping A function viewed as a mapping of the elements of the domain onto the elements of the range, p. A2.

Maximum r-value The value of $|r|$ at the point on the graph of a polar equation that has the maximum distance from the pole, p. H106.

Modulus See *Absolute value of a complex number.*

Natural exponential function The function $f(x) = e^x$, p. H6.

Natural logarithm A logarithm with base e, p. H26.

Natural logarithmic function The inverse of the exponential function $y = e^x$, denoted by $y = \ln x$, p. H27.

Negative angle Angle generated by clockwise rotation, p. H53.

Newton's law of cooling $T(t) = T_m + (T_0 - T_m)e^{-kt}$, p. H45.

nth root See *Principal nth root.*

nth root of a complex number z A complex number v such that $v^n = z$, p. H117.

nth root of unity A complex number v such that $v^n = 1$, p. H117.

Odd function A function whose graph is symmetric about the origin ($f(-x) = -f(x)$ for all x in the domain of f), p. A13.

One-to-one rule of exponents $x = y$ if and only if $b^x = b^y$, p. H41.

One-to-one rule of logarithms $x = y$ if and only if $\log_b x = \log_b y$, p. H41.

Order of magnitude (of n) $\log n$, p. H43.

Partial sums See *Sequence of partial sums.*

Period See *Periodic function.*

Periodic function A function f for which there is a positive number c such that $f(t + c) = f(t)$ for every value t in the domain of f. The smallest such number c is the period of the function, p. H60.

pH The measure of acidity, p. H44.

Phase shift See *Sinusoid.*

Piecewise-defined function A function whose domain is divided into several parts with a different function rule applied to each part, p. A26.

Polar axis See *Polar coordinate system.*

Polar coordinate system A coordinate system whose ordered pair is based on the directed distance from a central point (the pole) and the angle measured from a ray from the pole (the polar axis), p. H97.

Polar coordinates The numbers (r, θ) that determine a point's location in a polar coordinate system. The number r is the directed distance and θ is the directed angle, p. H97.

Polar distance formula The distance between the points with polar coordinates (r_1, θ_1) and (r_2, θ_2) $= \sqrt{r_1^2 + r_2^2 - 2r_1r_2 \cos (\theta_1 - \theta_2)}$, p. H103.

Polar equation An equation in r and θ, p. H100.

Polar form of a complex number See *Trigonometric form of a complex number*.

Pole See *Polar coordinate system*.

Positive angle Angle generated by a counterclockwise rotation, p. H53.

Power rule of logarithms $\log_b R^c = c \log_b R, R > 0$, p. H32.

Principal nth root If $b^n = a$, then b is an nth root of a. If $b^n = a$ and a and b have the same sign, b is the principal nth root of a (see *Radical*), p. H117.

Product of complex numbers $(a + bi)(c + di) = (ac - bd) + (ad + bc)i$, p. H114.

Product rule of logarithms
$\log_b (RS) = \log_b R + \log_b S, R > 0, S > 0$,
p. H32.

Quadrantal angle An angle in standard position whose terminal side lies on an axis, p. H57.

Quotient of complex numbers
$$\frac{a + bi}{c + di} = \frac{ac + bd}{c^2 + d^2} + \frac{bc - ad}{c^2 + d^2} i, \text{ p. H114.}$$

Quotient rule of logarithms
$$\log_b \left(\frac{R}{S}\right) = \log_b R - \log_b S, R > 0, S > 0,$$
p. H32.

Range of a function The set of all output values corresponding to elements in the domain, p. A2.

Real axis See *Complex plane*.

Reciprocal function The function $f(x) = \dfrac{1}{x}$, p. A22.

Recursively defined sequence A sequence defined by giving the first term (or the first few terms) along with a procedure for finding the subsequent terms, p. H122.

Re-expression of data A transformation of a data set, p. H36.

Reference angle See *Reference triangle*.

Reference triangle For an angle θ in standard position, a reference triangle is a triangle formed by the terminal side of angle θ, the x-axis, and a perpendicular dropped from a point on the terminal side to the x-axis. The angle in a reference triangle at the origin is the reference angle, p. H56.

Relevant domain The portion of the domain applicable to the situation being modeled, p. A4.

Removable discontinuity at $x = a$
$$\lim_{x \to a^-} f(x) = \lim_{x \to a^+} f(x)$$
but either the common limit is not equal to $f(a)$ or $f(a)$ is not defined, p. A6.

Richter scale A logarithmic scale used in measuring the intensity of an earthquake, pp. H39, H44.

Root of a number See *Principal nth root*.

Rose curve A graph of a polar equation $r = a \cos n\theta$ or $r = a \sin n\theta$, p. H106.

Sequence See *Finite sequence, Infinite sequence*.

Sequence of partial sums The sequence $\{S_n\}$, where S_n is the nth partial sum of the series, that is, the sum of the first n terms of the series, p. H134.

Series A finite or infinite sum of terms, p. H130.

Simple harmonic motion Motion described by $d = a \sin \omega t$ or $d = a \cos \omega t$, p. H89.

Sine The function $y = \sin x$, p. H65.

Sinusoid A function that can be written in the form
$f(x) = a \sin (b(x - h)) + k$
or $f(x) = a \cos (b(x - h)) + k$. The number a is the amplitude, and the number h is the phase shift, p. H67.

Spiral of Archimedes The graph of the polar curve $r = \theta$, p. H109.

Standard position (angle) An angle positioned on a rectangular coordinate system with its vertex at the origin and its initial side on the positive x-axis, p. H53.

Sum of a finite arithmetic series
$$S_n = n\left(\frac{a_1 + a_2}{2}\right) = \frac{n}{2}[2a_1 + (n - 1)d], \text{ p. 679.}$$

Sum of a finite geometric series $S_n = \dfrac{a_1(1 - r^n)}{1 - r}$,
p. H132.

Sum of an infinite geometric series
$$S_n = \frac{a}{1 - r}, |r| < 1, \text{ p. H135.}$$

Sum of an infinite series See *Convergence of a series*.

Summation notation The series $\displaystyle\sum_{k=1}^{n} a_k$, where n is a natural number (or ∞) is in summation notation and is read "the sum of a_k from $k = 1$ to n (or infinity)." k is the index of summation, and a_k is the kth term of the series, p. H130.

Symmetric about the origin A graph in which $(-x, -y)$ is on the graph whenever (x, y) is; or a graph in which $(-r, \theta)$ or $(r, \theta + \pi)$ is on the graph whenever (r, θ) is, p. A13.

Symmetric about the x-axis A graph in which $(x, -y)$ is on the graph whenever (x, y) is; or a graph in which $(r, -\theta)$ or $(-r, \pi - \theta)$ is on the graph whenever (r, θ) is, p. A13.

Symmetric about the y-axis A graph in which $(-x, y)$ is on the graph whenever (x, y) is; or a graph in which $(-r, -\theta)$ or $(r, \pi - \theta)$ is on the graph whenever (r, θ) is, p. A12.

Terms of a sequence The range elements of a sequence, p. H122.

Trigonometric form of a complex number $r(\cos \theta + i \sin \theta)$, p. H113.

Unit circle A circle with radius 1 centered at the origin, p. H59.

Upper bound for f Any number B for which $f(x) \leq B$ for all x in the domain of f, p. A11.

Vertical asymptote The line $x = a$ is a vertical asymptote of the graph of the function f if
$$\lim_{x \to a^+} f(x) = \pm \infty \text{ or}$$
$$\lim_{x \to a^-} f(x) = \pm \infty, \text{ p. A15.}$$

Vertical line test A test for determining whether a graph is a function, p. A3.

Wrapping function The function that associates points on the unit circle with points on the real number line, p. H59.

Index

Index

Acknowledgments

Staff Credits

The people who made up the High School Mathematics team—representing composition services, core design digital and multimedia production services, digital product development, editorial, editorial services, manufacturing, marketing, and production management—are listed below.

Patty Fagan, Suzanne Finn, Matt Frueh, Cynthia Harvey, Linda Johnson, Roshni Kutty, Cheryl Mahan, Eve Melnechuk, Cynthia Metallides, Hope Morley, Michael Oster, Wynnette Outland, Brian Reardon, Matthew Rogers, Ann-Marie Sheehan, Kristen Siefers, Richard Sullivan, Susan Tauer, Mark Tricca, Oscar Vera, Paula Vergith

Additional Credits: Emily Bosak, Olivia Gerde, Alyse McGuire, Stephanie Mosely

Illustration

Stephen Durke: 580, 617; **Jeff Grunewald:** 578; **Phil Guzy:** 585, 588, 609; **Rob Schuster:** 78, 80, 93, 202, 214, 271, 500, 501; **Christopher Wilson:** 161

Technical Illustration

Aptara, Inc.; Datagrafix, Inc.; GGS Book Services

Photography

Every effort has been made to secure permission and provide appropriate credit for photographic material. The publisher deeply regrets any omission and pledges to correct errors called to its attention in subsequent editions.

Unless otherwise acknowledged, all photographs are the property of Pearson Education, Inc.

190 NASA; **347** Jerry Lodriguss/Science Photo Library/ Photo Researchers, Inc.; **356** Dave King/©DK Images; **399** Finalphotos/Dreamstime LLC; **455** Demetrio Carrasco/©DK Images; **599** Sports Bokeh/Alamy; **616** ©matthiasengelian/ Alamy; **A1** © Shutterstock; **A30** © PhotoDisc Red; **H11** © PhotoDisc; **H19** © PhotoDisc; **H30** © NASA; **H37** © Corbis; **H40** © PhotoDisc; **H44** © PhotoDisc; **H71** © iStockphoto; **H101** © PhotoDisc/Getty Royalty Free; **H107** © Getty Royalty Free; **H128** © PhotoDisc/Getty Royalty Free.

Chapter 1: Whole chapter taken from Chapter 1 of *Pearson High School Math 2014 Common Core Integrated Math 3 Write-In Student Edition Volume 1.*

Chapter 2: Lessons 1-7 taken from Chapter 4, Lessons 1-7 of *Pearson High School Math 2014 Common Core Integrated Math 3 Write-In Student Edition Volume 1.* Lessons 8-9 taken from Chapter 4, Lessons 9-10 of *Pearson High School Math 2014 Common Core Integrated Math 3 Write-In Student Edition Volume 1.*

Chapter 3: Whole chapter taken from Chapter 5 of *Pearson High School Math 2014 Common Core Integrated Math 3 Write-In Student Edition Volume 1.*

Chapter 4: Whole chapter taken from Chapter 6 of *Pearson High School Math 2014 Common Core Integrated Math 3 Write-In Student Edition Volume 1.*

Chapter 5: Whole chapter taken from Chapter 7 of *Pearson High School Math 2014 Common Core Integrated Math 3 Write-In Student Edition Volume 2.*

Chapter 6: Whole chapter taken from Chapter 8 of *Pearson High School Math 2014 Common Core Integrated Math 3 Write-In Student Edition Volume 2.*

Chapter 7: Lessons 1-5 taken from Chapter 9, Lessons 1-5 of *Pearson High School Math 2014 Common Core Integrated Math 3 Write-In Student Edition Volume 2.* Lesson 6 taken from Chapter 4, Lesson 8 of *Pearson High School Math 2014 Common Core Integrated Math 3 Write-In Student Edition Volume 1.*

Chapter 8: Whole chapter taken from Chapter 10 of *Pearson High School Math 2014 Common Core Integrated Math 3 Write-In Student Edition Volume 2.*

Appendix A: Lessons A-1 and A-2 taken from Chapter 1, Sections 2 and 3 of *Precalculus: Graphical, Numerical, Algebraic, Eighth Edition.*

Honors Appendix: Lessons H-1 through H-5 taken from Chapter 3, Sections 1-5 of *Precalculus: Graphical, Numerical, Algebraic, Eighth Edition.* Lessons H-6 through H-9 taken from Chapter 4, Sections 3, 4, 7, 8 of *Precalculus: Graphical, Numerical, Algebraic, Eighth Edition.* Lessons H-10 through H-12 taken from Chapter 6, Sections 4-6 of *Precalculus: Graphical, Numerical, Algebraic, Eighth Edition.* Lessons H-13 and H-14 taken from Chapter 9, Sections 4 and 5 of *Precalculus: Graphical, Numerical, Algebraic, Eighth Edition.*